ENERGY AUDITING
CERTIFICATION GUIDE

Copyright © 2010 by Educational Technologies Group

This book was set in Times New Roman and Arial by Cathy J. Boulay, ETG.

Written by: Jay and Annie Warmke

Graphics by: Luke Johns

MARCRAFT

ISBN-13:   978-1-58122-125-1
ISBN-10:   1-58122-125-8

1 2 3 4 5 6 7 8 9 10

PREFACE

While there is already a great rush to develop additional energy sources to meet the exponentially growing demand around the world, we are not keeping up. Conventional carbon-based energy sources (dirty fuels) are quickly being depleted while newer alternative energy (clean energy) sources are working toward "silver bullet" technology breakthroughs that will make them a viable replacement for the diminishing conventional energy sources.

While it is essential to accelerate the development of most energy sources, it is equally essential that we develop much better methods of using the energy we do create. If not, we may not be able to meet future energy demands.

One key element in conserving large amounts of energy worldwide is to create sustainable, long-term energy conservation through improved building techniques, materials and technologies. We must build residential and commercial structures that use energy more efficiently (i.e., Green Buildings). In addition, we must renovate older structures to be as efficient as possible to minimize their impact on world energy demand and the carbon byproducts it produces.

While there is much discussion around conserving and replacing carbon-based fuels and minimizing the resulting carbon byproducts in the transportation arena, the energy consumption and the carbon emissions associated with the residential and commercial/industrial buildings in just two emerging Chinese cities will, within half a day, wipe out more than all of the energy conservation created by the influx of hybrid cars taking to the roads in the United States or Europe.

It is for exactly this reason that we have produced this Energy Auditing Experiment Panel and its accompanying Text/Lab manual. The three major areas of Energy Auditing featured in this course—Insulation and Lighting, Passive Solar Heating and Ventilation and RESNET National Rater Certification—represent the most effective energy conservation options for achieving high levels of energy conservation and minimizing carbon emissions. It also prepares the reader for Green Collar employment and certification in the Energy Auditing field. The RESNET national home energy rating standard provides an industry recognizable standard for the knowledge base and skills set required for Home Energy Raters.

Pedagogical Features

The pedagogical features of this book were carefully developed to provide readers with key content information, as well as review and testing opportunities. These include:

- Over 200 diagrams and tables designed to provide regular visual reinforcement and clarity of the concepts being discussed.

- The text follows closely the principles of STEM learning, exploring the basic Science that provides the foundation for each Technology discussed. The Engineering principles that make the technology work are explored in detail, as are the Mathematical concepts and equations that students must be able to complete if they are to have a well-rounded understanding of the technology.

- Each chapter begins with a list of learning objectives that establishes a foundation and preview of important concepts explored within the chapter.

- Key terms are presented in bold and highlighted in the margin for easy reference. They are also each defined in context within the chapter.

- Each chapter concludes with a 10-question multiple-choice section and a 15-question section of open-ended review questions. The multiple-choice questions test the knowledge of basic concepts presented within the chapter. The open-ended questions are designed to test and demonstrate critical thinking abilities.

- Special Let's Do The Math and Science Note inserts call attention to STEM features throughout the book.

- Appendix A contains the RESNET National Rater Test Objective Map.

- Appendix B is a comprehensive Glossary of terms to provide quick, easy access to key term definitions that appear throughout the text. The key terms highlighted throughout the text work in conjunction with the Glossary.

- Appendix C provides a list of common acronyms used in the green technology industry.

Organization

This section explains the reasons the Green Movement has taken on such importance in a relatively short amount of time. It describes the breath of the green movement and then focuses on the Green Power technology portion of the movement.

Chapter 1 – *Energy Auditing* introduces students to the concepts and history of global warming, greenhouse gases and their role with the Earth's atmosphere. This historical foundation will enable students to jump right in to the fascinating cutting edge issues that are at the heart of green technology. Students will find this historical perspective helpful as they learn the problems faced by the inadequacy of the electrical grid, and how society has evolved from an economy based on wood to one based on coal to one based on oil.

Chapter 2 – *Energy and Power* provides much of the fundamental physical science upon which all Green Technology systems are based. Students will develop a general understanding of the various forms of energy and understand the various physical laws of conservation of energy and thermodynamics, and their relevance to alternative power systems. This chapter also gets into basic electrical concepts such as Ohm's Law and the relationship between amps, volts and watts. Students will develop a working knowledge of electrical circuits, how batteries function and the difference between AC and DC power.

Chapter 3 – *Residential and Commercial Structures* will introduce the importance of reducing energy consumption within residential and commercial buildings, due to the large amounts they require, and the high percentage of greenhouse gas emissions for which they are responsible. The proper designs and functions of foundations, basements, crawl spaces, walls, doors, windows, ceilings, attics, and roofs are carefully examined. The importance of insulation and the use of vapor barriers are also discussed.

Chapter 4 – *Energy Conservation* is the a core concept of green technology and holds the promise of the most immediate and cost-effective reductions in personal and global energy consumption. Students will learn of the inefficiencies built into the current systems, as well as the various governmental initiatives (such as Energy Star) currently in place to boost energy efficiency. They will learn how energy is currently being used and how best to make this use more efficient. Students will be able to conduct a complete energy audit, and make informed recommendations regarding building shell integrity, insulation, window efficiencies, venting and air balancing options. Students will also come to understand the various heating (both air and water), cooling, and lighting options available that can save vast amounts of energy. They will see how habits and behavior contribute to energy inefficiencies.

Chapter 5 – *Passive Solar Systems* outlines the important basic concepts of passive and active solar energy systems that serve as the basis for some forms of green technology—including green building. They will also understand how passive daylighting systems, thermal mass, thermal lag, and the thermal storage capacity of building materials are an effective energy source. Attention is focused on the importance of the angle and location of the Sun in relation to a specific location and how to calculate the Sun's position. Students will also learn the difference between direct, indirect and isolated solar gain. Solar cooling systems are also addressed in this chapter.

Chapter 6 – *Green Building* will introduce the student to the processes and design concepts that make a building or community green. This chapter will discuss the advantages and barriers to this form of design, as well as certification programs such as LEED. The student will become familiar with concepts that seek to minimize the amount of land, landscaping, materials and general environmental impact a building has in its surroundings. They will learn what is meant by the urban heat island effect and how materials selected can have a big impact on how resource efficient, as well as how healthy and comfortable a building can be.

Chapter 7 – *Safety* introduces the student to the safety concerns faced by energy auditors in the normal flow of their work. It begins by discussing different types of protective gear available and the circumstances under which each type should be used. It also examines a number of safety issues related to the working environment. The chapter concludes with an extended presentation of emergency response information.

Chapter 8 – *Building Codes and Compliance* – There are many levels of rules (standards, codes, regulations and laws) associated with energy auditing. These regulations vary from location to location and may come from different levels of authority. However, they must be complied with to have a legal installation. This chapter will introduce you to the most common standards and regulations associated with energy auditing.

Chapter 9 – *Understanding Blueprints* offers a basic knowledge of blueprint reading. This final chapter is essential. Without blueprints, energy auditing would be haphazard and unruly. To understand blueprints is to have clarity for the energy auditor. The hands-on procedure in this chapter provides an activity in examining and identifying items associated with blueprints.

The Hands-On Lab Procedures

The second half of the GT-750 Text/Lab Guide contains an excellent set of hands on procedures that build upon the wealth of theoretical materials from the front of the book to prepare the reader for a successful career in the energy auditing workforce.

The lab guide section of the book contains four types of labs—multiple hands on labs designed to provide an introduction to the major technologies commonly found in the energy auditing workplace. A Guided Research lab that expands the reader's knowledge base of current and extended energy auditing follows the hands on labs. This lab procedure is followed by one or more Guided Design labs that present a scenario and expected outcomes and asks the reader to apply their acquired knowledge from the hands-on and research labs to evaluate, design and implement the requested scenario.

Lab Procedure 1 – *Introduction to the IR Camera* – This procedure introduces you to the IR Camera to locate and identify the important components. You will find an unknown emissivity value using the IR camera.

Lab Procedure 2 – *Evaluating Lighting and Heating Systems* – In this procedure, you will measure and record the power usage of various light bulb types and ratings, and then use a formula to determine the kilowatts per hour (kWh) of each bulb. You will use the passive water heater to heat a specific amount of water and then heat the water to the same temperature using the active water heater. You will calculate the energy used by both systems and evaluate the costs of the water heaters.

Lab Procedure 3 – *Evaluating Insulation Materials* – In this procedure, you will evaluate insulation quality of various types of insulation with an IR camera.

Lab Procedure 4 – *Energy Auditing Tests* – In this procedure, you will perform energy auditing tests.

Lab Procedure 5 – *Energy Auditing Research* – This guided Research lab is designed to guide you into deeper investigations of the current energy auditing market, its equipment, requirements and regulations.

Lab Procedure 6 – *Energy Auditing Design* – The guided Design lab(s) ask you to apply the knowledge you've acquired throughout the hands-on and research procedures to a real world scenario to evaluate and provide an acceptable design that will meet the requirements of the project scenario.

Lab Procedure 7 – *Understanding Blueprints* – In this procedure you will examine an actual blueprint of a commercial facility and be asked to locate and identify standard blueprint symbols.

Lab Procedure 8 – *Let's Take it Outside – Energy Auditing* – This procedure is designed to guide you through an independent energy auditing process. This process can be performed using the components from the GT-7500 Energy Auditing Technology panel, equipment from other sources, or a combination of the two.

Teacher Support Materials

A full-featured instructor's guide is available for the course. The instructor's guide includes:

- Answers for all of the end-of-chapter quiz questions are included along with a reference point in the chapter where a particular item is covered.

- Sample schedules are included as guidelines for possible course implementations.

- Answers to all lab review questions and fill-in-the-blank steps are provided so that there is an indication of what the expected outcomes should be.

- Full Power Point Slide Presentations including every graphic, table, question, and objective in the book. These slide sets can be edited to fit the class length and your delivery preference.

- An electronic copy of the textbook is included on the Instructor's Guide CD-ROM disc.

Optional System Support

- Online LMS Delivery and Management System—ETG/Marcraft also provides interactive, online classrooms and self study seats for all of its products. The LMS tracks student progress, automatically grades exams and quizzes and places the scores in the electronic grade book.

- Online Updates System—All the latest updates for all ETG/Marcraft curriculum is available online at *http://updates.etg-corp.com*. The first time you access the site, you will need to register by providing your email address and the ISBN numbers for each book you wish to see the updated pages for. Be sure to always provide the same email address and password when accessing the updates, this way you can see all updates for the ISBN numbers you have registered. The pages are in PDF format and can be printed out. You will want to check this site often to make sure you always have the latest information.

ABOUT THE AUTHORS

Annie and Jay Warmke are pioneers in the field of green technology and sustainable living. Together they have co-authored a number of books related to green living, founded the Ohio Green Living association, spoken to groups large and small around the world on Green Technology and generally made it their business to be a pest to as many elected officials as possible. In 2009, they were awarded the Sustainable Living Award by Rural Action for their pioneering work.

Annie began her career working on women's issues—particularly those focused on assisting battered women. She is a graduate of Ohio University. Her work has garnered her appearances on local, national (including Larry King Live), and international radio and television programs. Annie has written for a number of publications, including *The Beirut Daily Star* (Lebanon), *The Little Blue Book* (France), and the book *Women of Spirit*. In 1997 she introduced President Bill Clinton at a White House news conference held to announce the unveiling of The National Domestic Violence Hotline. She has received numerous local and national awards for her work and her volunteer efforts. Currently she serves as a board member of Ohio Green Living and on the advisory committee for the National Gardening Association's Kid's Garden Website. AND every Wednesday during the school year she leads The League of Extraordinary Girl Scientists (LEGS), a science club at the local junior high school.

Jay earned a degree in journalism from Ohio University and says he learned just enough about journalism to know he didn't want to be one. He also attended the MBA program at the University of South Florida, but eventually decided he had no business being in "business". He has written for a variety of publications, given countless presentations, served on more technical committees than he cares to remember, and sat through endless board meetings in his role as executive director of BICSI (an international telecommunications associations), as well as a board member of Ohio Green Living, Green Energy Ohio, the International Certification and Accreditation Council—just to name a few of the more recent groups. In 1998 he was named one of the "10 Most Influential People" in the telecommunications industry by a prominent industry magazine.

A number of years back, Annie and Jay decided to drop out of the corporate world to create Blue Rock Station—a 38-acre sustainable living center in rural Ohio. Together with their granddaughter Catlyn, they built Ohio's first Earthship, a self-contained passive solar home made of tires, cans, bottles and straw bales—a home that incorporates many of the techniques written about in this textbook. Since 2005 over 15,000 people have visited Blue Rock Station to tour the Earthship, attend workshops, and learn sustainable living concepts (as well as visit with the goats, llamas, and chickens). Their summers are spent being inspired by young people who work as interns at Blue Rock Station. Their winters are spent watching old movies, discussing the politics of life, and making sure the goats and llamas have plenty of water.

It is our hope that as you read this book, and learn more about how green technology and renewable energy can be incorporated into your everyday life, you will re-think how all of this fits into your own life practices. Remember... you WILL be green (whether you want to be or not). Best to know what the planet has in store for you.

ACKNOWLEDGEMENTS

Text book dedications are bizarre at best. This is the place where we get to thank a bunch of people that you don't know for doing things that helped create a book that—be honest—on most days you feel is more a burden to slog through than a pleasure to sit back and enjoy.

But none-the-less, there are folks who contributed a huge portion of their time, kindness, generosity, blood, sweat and tears to making this book a reality. Green technology is first and foremost about community. The community that contributed to this effort include:

All the folks down at Green Acres Country Store (John, Sandy, Sherry and crew) who put up with Jay for months on end as he used the wireless broadband for research and drank one big endless cup of coffee.

The interns at Blue Rock Station (Alicia McCormick and Mathews Silva) who kept the animals, as well as our bodies and souls fed while we were distracted. Also thanks to Sam Sheets for helping with the cooking and doing the dishes… always with a smile.

Thanks to all the teachers in our lives who have motivated us. The third grade teacher who told Jay he would never get into college because he held his pencil the wrong way. The seventh grade art teacher at Clinton Junior High in Columbus Ohio who made Annie stand in the corner for hours for asking too many questions. To Corwin Croy, journalism teacher from Athens High School who pushed his students to always be better than they thought they could be. These lessons have stayed with us over the decades. You never know where inspiration and motivation may originate.

Thanks to Matt Bennett from Dovetail Solar for his real world advice.

Thanks of course to Bethany Filipow for her insights on teaching science.

Thanks to Kelly Lewis for reading through the final draft, constantly asking - "What the heck does this mean?"

And a special thanks to Laura Wies who meticulously worked through every equation in the book and insisted that all the units of measure be complete and accurate. Oh, and she also insisted that we use proper English, go figure!?

Thanks also to all the good folks over at Marcraft, Cathy Boulay for compiling all the various scribbles into a form that can be read and understood, Luke Johns for his amazing graphics, and Chuck Brooks for shepherding the project through the hills and valleys of the publishing world (to really stretch an analogy).

Most of all, thanks to our granddaughter Catlyn who, just by being, sustains us.

Table of Contents

CHAPTER 3   RESIDENTIAL AND COMMERCIAL STRUCTURES

CHAPTER 4   ENERGY CONSERVATION

CHAPTER 5   PASSIVE SOLAR SYSTEMS

CHAPTER 6   GREEN BUILDING

CHAPTER 7 SAFETY

CHAPTER 8   BUILDING CODES AND COMPLIANCE

CHAPTER 9 UNDERSTANDING BLUEPRINTS

ENERGY AUDITING LAB PROCEDURES

INTRODUCTION TO LAB PROCEDURES

LAB PROCEDURE 1 – INTRODUCTION TO THE IR CAMERA

LAB PROCEDURE 2 – EVALUATING LIGHTING AND HEATING SYSTEMS

LAB PROCEDURE 6 – ENERGY AUDITING DESIGN

LAB PROCEDURE 7 – UNDERSTANDING BLUEPRINTS

LAB PROCEDURE 8 – LET'S TAKE IT OUTSIDE – ENERGY AUDITING

APPENDIX A

APPENDIX B

APPENDIX C

INDEX

CHAPTER 1

ENERGY AUDITING

OBJECTIVES

Upon completion of this chapter, you will be able to perform the following tasks:

1. Understand what is meant by the term *green technology*.

2. Be able to define the factors which have combined in recent years leading to an explosion in interest in green technologies.

3. Discuss in broad terms the various energy transitions that societies have undergone over the past century.

4. Understand how population growth, the emergence of a vast middle class, as well as declining fossil fuel reserves have led to mounting pressure on the world's energy supply.

5. Discuss how the burning of fossil fuels impacts the environment as well as contributes to climate change.

6. Understand how price convergence (increasing fossil fuel prices and declining costs of green technology) will impact energy production over the next few decades.

Energy Auditing

INTRODUCTION

For the last century or more, the economies of the world's societies have been linked together by a common bond; a dependency on increasingly limited fossil fuel reserves. This stored energy has been tapped to produce the **Work** that has lead to an unprecedented growth in standards of living and industrial activity across the globe. But this situation is rapidly changing.

The growth of the last century, a massive transition from an agricultural economy to an industrial economy, to an informational economy - has at its heart been fueled by the seemingly endless supply of relatively inexpensive stored energy. For example: the amount of energy contained in one barrel of oil is roughly equivalent to 25,000 hours of human labor (or 12 people working 40 hours a week for an entire year). Assuming a minimum wage of US$7.25 per hour, that means a barrel of oil contains an equivalent value of US$181,250 of human labor. Cheap energy indeed at US$80 a barrel, or US$100 or even US$200 a barrel (when compared to human labor, at least).

With such a bountiful energy resource at hand, it is little wonder that the last century has seen astronomical increases in wealth (from an energy point of view). But sadly, this resource is not unlimited—and we are beginning to bump up against those limitations.

In recent years, our society has responded to these limitations with an increasing interest in sources of **Green Energy**. The fields of transportation, industry, agriculture, and residential/commercial construction have found ever increasing need to reduce their dependency on fossil fuels (as well as most other limited resources). A shift is underway from systems and processes that rely almost entirely on previously inexpensive and abundant fossil fuels to a heavier reliance on wind, solar, hydro and perhaps most importantly (at least in the short term), more efficient uses of existing fossil fuel resources.

WHAT IS GREEN?

It seems that suddenly there are references to "being green" or "renewable energy" all around us. There are advertisements for green companies and green products everywhere. Power companies are talking about intelligent **Smart Grids** and equipment and techniques for saving energy. But what is "**Green Technology**" and why is it important?

Like any concept that suddenly gains widespread acceptance, it can (and does) mean different things to different people. For some, green technology is a design process that seeks to minimize the use of resources while maximizing efficiency. Still others view green from a scientific perspective, replacing one technology with another in order to reduce harmful (and climate changing) emissions.

Work

Green Energy

Smart Grids

Green Technology

Kermit the Frog may have summed up the reality of "green" in his famous quote "*It's not easy being green.*" There is no simple or easy method of moving society from a fossil-fuel based economy to a green economy. Despite the difficulty of the task, it is one that must and will occur. As is becoming abundantly clear, there is simply no choice.

There is also no single step or process that will achieve a sustainable green world. Green technology is actually a collection of ideas that include:

- Generating power from sources that do not produce carbon (**Greenhouse Gases**) as a bi-product.

- Limiting energy usage through personal behavior modification and technology.

- Conserving resources through personal behavior modification and technology.

- Fostering sustainable energy conservation through improved building techniques, materials and technologies.

- Creating and using transportation systems and techniques that do not rely on carbon-based products.

Why go Green?

Why does it seem that suddenly the idea of green technology has gained such prominence? The answer lies in the convergence of a number of factors. These include:

- The pressure placed on resources by a continued human population growth.

- Rapidly declining fossil fuel reserves.

- The dramatic rise of a middle class in developing nations (such as China and India) that places further demands on limited resources.

- A growing understanding of the effect carbon emissions are producing on the global climate.

- Advances in alternative technologies that, for the first time, make green technologies price competitive with fossil fuel energy sources.

The human population on Earth continues to increase. This in itself is not new, as seen by Figure 1-1, world population has increased dramatically over the years. What is new is that a significant portion of this burgeoning population is becoming relatively affluent—placing huge and growing strains on the limited resources of the planet.

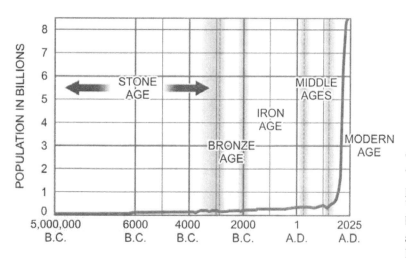

Figure 1-1: World Population Growth Through History

Scientists, as well as the population in general, have recently become aware of the tremendous negative environmental impact the emission of greenhouse gases (such as CO_2) are having on the planet's ecosystem. These gases, the waste from decades of ever-expanded combustion of **Fossil Fuels** are not only polluting the land, water and air of the planet, they are also contributing to **Climate Change**, the effects of which are predicted to be widespread and possibly catastrophic over the coming decades.

Two additional global trends are also combining at this moment in history to push green technology to the forefront. Fossil fuels are running out. In 1956, a geoscientist working for Shell Oil named M. King Hubbert made a startling prediction. He suggested that in 1970 the U.S. (at that time the largest producer of crude oil in the world) would reach **Peak Oil** (a situation where half of all the oil reserves present would be exhausted). He later predicted that worldwide oil production would reach a peak in 1995, as illustrated in Figure 1-2. While his prediction regarding U.S. oil reserves proved remarkably accurate (U.S. oil production reached a peak in 1970 and has declined each year since), world oil reserves extraction did not peak until 2004.

The impact of peak oil is that each barrel of oil now pumped from the ground is more difficult, and more expensive to obtain. As a result, fossil fuels have increased dramatically in cost. Economic theory suggests that with declining supply, fossil fuels will continue to do so (perhaps dramatically) into the future.

The final trend that is converging is the economic competitiveness of alternative technologies. With advances in technology as well as governmental incentives, alternative energy sources such as wind and solar power are, for the first time, becoming economically attractive alternatives to traditionally low-cost fossil fuels.

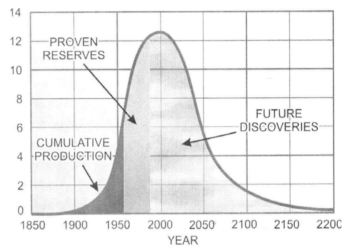

Figure 1-2: Hubbert's Peak Oil Curve

The Brief History of Fossil Fuels

So how did we get from there to here? How did society transition from a largely local agricultural economy to a global economy with wealth based almost entirely on the extraction of limited fossil fuel reserves?

Some say it began with steam.

In the late 1700's a period of innovation and growth called the **Industrial Revolution** began. Prior to this time, manual labor, domesticated animals and water power were the predominate methods of performing work. During the industrial revolution, these methods began to be replaced by, and enhanced through, the use of **Machines**.

This movement brought widespread and relatively rapid changes to societies across the globe. It shifted largely agricultural societies in Europe and North America into machine-based manufacturing communities. These societies became increasingly dependent upon **Energy** and **Power**. No longer were people restricted to living off the limited output of human and animal energy. Society could tap into the vast amounts of stored energy contained within fossil fuels. This began a sustained period of economic growth and inventiveness.

The first major innovation of this period was evident in the development and widespread adoption of the **Steam Engine**, as shown in Figure 1-3. The steam engine relies on energy derived from burning fuels such as **Wood** or **Coal** to heat water, converting it into steam. The steam can then be used to perform **Mechanical Work**. Coal eventually emerged as the favorite fuel of the day, because it offered twice as much energy output potential (a greater **Energy Density**) as the same amount of wood.

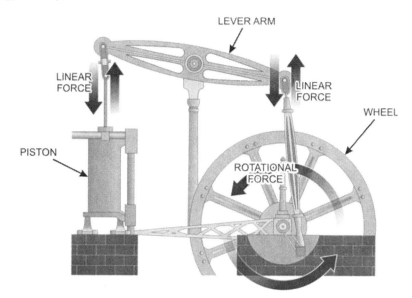

Figure 1-3: The Steam Engine

Coal, **Natural Gas**, and **Crude Oil** were used in the industrial production processes, as well as to heat homes and buildings. **Whale Oil**, the traditional source of light within homes, was replaced with **Kerosene** (first refined from coal, then from crude oil), which was in turn replaced by the electric light.

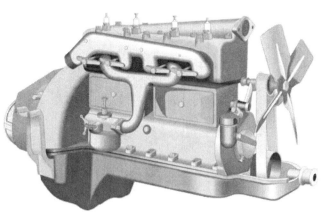

A byproduct of kerosene refining called **Gasoline**, found a ready market in the emerging automobile industry. Toward the end of the 1800's (the late 19th century), the **Internal Combustion Engine**, as shown in Figure 1-4, was developed. This machine created a major shift in the transportation of goods and people.

Figure 1-4: The Internal Combustion Engine

The development of the modern industrial assembly line by the inventor Henry Ford enabled the general public to purchase automobiles at an affordable price. The process (changes in technology) made the automobile inexpensive enough for working-class individuals to own. An abundance of inexpensive personal vehicles, along with a glut of low-price gasoline, led to dramatic changes in infrastructure. Cities, shops and suburbs sprang up along roads and highways designed for the automobile.

The industrial revolution also produced a commercial power revolution in the form of industrial and residential **Electricity**. Electricity emerged as an energy source that could be used to generate heat and light, as well as to produce mechanical and motive (moving things from one place to another) forces.

Early electrical power plants were dependent upon **Hydro Power**, located near water sources that served as the plant's energy source. As demand increased, water alone could not meet this demand. Oil, gas, coal and even **Nuclear** power plants sprang up across the globe.

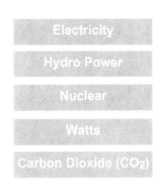

The demand for electricity has produced a world full of electrical generation plants. In the year 2000, the worldwide rate of electrical energy consumption was about 13 trillion **Watts** at any given moment. This amount is expected to double by the year 2050.

While there are electrical generation plants powered by water (hydro), wind, sunlight (solar), and nuclear reactors, the majority of the power plants in existence are powered by fossil fuels (as demonstrated in Figure 1-5) that produce **Carbon Dioxide (CO_2)** and other greenhouse gases as a byproduct of their processes.

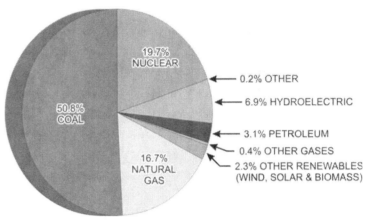

Figure 1-5: Fuel Sources for U.S. Electrical Power Generation

Rising World Populations

The current human population of the world is roughly 6.7 billion people. This is up from approximately 2.8 billion people in 1955. The number of people living on Earth is expected to climb to 9.2 billion by 2050. The expected INCREASE in population over the next forty to fifty years is equal to the TOTAL population that was present on earth just fifty years ago.

According to the United Nations (UN), more than half of all people on Earth live in cities (as opposed to suburbs and rural locations). The continued increase of people dwelling in cities will place growing stress on urban **Infrastructures** such as roads and streets, electrical supply, and sanitation systems, water, sewage and garbage.

Dramatically increasing populations place a strain on limited or diminishing resources such as oil. The first commercially productive oil well in Saudi Arabia (a nation that controls nearly 20% of the world's known oil reserves) was placed into service a mere 75 years ago. During that period of time, half the world's oil reserves have been consumed. What will be the impact when the population demanding the oil that is left doubles in size?

A Rising World Middle Class

While many poor countries are struggling to obtain basic resources and technology, several nations with historically poorer populations are developing a growing middle class within their societies. Leading the way are China and India, whose combined populations account for one-third (37.5%) of the world's total population. Since 2000, China and India combined have added more than 59 million people per year to the global middle class (defined as people with an annual income of $6,000 or more) - representing over 75 % of the world's increase in this group.

These countries are followed closely by a growing middle class in Russia and South East Asian nations. With this comparative affluence, comes further strain on limited resources. Literally millions of new consumers seek to increase their level of comfort and security through the purchase of commodities (things) and increasing their use of resources (such as energy, food and water).

The "things" that upwardly mobile people add to their lives (such as refrigerators, air conditioners, heaters, computers, microwave ovens, and automobiles) require metals, plastics, wood, chemicals and other raw materials to produce. They also require fuel to produce these things, and to operate them. As seen in Figure 1-6, worldwide demand for oil is increasing as supplies become more limited.

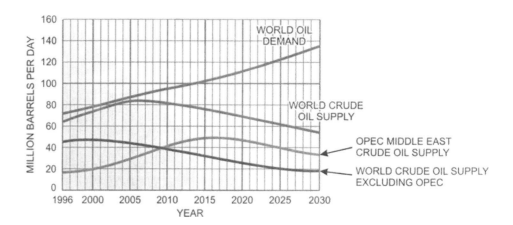

Figure 1-6: World Oil Supplies vs. Demand

Not only oil, but coal, natural gas, water, land and electricity are under pressure of this ever-increasing demand. For example, China is putting a new power plant into operation every two weeks in order to produce an additional billion watts (one Gigawatt) of electrical power, just to keep up with that nation's growing demand for energy.

As the affluence of a population increases, so too does the amount of energy consumed per capita within a nation. A person living in Japan, for example, consumes more than six times the amount of energy each year than someone living in China (a U.S. resident consumes 18 times as much). A resident of Singapore consumes 14 times as much energy each year than someone living in India.

Diminishing World Resources

If, as the U.S. government has reported, the world passed peak oil production in 2004, it might seem logical to assume that in the year 2030, worldwide oil production will be the same as it was in 1980 (a standard bell curve, where production is the same 25 years before the peak as 25 years after the peak). This would only be the case, however, if demand over the years remained stable.

But demand for oil is predicted to increase sharply over the next two decades, due to rising populations and comparative affluence (oil producing states estimate demand will increase 27% during this time period).

Another complicating factor is that the oil that was easy to extract is already used up. Each new barrel of oil is increasingly difficult to obtain. So just as demand is skyrocketing, industry experts predict that production will DECLINE dramatically. The Energy Information Administration (part of the U.S. Department of Energy) estimates that Middle East oil production has already declined dramatically in recent years and that worldwide production will decline by 8% annually (some estimates place this annual production decline as high as 12%).

As oil reserves are rapidly used up, it is envisioned that industry will increasingly turn to natural gas to power factories and electrical generating plants. Government projections indicate that demand for natural gas will increase by about 2.4% annually, making it the dominant fossil fuel source for industry by 2030. But as seen in Figure 1-7, all fossil fuel sources will see declining production in the not-too-distant future.

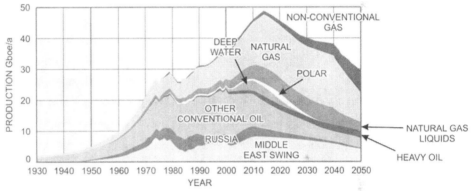

**Figure 1-7:
Carbon-Based
Fuel Supplies**

Coal is still the most abundant of all fossil fuels. Scientists estimate that, at the current rate of extraction, the known reserves (27% of the world's coal reserves are in the United States) will last about 130 years before the last bit of coal is removed from the ground. But the rate of extraction has been growing, by between 2-3% per year. As a result of compounding, a small increase of 2.3% each year results in the amount of coal used doubling every 31 years. Calculating for a 2.5% annual growth in the use of coal (which is the rate projected by the U.S. government), it is estimated that known coal reserves will only last about 60 years.

Environmental Concerns

In the second half of the 20th century, many groups began to evaluate the effect that modern life was having on planet Earth. People and organizations began to assess the impact that decades of burning fossil fuels was having on the atmosphere, lakes, rivers, streams and aquifers, forests, climate and wildlife species.

This examination led to a growing awareness of the impact humans in industrialized regions were having on the world. The first waves of understanding were focused on water and air pollution, decreases in biodiversity and changing world environments. Landmark U.S. legislation such as the *Clean Air Act* (1963), the *Clean Water Act* (1972) and the *Endangered Species Act* (1973), were passed to address specific areas of environmental concern.

In recent years, one of the most pressing environmental realizations is how the global climate has been damaged by the burning of fossil fuels. Large amounts of pollutants, known as greenhouse gases, have been accumulating in the atmosphere, disrupting its delicate balance. These gases (primarily carbon dioxide) accumulate within the **Ozone Layer** of the atmosphere and act as an insulating layer wrapped around the Earth. Through this ozone layer, radiant energy from the Sun is able to enter the Earth's atmosphere, but only a portion of that energy can escape back into space.

The balance of this system is critical. Too much energy escaping, and the Earth will become a cold and lifeless body floating in space (like the moon). Too little energy escaping (as a result of an excess of greenhouse gases within the layer) and the surface of the planet will begin to heat up. Many scientists believe that the planet is rapidly approaching a **Tipping Point**, where the level of these greenhouse gases may cause irreversible changes in the environment. This will result in **Global Warming** and adverse **Climate Change**.

As seen in Figure 1-8, there is a clear connection between historic levels of CO_2 within the atmosphere and the surface temperature of the planet.

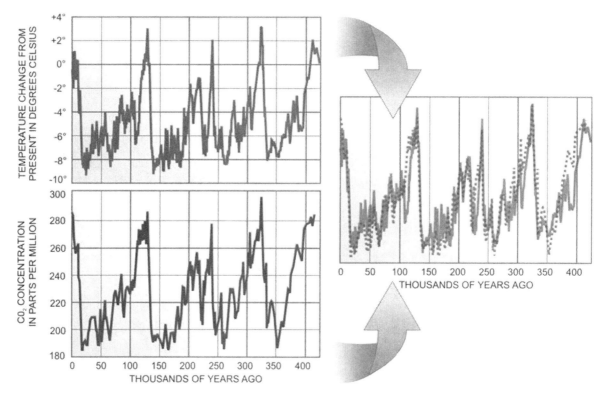

Figure 1-8: Historic CO_2 Levels and Global Temperature

Greenhouse gases are mainly the byproduct of industrial, residential and transportation systems operating within developed countries. However, the accumulation of the greenhouse gases in the atmosphere has worsened because of an accelerated loss of green areas (forests and prairies) around the globe. These green areas are important in the world's carbon dioxide exchange process. Trees and plants remove CO_2 from the atmosphere and produce oxygen (O_2) through **Photosynthesis**.

The destruction of green areas affect the balance of greenhouse gases within the atmosphere in two ways. First, the reduction in the number of trees and plants means that there are fewer available to draw CO_2 from the air and convert it to oxygen. Secondly, the destruction of the green plant material releases the carbon stored within the trees and plants back into the atmosphere. The impact of **Deforestation** is enormous. The destruction of vast forested areas in countries such as Brazil and Indonesia has contributed more CO_2 to the atmosphere than the emissions of all of the transportation vehicles operating worldwide.

CO_2 is not the only greenhouse gas piling up in the atmosphere. Other gases include methane (CH_4), a colorless, odorless gas produces by cattle as part of their digestive process.

ENERGY AUDITS

Clearly the least expensive form of energy is that which is not used. But before savings and efficiencies can be discovered and implemented, one must first figure out just how and how much energy is currently being used. In most cases, this process involves an **Energy Audit**. Like any journey from one place to another, you cannot know where you are going unless you have a pretty good idea of where you are.

An energy audit generally consists of an inspection and analysis of the energy flows within a system (such as a heating/air conditioning system in a commercial building), process (energy use within a manufacturing process, for example), and/or building. The energy auditor first identifies what energy consumption is currently taking place within the structure (or system or process) and then identifies alternatives (and indicates the energy consumption that will occur in the future should changes be made).

Home Energy Audits have become increasingly adopted as a way for home owners to minimize their consumption of limited (and increasingly more expensive) fossil fuels. These audits typically consist of all or some of the following:

- An interview with the homeowner/resident to determine existing comfort and energy problems, goals, priorities, etc.

- Inspection and evaluation of the:
  - **Building Envelope** (including the walls, ceilings, floors, doors, windows, and skylights). Each portion or component of the building's envelope (or shell) is inspected and tested (or estimated) for resistance to heat flow (known as the component's R-value). Leaks, weaknesses and other points of air infiltration are also identified and/or measured.

  - Building's lighting systems (including lighting levels, controls, lamp types and characteristics, and other energy management opportunities).
  - Heating/air conditioning systems. These systems consume a large percentage of a home's energy budget. The audit should inspect not only the units, but the distribution system (air or water handlers) as well.
  - Ventilation systems. Not only will proper indoor air flow help minimize energy consumption - but maintaining a healthy indoor air quality is of primary concern when conducting a home energy audit.
  - Hot water systems. Hot water systems typically consume 11% of all the energy used within a residential structure.

- Water usage of the various systems. As water increasingly becomes more and more scarce in many locations, the efficient use of water resources is often a part of a comprehensive home energy audit.
- Utility bills. Many a utility company has been known to allow inaccuracies to creep into their billing systems. An evaluation of billing, as well as an analysis of the various incentive programs offered by utility companies can assist in dramatically reducing energy costs.

- Combustion appliance safety testing (including CO tests of units with outdoor combustion air sources, sealed combustion units, and power ventilated equipment to verify that they are properly installed and operating).

- Analysis (typically computer-aided modeling) of the home's current energy performance.

- A prioritized list of recommended repairs and/or improvements designed to enhance the building's health, safety and energy conservation. Energy conservation measures should be rated for cost effectiveness in terms of units of energy saved.

Just what constitutes an energy audit is a matter of some debate in this newly emerging field. Local codes, rules, and regulations apply, but a number of organizations have published standards and provide professional credentials that target those conducting energy audits. ASHRAE (the American Society of Heating, Refrigerating and Air-Conditioning Engineers) have published standards concerned with the conducting of energy audits within commercial buildings. They identify four audit levels:

- Level 0 – Benchmarking: This consists of a Whole Building Energy Use (WBEU) analysis based on comparisons with known performance levels of similar buildings. For instance, a 20,000 sq. ft. commercial building constructed of brick at around 1940 would be compared to other similarly constructed buildings of a similar age to determine possible future savings (based on the experience of other similar structures).

- Level I – A Walk-Through audit: An auditor performs a limited physical inspection of the property (a "Walk-Through") to identify simple, low-cost improvements. This audit typically also provides the building owner with a list of energy conservation measures (ECMs) that might be implemented to realize additional energy savings. Level I audits are by design - limited. As a result, the information obtained and provided often lacks detail and typically does not and can not identify all the possible energy savings.

- Level II – Detailed/General energy audit: A comprehensive Level II energy audit typically includes: an evaluation of energy loads (both directly connected and all items plugged into outlets) in the building: the HVAC system (equipment as well as the distribution system); building envelope improvements (walls, windows, roof, foundations, insulation); lighting; equipment and system operation and maintenance improvements; and even tenant education. This level of analysis can also include detailed on-site measurements and computer-based simulation tools to evaluate precisely the benefits and costs of selected energy retrofits. The financial analysis allows the owner to understand the financial benefits of installing specific energy efficient measures.

- Level III – Investment-Grade audit: The investment-grade audit expands on the Level II audit and further relies on a complete engineering study in order to satisfy the requirements of investors on large capital-intensive projects. These audits typically stress the return on investment (ROI) and the rigorous detail is to provide a high level of confidence (if not a guarantee) of these projected returns.

Other organizations, such as the BPI (Building Performance Institute) and RESNET (Residential Energy Services Network) have focused on attempting to define energy audits within residential structures. The RESNET Home Energy Rating System (HERS) is utilized by the ENERGY STAR Homes program developed by the Environmental Protection Agency (EPA). Both organizations (as well as others) offer home energy auditing certifications. Increasingly, many jurisdictions are requiring that home energy auditors be certified to perform audits within that locale.

REVIEW QUESTIONS

The following questions test your knowledge of the material presented in this chapter:

1. Discuss what is meant when we speak of green technologies.

2. How has the increase in world population, as well as the relative affluence of this population affected interest in green technology?

3. Explain what is meant by the term *peak oil* and its impact on fossil fuel prices as well as its impact on the adoption of green technologies.

4. Discuss how the Industrial Revolution transformed society.

5. Discuss how the development of the internal combustion engine as well as refinements in manufacturing processes (such as the assembly line) impacted the development of cities and infrastructure during the 20th century.

6. Discuss how small annual increases in the consumption in fossil fuels (such as a 2.5% increase in the use of coal) can dramatically affect the available reserves.

7. Discuss why the idea of green technology has recently gained such prominence.

8. In what way does the burning of fossil fuels affect global climate?

9. Discuss the complex relationship that plant material have in maintaining a balance of greenhouse gases within the atmosphere.

10. What is one key element in conserving large amounts of energy worldwide?

11. What is still the most abundant fossil fuel?

12. Explain why the emergence of a large middle class within historically poorer nations has a significant impact on world energy demand.

13. What is still the most abundant fossil fuel?

14. What impact might the development of a "Smart Grid" have on the consumption of electricity?

15. Discuss the overall process of an energy audit performed by a professional energy auditor.

1. Which of the following would NOT be considered part of a green technology approach?
   a. Generating power from sources that do not produce greenhouse gases.
   b. Exploring for and exploiting additional sources of fossil fuel.
   c. Changing behavior to conserve energy and resources.
   d. Designing and producing more efficient products.

2. One factor in the growing interest in green technology in recent years is:
   a. a rapidly expanding middle class in historically poor nations.
   b. declining populations within industrialized nations.
   c. increases in the fuel efficiency of automobiles since 1970.
   d. the world-wide economic recession.

3. Prior to the late 1960s, which nation dominated world oil production?
   a. The United States
   b. Iraq (Mesopotamia)
   c. Saudi Arabia
   d. Great Britain

4. The person largely credited with predicting the peaking of world oil reserves is:
   a. British Prime Minister Winston Churchill
   b. King Hubbert
   c. King Abdul Aziz ibn-Saud
   d. U.S. President Franklin Roosevelt

5. Early electrical power plants were almost entirely dependent upon which energy source?
   a. hydro
   b. wood
   c. coal
   d. steam

6. World population in 2050 is expected to:
   a. be over three times what it was in 1955.
   b. decrease slightly from today's levels.
   c. be located primarily in rural areas that have the space and resources to absorb the expected increase.
   d. benefit from peak oil – expected to occur globally in 2049.

7. The U.S. government projects that worldwide oil production will:
   a. increase over the coming years as newly discovered off-shore reserves come on line.
   b. reach peak oil as predicted in 2049.
   c. decline by 8-12% each year over the coming decade.
   d. exceed projections, since OPEC has vastly understated their reserves.

8. Industry experts predict that which of the following will become the dominant fossil fuel source for industry by 2030?
   a. natural gas
   b. solar energy
   c. hydro power
   d. coal

9. When conditions have reached a level where their impact is considered irreversible, this is known as?
    a. climate change
    b. convergence
    c. tipping point
    d. energy density

10. What is photosynthesis?
    a. The conversion of carbon dioxide into H_2O
    b. The process wherein trees and plants take CO_2 from the atmosphere and produce oxygen.
    c. The process of converting oxygen to carbon dioxide.
    d. The process of converting CO_2 to O_3

CHAPTER 2

ENERGY AND POWER

OBJECTIVES

Upon completion of this chapter and its related lab procedures you will be able to perform the following tasks:

1. Understand basic electrical concepts.

2. Display a general understanding of the various forms of energy.

3. Understand the various physical laws of conservation of energy and thermodynamics, and their relevance to solar power systems.

4. List the various ways solar radiation levels are effected by the physical environment.

5. Compute the relationship between amps, volts and watts.

6. Understand and apply Ohm's Law.

7. Describe and diagram electrical circuits in parallel and in series and understand how the different configurations will effect the output of each circuit.

8. Identify the key differences between AC and DC power.

9. Understand how batteries function.

Energy and Power

INTRODUCTION

What is energy? Things are always happening. They are constantly moving from one place to another, changing from one form to another.

When you breathe, you use energy. When sunlight shines on your face, you feel this energy as heat and light. When an alarm clock goes off in the morning, it uses energy—and of course it requires energy to get up out of a nice warm bed.

In science this is called **Work**. It is not work, necessarily, in the way work is typically defined (as in making a living), but work in the sense that something is moved from one place to another. This movement can be something visible to the human eye (like moving a glass of milk from the refrigerator to the table) or movement that cannot be seen (like movement on the molecular level that causes that glass of milk to get warmer the longer it is out of the refrigerator).

These forms of energy appear to be very different from each other—and in many ways they are. One thing that they have in common is the fact that they cause change to happen.

Work

POTENTIAL ENERGY AND KINETIC ENERGY

What is energy? In building an understanding of how energy works, it is often best to start at the very beginning. A basic discussion begins by focusing on two broad categories of energy. Energy in motion (Kinetic) and energy at rest (Potential).

Potential Energy

The word potential pretty much says it all. It just hasn't happened yet. **Potential Energy** is like money in the bank. It is just sitting there—but it has the potential to be used to buy things in the future. A ripe apple hanging from a tree might fall to the ground at any moment. But while it is hanging there on the branch—its energy is Potential Energy. This might also be referred to as "Stored Energy".

When an apple is about to fall from a tree, or an archer aims an arrow at a target—it is clear that something is about to happen (or might happen). There is clearly the potential for something to happen. But potential energy can exist in less clear forms.

Potential Energy

For example, someone might want to eat that apple rather than let it fall to the ground. Once the apple is eaten, then it becomes food (or fuel) that the body uses for energy. Energy that can be used to run or sit or breath or play tennis is still potential energy until these tasks are actually performed. And if too many apples are eaten, then the energy gets converted into fat cells within the body. This stored energy is not being used at the moment—so it is stored as potential energy.

Another example can be found in a stick of wood. A regular old stick hanging in the branches of a tree has many kinds of potential energy. The branch might fall to the ground. An elephant might eat it for food. That same branch could be set on fire. But while it is still up there in the tree—the stick's energy is all potential.

Potential energy (as well as kinetic energy) can take many forms (such as chemical energy, mechanical energy, nuclear energy, heat energy, light energy and electrical energy). Energy can also be studied based on characteristics within the forms. Two common forms of potential energy include elastic and gravitational energy. Both forms are useful in the generation of power.

Potential Energy

Joules

LET'S DO THE MATH

Gravitational potential energy can actually be measured mathematically. The equation is really quite simple. For any object, the gravitational potential energy (GPE) is equal to its mass (m, measured in kilograms) times its acceleration due to gravity (measured in meters per second squared and called "g" in our equation—for gravity—just to keep things simple) times its height (h, measured in meters).

So let's say that there is a big coconut hanging from a palm tree. If the coconut weighs 2 kg (about 4.4 pounds) and is 4 meters (about 13 feet) up there, it is easy to figure out how much gravitational potential energy that coconut contains.

GPE = mgh (gravitational potential energy = mass x gravity x height)

The result of this equation will tell us how many **Joules** (pronounced like "jewels") of gravitational potential energy there are in the coconut (we measure this kind of energy in joules-which is a metric measurement so we must use other metric measurements to get a result that makes sense).

GPE = 2 kg x g x 4 meters

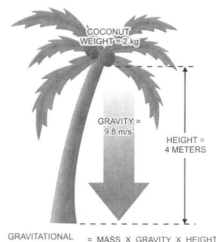

So, in order to solve this equation, all we need to know is the value of "g". On Earth, scientists have figured out that gravity is 9.8 m/s^2 (stuff will fall at a rate of 9.8 meters per second squared) so we just have to plug this number into the equation. We will assume, of course, that you are doing this experiment somewhere on Earth.

GPE = 2 kg x 9.8 m/s^2 x 4 = 78.4 kg (m^{2}s^2) = 78.4 Joules

So, the bigger something is (the bigger its mass) or the higher it is away from the ground, the more gravitational potential energy that thing has.

Kinetic Energy

Kinetic Energy is energy in motion. When that apple falls to the ground, some of its potential energy suddenly becomes kinetic energy. In fact, the word kinetic comes from the Greek word that means "to move."

Sometimes this motion can easily be seen—like when an apple falls to the ground. But sometimes the movement is quite small. Often the movement takes place on a molecular level. Even though these movements are too small to see with the human eye—they are still extremely important.

LET'S DO THE MATH

Kinetic Energy (KE), like potential energy, can be calculated using math. Kinetic energy (KE) is simply half of the mass (m) of the object times its speed (v for velocity) squared.

$$KE = \frac{1}{2} mv^2$$

So, if we use our example of the 2 kg coconut that is 4 m up in a palm tree, we can figure out how much kinetic energy is used as it falls to the ground. If it takes 2 seconds for the coconut to fall to the ground—we know that its velocity (v) is 4 meters in 2 seconds (s) or 2 meters per second (m/s).

So now we have everything we need to figure out its kinetic energy.

$$KE = \frac{1}{2} (2 \text{ kg})(2 \text{ m/s})^2 = \frac{1}{2} (2 \text{ kg})(4 \text{ m}^2/\text{s}^2) = 4 \text{ J}$$

Again, if you increase the weight of the item, or make it travel at a faster speed—the amount of energy will increase. If you increase the weight of the coconut to 8 kg (now, that is a big coconut) the equation would be:

$$KE = \frac{1}{2} (8 \text{ kg})(2 \text{ m/s})^2 = \frac{1}{2} (8 \text{ kg})(4 \text{ m}^2/\text{s}^2) = 16 \text{ J}$$

If we increase the speed of the object, this will have an even more dramatic effect on the energy—since the speed is squared in this equation. So if we make the original 2 kg coconut travel four times as fast (8 m/s rather than 2 m/s), the equation would be:

$$KE = \frac{1}{2} (2 \text{ kg})(8 \text{ m/s})^2 = \frac{1}{2} (2 \text{ kg})(64 \text{ m}^2/\text{s}^2) = 64 \text{ J}$$

Molecules and Atoms

Molecules

All matter in the universe is made up of **Molecules**. A molecule is extremely small (in fact its name comes from the French word that means "extremely small particle"). There are many types and forms of stuff that make up the universe, but it is safe to assume that anything that can be touched is made up of molecules.

But as happens with most things that are big or small—there is always something out there that is bigger or smaller still. Molecules are actually made up of even smaller bits called **Atoms**. At one point in time, scientists thought that an atom was as small as things could get. It was felt that atoms were the fundamental building blocks of all matter.

Atoms

Protons

Neutrons

Electrons

Well, it turns out that there are smaller bits still. Atoms are made up of a combination of the sub-atomic (smaller than atoms) particles called **Protons**, **Neutrons**, and **Electrons**, as illustrated in Figure 2-1. In most cases (but not all) each atom has at least one of each of these.

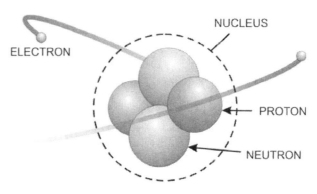

Figure 2-1: Basic Model of an Atom

Some models of an atom appear quite similar to a typical model of a planetary solar system. The center of this system is the nucleus, which consists of at least one proton and typically one neutron for every proton (although hydrogen, the lightest of all elements, gets by without this neutron). At least one electron is in orbit around the nucleus.

In a planetary system, the sun and the planets are held together through gravitational forces. In an atom, the protons and electrons are held together through electrical charges. A proton has a positive charge. An electron has an equal negative charge. When an atom is in balance, these charges are in balance with one electron present for every proton.

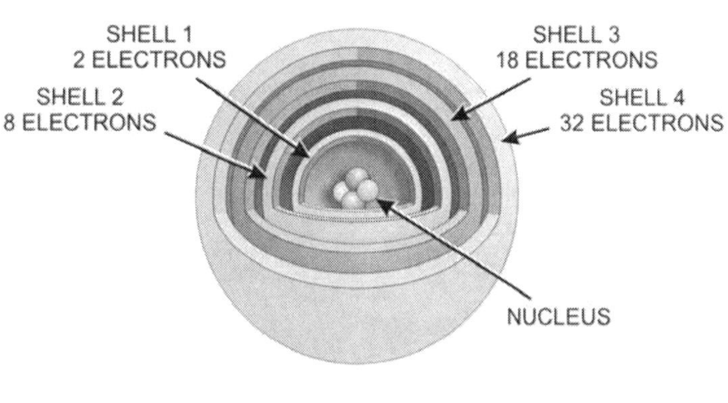

Electrical Energy

SHELL 1
2 ELECTRONS

SHELL 2
8 ELECTRONS

SHELL 3
18 ELECTRONS

SHELL 4
32 ELECTRONS

NUCLEUS

Figure 2-2: Atomic Shells

Like planets orbiting the sun, these electrons typically stay within a specific range in relation to the nucleus. These orbits are usually referred to as shells (rather than circles), since they orbit in three dimensions, as shown in Figure 2-2. The closer the orbital shell is to the nucleus, the stronger the electrical attraction.

When acted upon by some force, electrons in the outer shell can be pushed from their orbits. If these electrically charged electrons are forced to move from one atom to another, the result is **Electrical Energy**.

Covalent Bonds

It is impossible to know where an electron in an atom is located at any given moment (they don't orbit the nucleus in a predictably fixed orbit like the moon orbits the Earth. Electrons are much more random than that). So their location is found by making an educated guess as to where they might be at any given time. Since electrons move very very fast, it is probably easier to imagine the nucleus surrounded by a cloud that represents where the electron might be at any given time (in fact this model of an atom is called an **Electron Cloud**).

When two atoms come together (or bond), the region where these clouds overlap creates a slightly stronger electrical charge within that area. The nuclei of both molecules are attracted to this area just a bit stronger than to other areas where the clouds do not overlap. This electrical charge helps to hold them together. The attraction between the two molecules, as illustrated in Figure 2-3, is called a **Covalent Bond**.

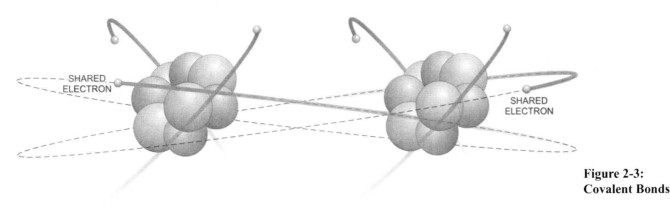

**Figure 2-3:
Covalent Bonds**

Energy Conversion

Before discussing the various types of energy, it is important to understand that energy can change from one type to another. In fact, for anything to actually happen, energy MUST change from one form to another.

SCIENCE NOTE:
THE LAW OF CONSERVATION OF ENERGY

There is just so much energy in the universe and there just isn't any more. Kind of makes sense, if you think about it. Since the universe contains everything—if you added more energy—where would it come from? And if energy disappeared—where would it go?

So the amount of energy in the universe always stays the same. This is called the **Law of Conservation of Energy**. Energy cannot be created or destroyed – but can simply change from one form to another.

Albert Einstein's theory of relativity added to the understanding of this theory by demonstrating that energy can also be converted into mass (called rest mass), and that mass can be converted into energy. So in recent years, the law of conservation of energy and the law of conservation of mass (that matter within a closed system cannot be created or destroyed) are often considered integrated, stating that the mass-energy of a closed system can neither be created or destroyed but simply changes forms.

According to the Law of Conservation of Energy, energy can never be created or destroyed. It just changes form. In fact, for anything to happen, energy must change from one form to another. When a light is switched on, the electrical energy in the wire is changed into light energy and heat energy (many light bulbs can become quite hot).

The Law of Conservation of Energy states that energy cannot be created or destroyed, but can change its form.

The total quantity of matter and energy available in the universe is a fixed amount and never any more or less.

When a person runs, the chemical energy in the food they ate for breakfast converts into mechanical energy (running). When a stick of wood is burned, its chemical energy is converted to heat and light energy.

SCIENCE NOTE: THE LAWS OF THERMODYNAMICS

First Law of Thermodynamics

Entropy

Second Law of Thermodynamics

Zeroth Law of Thermodynamics

Third Law of Thermodynamics

When people started looking at the nature of the universe, they decided to organize their observations into some rules (or laws). When folks started discussing the nature of heat (a form of energy) the law of conservation of energy became known as the **First Law of Thermodynamics**. It basically says that in a closed system (like the universe) heat (energy) can not be created or destroyed.

When we light a candle, we are not "creating" energy. We are simply beginning the process of transforming the stored chemical energy of the candle into heat and light.

They also noticed that as work is done (things moving about), heat always moves from where it is warm to where it is cooler. Energy goes from where it is more concentrated to where it is less concentrated. This "evening out" of energy or temperature is called **Entropy**. And if left alone, entropy (the evening out of energy) in a closed system always increases. This is known as the **Second Law of Thermodynamics**.

So what happens if the two things are already the same temperature (of equal energy)? Well, it turns out that heat will not flow between objects that are the same temperature (since they are already in balance). But this realization seemed pretty fundamental to the folks thinking these things up, so they didn't want to name it the third law. They decided that it really should come first. But the first law was already taken. So they named this observation the **Zeroth Law of Thermodynamics** (good thing they didn't come up with any more, or we might have gone to negative numbers).

As these great thinkers sat around thinking, they wondered what would happen if they took energy from one place to another (increasing entropy), and then tried to put it back again. Could they somehow perfectly reverse the process (get back to exactly where they started)?

Well, it turns out that nothing is perfect. So you can never quite get back to where you started. Energy is always lost (like the exhaust from a car engine) as a system does work. As work takes place (energy is moving about), it is always moving in a steady direction towards increased entropy (in other words, the temperatures are always getting just a bit more even). This is the **Third Law of Thermodynamics**.

TYPES OF ENERGY

The electrical charges within and between atoms are fundamental in understanding how various forms of energy function. Each energy form holds the promise of solving society's energy needs. These forms of energy include:

- Chemical energy
- Electrical energy
- Thermal energy (heat)
- Radiant energy (light)
- Mechanical energy
- Nuclear energy

Chemical Energy

The energy used or stored when atoms bond together is called **Chemical Energy**. If the atoms just sit there, bonded together, then the energy held within that bond is potential energy. This energy can sit around for a long time before it is used. It doesn't mean the energy doesn't exist—it is simply not being used at the moment.

Atoms generally don't just sit there, however. They change from one form to another. Chemical energy conversions are more commonly referred to as **Chemical Reactions**. Change of some sort (in this case a chemical change) has taken place when two materials are mixed together, resulting in a third, completely different material.

These reactions may be purely chemical in nature, for example hydrogen and oxygen combining to form water (H_2O). Or they may be a combination of various energy conversions. For example, gasoline inside a car's engine is ignited. The potential chemical energy within the gasoline converts to thermal energy, radiant energy, mechanical energy (the explosion pushes the pistons), as well as chemical (as some of the gasoline is converted into chemical pollutants that leave through the exhaust system).

Often a chemical reaction will release heat, or light, or sound—or all three. When this happens, the "mad scientist" responsible for the experiment has converted potential chemical energy into heat energy (**Thermal Energy**), light (**Radiant Energy**) and sound waves (and perhaps even a bit of smell). There is probably still some chemical energy present, unless every bit of the original compound was consumed in the explosion. If, during this chemical reaction, heat is given off, it would be an example of an **Exothermic Reaction**.

For example, when a piece of wood is burned, as shown in Figure 2-4, the carbon ©) in the wood (its primary component) mixes with the oxygen in the air (O_2). The result is heat (an exothermic reaction) as well as carbon dioxide (CO_2). The smoke is likely comprised of gases from other materials in the wood combining with the oxygen (some of these can be highly toxic), water vapor, as well as carbon (soot) that is not completely reduced to CO_2.

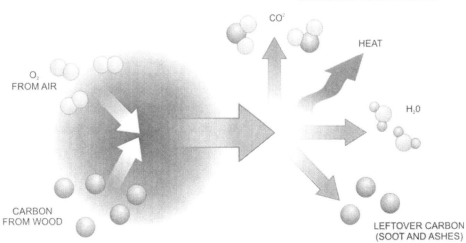

Figure 2-4: Molecular Model of Wood Burning

Endothermic
Reactions

Photosynthesis

There are also cases where the chemical reaction will actually absorb heat. These are called **Endothermic Reactions**. A good example of an endothermic reaction is **Photosynthesis**. Plants use the heat and light from the sun, along with carbon dioxide and water, converting it into glucose (sugar) and oxygen. In this way, the plants effectively "store" the energy of the sun.

Thermal Energy (Heat)

Thermal (heat)
Energy

Another type of energy is called **Thermal Energy (heat)**. It is important to understand how heat works, since generating heat (or cool) is an important goal of all energy sources. Why is one thing hot and another is cold? Why do things get hot when the are cooked? All this has to do with how thermal energy functions.

Everything that can be touched is made of molecules and even smaller bits that are called atoms. These atoms are always in motion. The electrons zip around the nuclei, the atoms bang into each other, sometimes sticking together, sometimes bouncing off. The molecules are bumping and bouncing and moving. This movement requires energy. This movement always generates heat.

Absolute Zero

It is theoretically possible for all molecular motion to stop, resulting in a situation where the temperature is as cold as it can possibly get (it is impossible to move slower than standing still). This thermal situation is referred to as **Absolute Zero**.

SCIENCE NOTE: ABSOLUTE ZERO

If temperature is really just a measurement of how fast molecules are moving around within a substance, what would happen if these molecules were slowed down until they stopped completely?

While this is fine to think about in theory, it simply does not happen in reality (although scientists have gotten really really close in those laboratories where scientists hang out). In theory, the temperature at which all molecular motion stops is called absolute zero.

But the problem with absolute zero is that in order to cool something down, the energy has to go somewhere. And energy always has to go from something that is warm to something that is cooler. So, as you take the energy away, you have to put it somewhere that is colder. So in order to get to absolute zero, something already has to exist that is colder than absolute zero.

Scientists have figured out that absolute zero (that doesn't exist) would exist at -459.67° F (-273.15° C) if it could get that cold... but it can't... so it won't.

Temperature

Pressure

Any given object, or even the air we breath, is comprised of moving molecules. Some of these molecules are moving slowly, some are moving quite quickly. But they are all so small that it is nearly impossible to measure each one. The best that can be done (from a practical perspective) is to simply measure the average of this motion. This average is referred to as either **Temperature** or **Pressure**.

If the atoms in something move faster and faster—then the temperature (or pressure if that is what is being measured) will increase. Imagine a dance where everyone is jumping and banging into each other. As they jump and dance and run around—they get warmer. In fact nearly everyone and potentially everything in the room gets warmer. Even the air in the room gets warmer. The temperature increases. Mechanical energy (dancing) has been converted into thermal energy.

It is important to understand that this energy is always trying to move from where it is highly concentrated—to a less concentrated place. The dancers will spread out so they have room to move.

As the air temperature in the room rises to an uncomfortable level, an open window might allow the warmer air to flow outdoors and the cooler outside air to come inside. Eventually all the various temperatures of air will mix until (if given enough time and no outside force acts upon it) all the air in the world will become the same temperature. But the air all over the world will be just a little bit warmer because of the dance.

Conduction

So how does heat go from where it is concentrated to where it is less concentrated (from where it is warmer to where it is cooler)? One way is through **Conduction**.

Conduction occurs when heat moves directly through physical contact (touching) from where it is hot (concentrated thermal energy) to where it is cooler (less concentrated).

If a candle is lit, for example, the potential chemical energy within wax and the wick is converted into heat and light (and a bit of smoke). If the metal rod is placed directly into the flame, as illustrated in Figure 2-5, over time, more and more heat will move through the metal rod from where it is concentrated (the flame) to where it is less concentrated (the hand, in this case). Eventually the rod will get too hot to touch. This form of heat transfer is known as conduction.

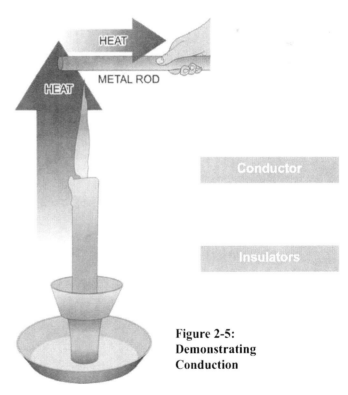

Since metal is a good **Conductor**, a large amount of the heat will be transferred along the rod. Remember, the rod and the hand are cooler than the flame, so the thermal energy will attempt to travel from where it is more concentrated (the flame) to where it is less concentrated.

Some materials do not conduct energy very well at all. These are called **Insulators**. Homes use insulators (such as fiberglass, wood fiber, wool) to keep the warmer air from traveling outside, where the cool air has an even lower concentration of thermal energy. If, in the above example of the candle flame and metal rod, well-insulated gloves were worn while holding the metal rod, the heat would not transfer from the rod to the hand. So insulators are important in blocking the flow of energy (usually thermal or electrical energy).

**Figure 2-5:
Demonstrating
Conduction**

Convection

Another way thermal energy might move and mix is through a process known as **Convection**. As a liquid or a gas heats up, it becomes less dense (the area it occupies expands, but the quantity of matter remains the same). Warmer, lighter air will rise within a room as cooler, more dense air fills the space below it, as demonstrated in Figure 2-6.

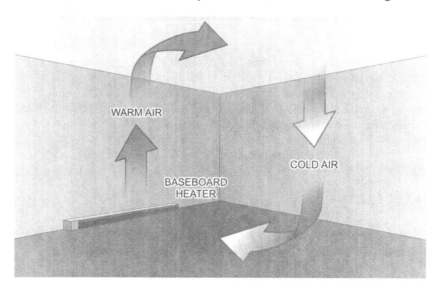

Figure 2-6:
Convection within a Room

If a heater is located on the floor within a closed room, the cooler air near it will warm. This warmer air will expand, becoming less dense, and rise until blocked by the ceiling (which is hopefully well insulated). If this air is warmer than the air already occupying that space, the cooler air will sink, completing the circular cycle. In this way the warmer and cooler air within the room will move and mix, without the help of a fan.

Radiation (Light)

All matter radiates energy. It might be helpful to think about this form of energy as waves flowing from an object that is warm to an object that is cooler. These **Electromagnetic Waves** flow from one place to another—even through the vacuum of space (such as the radiated energy that flows from the Sun to the Earth).

The amount of incoming solar electromagnetic radiation per unit of area (usually considered in terms of square meters) at a distance of one **Astronomical Unit** (**AU**)—the average distance of the Earth from the Sun, or about 93 million miles (150 million kilometers)— is referred to as the **Solar Constant**. When measured at the outer edges of Earth's atmosphere, sunlight contains roughly 1,366 watts of energy per square meter (W/m^2). This energy is reduced dramatically as sunlight passes through the Earth's atmosphere. The amount of energy contained in sunlight striking the surface of the planet is only about 342 W/m^2.

The actual direct solar irradiance striking the top of the atmosphere fluctuates throughout the year as well by about 6.9% (from 1,412 W/m^2 in early January to 1,321 W/m^2 in early July) due to orbital variations in the Earth's distance from the Sun.

Like any wave (such as those on the ocean), the direction of the wave is both vertical (up and down), as well as lateral (side-to-side) in the direction of the current flow. This movement is measured in terms of frequency (or wavelength)—how much or how little time there is between wave crests. The entire range of these frequencies is called the **Electromagnetic Spectrum**.

As shown in Figure 2-7, the electromagnetic spectrum covers a wide range from short gamma rays to incredibly long radio waves. The visible light portion of the spectrum occupies only a very narrow portion of the overall system.

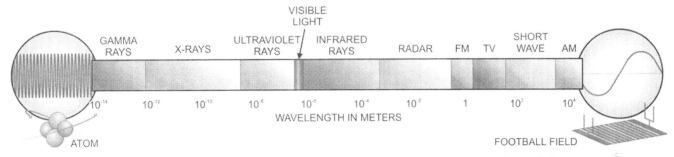

When an object is struck by light radiation, that energy is either **Absorbed**, **Reflected** or **Transmitted** through to some other object. If it is absorbed, it is absorbed in the form of heat. If it is reflected, it can either be reflected as light or as heat energy.

Figure 2-7: Electromagnetic Spectrum

Imagine sunlight hitting a pool of water. The energy of that sunlight can either be absorbed by the water (making it warmer), or be reflected off its surface (bouncing off and warming up whatever it hits next) or it might travel through the water and heat up the bottom of the pond.

In the case of light striking a pond, the radiant energy is absorbed, reflected AND transmitted. But if sunlight hits a basketball—not much of it would travel through the ball (if any) so all the energy is either absorbed or reflected.

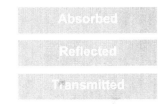

Properties Affecting the Absorption of Radiant Energy

Just how much heat energy an object absorbs through radiation is determined by several properties of that object. These properties include:

Temperature

Remember, energy always moves from where it is concentrated (warmer) to where it is less concentrated (cooler). So the cooler an object is in relation to everything around it, the more of the available energy it will absorb.

For example, if an ice cube is placed into a cup of boiling water out in the sun, the ice cube will absorb more energy (its temperature will increase faster) than will the cup of boiling water. It doesn't mean that the temperature of the ice is higher than the boiling water (obviously not) but the rate of absorption is higher.

Albedo

The more reflective an object, the less energy it will absorb. More of the available energy will simply bounce off (dark objects get hotter in the sun, white objects stay cooler—and a mirror is even more reflective, so it will remain cooler still). Different surface materials absorb radiant energy at significantly different rates, as shown in Table 2-1.

Table 2-1: Albedo Characteristics of Various Surface Materials

SURFACE	TYPICAL ALBEDO
Fresh asphalt	0.04 (4% of radiant energy reflected)
Conifer forest (summer)	0.09 to 0.15
Worn asphalt	0.12
Deciduous trees	0.15 to 0.18
Bare soil	0.17
Green grass	0.25
Desert sand	0.4
New concrete	0.55
Fresh snow	0.80 to 0.90

SCIENCE NOTE: ALBEDO

Albedo

When we talk about **Albedo**, it is typically understood that it is the reflectivity of the visible light portion of the spectrum that is discussed. This reflectivity can range from 90% for fresh snow (meaning that only 10% of the visible light's energy will be absorbed by the snow, the rest will bounce off) to 4% for charcoal (where almost all the light's energy is absorbed as heat).

The term albedo is derived from Latin, meaning *whiteness*. So not surprisingly, the lighter the color of an object, the higher its albedo properties (such as in the comparison between snow and charcoal). On a global scale, this can have a profound impact in areas that are normally covered with snow. The area that once reflected 90% of the sun's heat energy (the snow covered areas) now may absorb 80% or more (once the snow melts), causing surrounding snow to melt faster, which in turn creates a larger area for heat absorption, and so on.

On a more local (and positive) scale, a designer can utilize the albedo characteristics of the surrounding landscape to augment the collection of radiant energy.

For example, anticipating that 90% of the energy falling on snow will be reflected may lead to a design that captures some of this reflected energy by situating solar panels in such a way as to capture this otherwise lost energy. Or grass might be used (such as on a living roof) rather than a darker material (such as asphalt shingles) to reduce the amount of energy absorbed into a building.

Size

The more surface area that is available to absorb the radiant energy, the more energy it will absorb.

Angle

And finally, the angle at which an object is oriented towards the thing that is radiating the energy (the sun, for example) will affect how much energy that object will absorb.

Think about skipping a flat rock on the surface of a pond. If the rock strikes the surface at a low enough angle, it will bounce off (perhaps many times). But if it is dropped straight down into the water, it will sink like… well, a rock.

In the case of the sun's energy, the greater the angle, the larger the resulting surface area to receive a fixed amount of energy. So that energy is less concentrated. Figure 2-8 illustrates that every square foot of sunlight striking the surface of the earth contains about 32 watts (342 watts per square meter) of energy. When the angle of the sun's rays is shifted to 45 degrees, the surface area this same amount of sunlight strikes increases by a factor of 1.41. As a result, the earth at this angle receives only 22.5 watts of energy per square foot (242 watts per square meter).

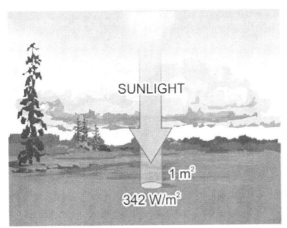 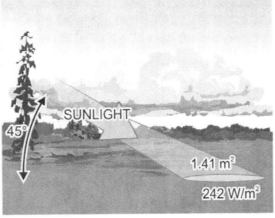

Figure 2-8: Angle of Sun

SCIENCE NOTE: THE ANGLE OF THE SUN

When calculating how much energy strikes the earth from the sun, the angle of the sun's rays will make a huge difference. This is not only because a greater amount of the energy will "skip off" the atmosphere (like a stone skipping off the water's surface) but also the surface area that this fixed amount of sunlight strikes gets larger.

For example, for every 10.76 square feet (1 square meter) of the earth's surface that the sun strikes directly, it receives 342 watts of energy each hour. If you tilt the angle of the sun to 45 degrees, the surface area of earth that same amount of sunlight will actually hit is 15.18 square feet (1.41 square meters). So this same 342 watts of energy is now absorbed over a much larger surface area. In fact, the concentration of energy is reduced to only about 242 watts per square meter simply by changing the angle of the energy source (in this case the sun).

This is the major reason why it is colder in the winter (when the angle of the sun striking the earth is greatest) and warmer in the summer (when the angle is less).

The Effect of Atmosphere on Solar Radiation

Scattered

Three atmospheric processes affect the radiant energy of the sun as it makes its way to the earth's surface. As solar radiation passes through the atmosphere, it can be **Scattered**, absorbed, or reflected by the atmosphere itself or by particles suspended in the atmosphere.

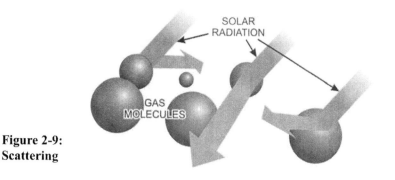

Figure 2-9: Scattering

- *Scattering*: As the light waves pass through the earth's atmosphere, they may be diffused in random directions as they hit gas molecules or suspended particles, as shown in Figure 2-9. The wavelengths of this energy are not altered although some of the shortwave energy is redirected back out into space (reducing the amount of energy that strikes the earth's surface). The effect of this scattering is what causes the sky to look blue (or more red if larger particles—such as pollution—are concentrated in the atmosphere). Without scattering, the daytime sky would be black (as is the case on the moon, for example).

- *Absorption*: Some particles and gases in the atmosphere are able to actually absorb solar radiation. This energy is converted into heat (just as the earth's surface heats when struck by solar radiation, the atmosphere heats as well). As this heat energy radiates from the particle, some of its energy will be radiated out into space, as illustrated in Figure 2-10.

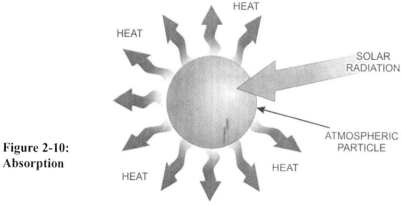

Figure 2-10: Absorption

- *Reflection*: And finally, if the radiant energy is reflected back at a 180 degree angle, 100% of its energy will bounce back into space, as shown in Figure 2-11. Most of this reflection takes place in clouds, where 40-90% of the sun's energy is reflected into space.

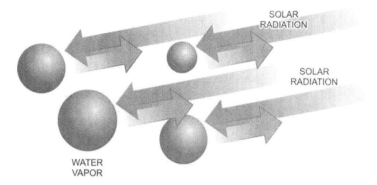

Figure 2-11: Reflection

In combination, these three factors result in only about 51% of the sun's radiant energy actually being absorbed by the surface of the earth. About 30% of the sun's radiant energy is reflected back into space (26% reflected by the atmosphere and 4% reflected by the earth itself) while another 19% is either absorbed or scattered within the atmosphere, as illustrated in Figure 2-12.

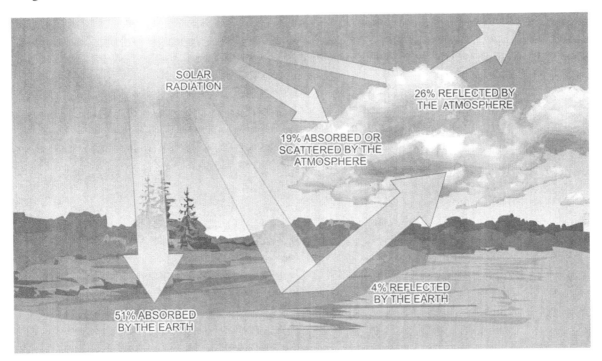

Figure 2-12: Solar Radiation Absorbed at Earth's Surface

Mechanical Energy

When an object is moved from one place to another (on an observable level rather than on a molecular level) most often this is **Mechanical Energy** in action. When anything falls, or turns, or spins or hops—it is mechanical energy at work.

And speaking of work, mechanical energy is often defined as the ability to do work. At a very basic level, **Work** happens when energy (a **Force**) makes something move from one place to another (it is displaced). When a nail is hammered into a board, the force to move that nail from outside the board to inside the board requires energy. That energy is mechanical energy. The use of this mechanical energy results in work (the nail has been moved).

LET'S DO THE MATH

In order to understand Work, you have to understand some of the terms and the math.

The first unit of measure we will discuss is called a **Newton** (after Sir Isaac). One newton is defined as the amount of force that is required to accelerate (move from a dead stop) something with a mass of one kilogram at a rate of one meter per second. This is a metric term, so again all measurements will be metric.

Its mathematical equation is:

One newton (N) = one kilogram (kg) times one meter (m) divided by one second squared (s^2)

$$1N = 1 \text{ kg} \times m / s^2$$

It is not so important to understand exactly what a newton is for the moment, but just to know that it is the way to measure force. For example, the earth's gravity can be measured and found to exert 9.80665 N (newtons) of downward force on an object with a mass of one kilogram.

Now that we know how to measure force, we can start to talk about measuring work. We know that work happens when a force makes something move a certain distance. So we can represent that with the following equation:

Work (w) = Force (F) $\times$ Distance (d) or w = F $\times$ d

But we measure work in terms of joules. And one joule (J) has been defined as equal to one newton (our measurement of force) traveling one meter (our measurement of distance). So, mathematically we can simply state:

1 joule (J) = one newton (N) $\times$ one meter (m)

If you substitute in the equation that defines a newton, you get:

$$J = (1 \text{ kg} \times m/s^2) \times m = 1 \text{ kg} \times m^2 /s^2$$

So, for example, since we know that the earth's gravity is 9.80665 N, we can figure out how much work (in joules) is done if we drop something that weighs 1 kilogram a distance of 20 meters (just to pick a number at random).

$$W = 9.80665 \text{ N} \times 20 \text{ m} = 196.133 \text{ J}$$

Wind energy is just one example of how humans have harnessed mechanical energy. For centuries, humans have converted the mechanical energy of the wind into useful power. A traditional windmill uses large blades to capture the lateral direction of the wind, converting it into a circular motion.

The resulting rotational energy can then be transferred to a grinding wheel to process grains into meal or to pump water from below the earth's surface, as shown in Figure 2-13. These are just a couple of simple examples of how mechanical energy can be harnessed.

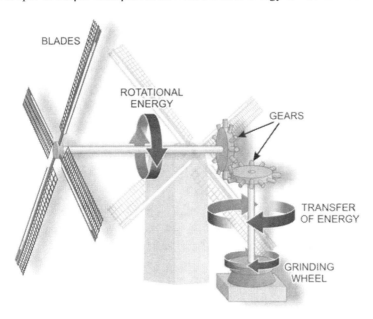

BLADES

ROTATIONAL ENERGY

GEARS

TRANSFER OF ENERGY

GRINDING WHEEL

Figure 2-13: Mechanical Energy

Power

If work is simply the force required to move something from one place to another—does it really matter how long it takes? After all, if a person carries a bucket of water up a hill, the same amount of work is done whether it takes a minute or an hour.

But time is important. So when time is factored into the work equation, the result is **Power**. The more power available, the faster the work will be accomplished.

Power is expressed as the amount of work divided by the amount of time it takes.

Power = Work/Time

Whenever a thing is measured—that measurement is given a name (otherwise no one would know what is being discussed). Distances are referred to in inches, or feet, or meters. Temperatures are measured in degrees. Power, however, is referred to in units of measure called **Watts**.

A watt is simply one joule per second (work/time). All of these things—watts, joules, even seconds, are just units of measure that are used to give people a common frame of reference.

LET'S DO THE MATH

So just how much power does it take to walk up a hill? Well, that depends on a lot of factors. How high is the hill? How fast are you walking? And how much force does it take to move yourself each step of the way?

So let's assume that it takes about 700 newtons (that's a measurement of force not a cookie made with figs) to move 1 meter straight up the hillside. We measure the hill and find that it is 30 meters high. With this information we can figure out how much work it take to climb the hill, but we will have no clue of the amount of power.

So the only thing left to know if we want to learn how much power it takes to climb the hill is the amount of time to do it.

If it takes 120 seconds, our equation will look like this:

Power = Work/Time = (Force x Distance)/Time = 700 N x 30m/120s = 21,000J/120s = 175 Watts

Remember, one joule (J) = one newton (N) x one meter (m)

Now, if we could hurry, how would this affect the amount of power used in our equation? If it took half the time, say 60 seconds, what happens?

Power = 700N x 30m/60s = 21,000J/60s = 350 Watts

Notice that the amount of work stayed the same, but the power doubled. Clearly, the faster the work gets done, the more power it takes.

SCIENCE FACT: HORSE POWER

In 1763 a young Scotsman named James Watt started tinkering around with steam engines (check it out in Figure 2-14). After years of messing with these things, he finally figured out how to make them much more efficient—so efficient in fact that many folks give Watt a big share of the credit (or his steam engines anyway) for helping launch the industrial revolution.

Since Watt didn't actually invent the steam engine, but just improved it. He came up with a way of getting paid based on how much coal his improvements saved his customers. But if they were using horses instead of an older version of the steam engine— Watt didn't get paid. Big problem. So Watt had to figure out just how much work a horse did, so he could show that his engine was saving money by doing more.

After doing the math, Watt came up with a number by estimating that a pony could lift 220 pounds 100 feet per minute for four hours. He then figured that a full grown horse could lift about 50% more than that. And from then on, Watt started talking about how much power his steam engines generated in terms of "**Horse Power**."

To honor Watt for his work with steam (and maybe horses) in 1889 the Second Congress of the British Association for the Advancement of Science decided that units of power should be named after our friend James.

It turns out that one horsepower is equal to about 746 watts.

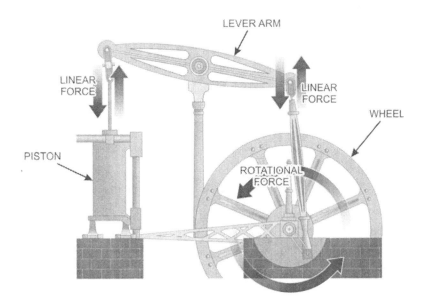

LEVER ARM

LINEAR FORCE

LINEAR FORCE

WHEEL

PISTON

ROTATIONAL FORCE

Figure 2-14: Watt's Steam Engine

Electrical Energy

Atoms are made up of sub-atomic components referred to as protons, neutrons and electrons. The tiny little electrons move around the outside, while the proton and neutrons form the center, or **Nucleus** of the atom.

These electrons have a **Negative Charge**, while the protons have a **Positive Charge**. Negative and positive charges are typically equal to each other and keep the atom in balance (since opposites attract). But as the electrons spin and rotate around the outside of the atom, they can fly off when prompted to do so by some outside force. Usually when this happens, an available electron that spins off from another atom quickly joins up with the lonely proton so that the electrical charge of the atom is balanced once again.

It might help to think of this process as a giant dance floor where couples are dancing around in couples, always together. But one person might decide to change partners. So she turns away from her current partner and starts dancing with someone else. For a moment there will be two people out on the dance floor who have no one to dance with (her original partner and the person who was dancing with the partner she is dancing with now).

Electrons and protons are not very fussy about who they dance with. So when they are forced out of balance (dancing alone, so to speak) they quickly pair up whenever possible.

When these electrons (or dancers) move from one partner to another—it is called **Electricity**.

Nucleus

Negative Charge

Positive Charge

Electricity

Electrical Charges

Each particle in the atom has energy associated with it and is identified by the type of energy it possesses. Protons possess a **Positive Electrical Charge**, electrons have a **Negative Electrical Charge** and neutrons are neutral and have no charge. What makes the atom interesting for alternative energy is in using its energy to perform **Work**, such as providing heat, light or driving an electric motor.

Energy can be obtained from an atom by causing it to give up an electron from its outer orbit (or shell). When the electron leaves its orbit around the atom, energy is given off in the form of heat or light. This is accomplished by applying energy to the electron to *push* (or *pull*) it away from the atom. To free an electron from its atom, enough energy must be applied to the electron to overcome the element's **Resistivity** to giving up its electron. Each element has its own resistivity level. Only the electrons in the atom's outer shell (called **Valence Electrons**) can be separated from an atom.

Once the electron has left its relatively stable orbit, it is referred to as a **Free Electron** and represents a negative electrical charge. The atom that gave up the electron is now out of balance and becomes a positive electrical charge. In this state the atom is referred to as an **Ion**. When a free electron comes into the vicinity of an ion (an atom that is missing an electron from its structure), it will fall into an orbit around that atom.

It is said that opposites attract, and this is certainly the case with electrical charges, as shown in Figure 2-15. Just as the negatively charged free electron is attracted to the positively charged ion, negatively charged free electrons are repelled by the electromagnetic properties of other negatively charged free electrons.

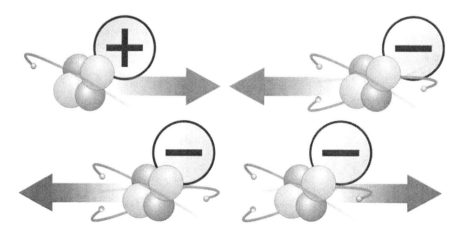

**Figure 2-15:
Electrical Charges**

Likewise, positively charged ions are repelled by other positively charged ions. While the process is not exactly the same, imagine two magnets held closely together. If the negative terminal of one magnet is matched with the positive terminal of the other, they pull together. If both negative (or both positive) terminals are placed together, they push apart from each other.

The attraction and repulsion of positive and negative charges in relation to each other results in an **Electrical Force** being applied to these objects. This occurs because similar electrically charged particles repel each other while unlike electrical charges attract each other—the positive ion attracts the negative electron. Once combined, the atom returns to its normally neutral state (all atoms seek to be electrically neutral).

It tends to be much easier to create free electrons with atoms that have three or less electrons in their valence shell. These materials are referred to as electrical **Conductors**. Materials that possess more then three electrons in their outer shell are referred to as **Insulators** and do not give up valence electrons easily. Common conductor materials include gold, silver, copper and aluminum.

Conductors

Insulators

Common electrical insulators include rubber, plastics, paper, and glass. Electrical insulators are typically not a single element. Instead, insulators are most often materials made up of different elements that have joined together to share their valence electrons. The sharing of valence electrons is referred to as covalent bonding and makes it much more difficult to create a free electron.

SCIENCE FACT: CONSERVATION OF CHARGE

Okay, so we learned earlier that the LAW of conservation of energy says that energy cannot be created or destroyed—it just is. Well, guess what? Electrical charges are a form of energy. So in any closed system (like, say, the universe) the charges will remain constant.

Of course a positive charge can be balanced out by a negative charge, so everything appears to have no charge. But don't let that fool you. It's still in there, waiting for its chance.

You might think this doesn't mean anything to anybody—but understanding this can lead to some interesting ideas (like batteries, for instance). So if you rub your feet along the carpet, you are losing electrons and becoming negatively charged.

But while you become negatively charged, the carpet is gaining electrons in an equal amount, becoming positively charged. The amount of charge remains the same (negative = positive). Nothing is created or destroyed.

Coulombs, Amps, Volts and Watts

This electrical force is measured in terms of **Coulombs** ©), which is defined by the International System of Units as being equal to the amount of electrical charge that is transmitted in one second (s) at a current rate of one ampere (A).

Coulombs ©)

1 Coulomb = 1 A x 1s

That said, just what is an **Ampere** (or amp)? Well, an ampere is simply the unit of measure to quantify the **Current**, or flow rate of electricity through a circuit. Imagine that electricity is water. With water, the current might be measured in gallons per minute (or liters per second)—how much quantity of water passes a given spot during a period of time.

Ampere

Current

Well, amps measure exactly the same concept, except for electricity. One ampere is $6,280,000,000,000,000,000$ (6.28×10^{18}) electrons passing by the point of measurement in one second.

While amps will show the rate at which the electrical current is flowing, it doesn't show how much electricity has actually been moved from one place to another. Electricity (as with water) does not move without pressure. No pressure, no flow. The more pressure, the greater the quantity (assuming the pipe size remains the same). So there are a few more terms that should be defined in order to discuss electrical flow.

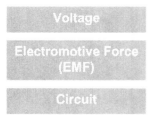

When discussing electrical pressure (the intensity or difference in potential), this factor is measured in terms of **Volts** (**V**). A volt is defined as the potential difference across a conductor when a current of one ampere dissipates one watt of power. In other words:

Watt = Volts x Amps
Amps = Watts/Volts
Volts = Watts/Amps

SCIENCE NOTE: AMPS, WATTS AND VOLTS

One of the most difficult electrical concepts for folks to understand is the concept of watts, amps and volts. This is because the definition of one depends upon the definition of the other.

For example, let's use the water analogy again. If I say we have a gallon (or a liter) or water, it really doesn't tell you anything about its power or flow or intensity. It just is. If I say that the water is flowing at a rate of 2 meters/second, again, it doesn't tell us much. How much water? A trickle or a river?

But if I say that the water is flowing at a rate of 5 gallons per second, then we have some information that is useful.

The same is true for electrical power. The watts refers to the total amount of power. By itself it doesn't really mean much (just like 10 gallons doesn't really tell us much). People often confuse the terms watt and watt-hour. A watt-hour is a rate at which power is used. A watt is just the amount of power used. They are different as, for example saying that we traveled 1,000 miles or that we were traveling at 1,000 miles per hour. A 100-watt light bulb uses 100-watts of energy each and every hour (100 watt-hours) it is turned on.

Let's say that the 100-watt bulb is like a very leaky barrel that needs to receive 50-gallons of water each hour to stay full. If we are filling the barrel through a very narrow straw (low current), we will need a very high water pressure (voltage) to keep up. If we are filling it with a big pipe (increased amps) we need less pressure (volts) to transport the same amount of water.

So you see, amps (current) times voltage (intensity) equals power (watts).

VOLTAGE AND CURRENT

Voltage is the term used to describe the **Electromotive Force** (**EMF**) that places the electrical push and pull on the different terminals of a power source. If an acceptable external pathway is provided for the movement of the electrons from the pushing end of the voltage source to the pulling end, an electrical **Circuit** is created. This concept is depicted in Figure 2-16. You can envision this as electrons hopping from one atom to the next to move around the circuit from the pushing end of the voltage source to the pulling end. The electromotive force is applied to all of the atoms between the two ends of the conductor, which causes a flow (or current) of electrons to move through the circuit.

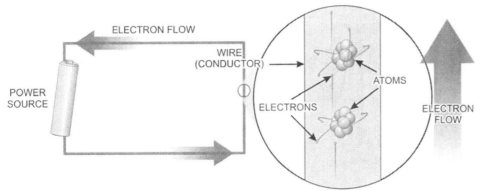

Figure 2-16: Electron Current Flow

After traveling through the external circuit, the electron reaches the **Anode** (+) side of the source where it recombines with one of the ions that gave up an electron.

If the movement of electrons around the circuit is always in one direction, this is referred to as **Direct Current (DC)**. Direct current is typically associated with batteries (or solar panels). On the other hand, there are electrical generation systems that obtain energy from electrons by causing them to periodically hop back and forth between atoms. This type of electrical current is referred to as **Alternating Current (AC)** and is usually the product of systems that generate electricity through some type of rotational mechanical system—such as generator and alternators. Direct and alternating currents are depicted in Figure 2-17.

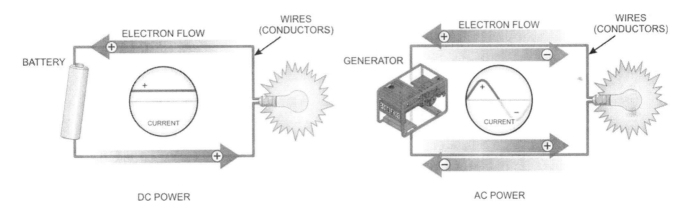

Figure 2-17: Direct and Alternating Current Flows

── NOTE ──

Be aware that technicians and engineers use different methods of describing current flow in circuits. Engineers use a method known as **Conventional Current Flow** to describe the movement of positive charges through the circuit, while technicians employ **Electron Current Flow**, which describes the movement of the electrons through the circuit.

Electrical Circuits

Circuit

An electrical current is comprised of electrons flowing along a path, each electron pushing the next as they move in a uniform direction. But in order for this flow to be maintained, the pathway must form a complete circle (or **Circuit**).

Figure 2-18 demonstrates a simple DC (Direct Current) circuit. The electricity will always flow in one direction, moving from an area of negative charge (more concentrated electrons) to an area of positive charge (where there are fewer electrons).

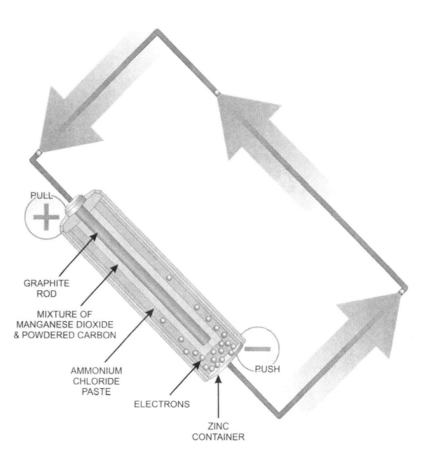

PULL

GRAPHITE
ROD

MIXTURE OF
MANGANESE DIOXIDE
& POWDERED CARBON

AMMONIUM
CHLORIDE
PASTE

ELECTRONS

PUSH

ZINC
CONTAINER

Figure 2-18:
Simple DC Circuit

Load

As this current passes along the circuit, it can be used to power a **Load**, such as a light bulb, as illustrated in Figure 2-19. When this occurs, some of the power is converted (from chemical energy within the battery to light and heat energy in the light bulb). Less energy returns to the battery over the circuit than left the battery (converted by the load) and the battery is slowly drained of energy.

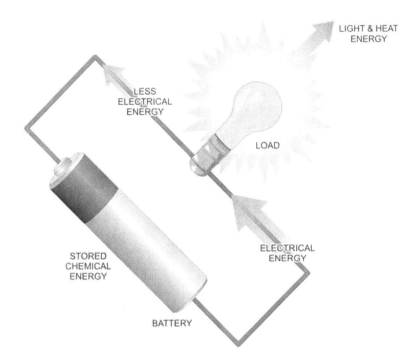

Figure 2-19:
Circuit with Load

Open Circuits

When the pathway of a circuit is broken (an **Open Circuit**), as shown in Figure 2-20, electricity stops along the entire circuit. A simple light switch is a practical example of this process. When the switch is turned "on" (the circuit is connected), the light bulb shines. When the switch is turned "off", the circuit is broken and the flow of electricity stops instantly along the entire circuit.

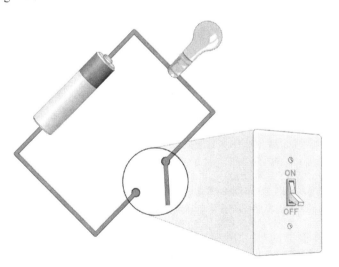

Figure 2-20:
Open Circuit

Often electrical circuits have fuses or breakers incorporated into them, as well as switches. These over voltage protection devices (fuses and breakers) will open the circuit, stopping the flow of electricity if there is a sudden increase in the voltage or amperes flowing across the wires.

Parallel and Series Circuits

Series Circuit

When there is only one pathway along which the electrons can flow in a circuit, this is called a **Series Circuit** (everything attached to it comes one after the other—in series). An old-fashioned string of Christmas tree lights is a good example of a series circuit. All the bulbs will shine when the string is plugged in, but when one light bulb burns out, the circuit is broken and no electricity will flow (making it a real chore to figure out which bulb needs to be replaced).

Parallel Circuits

Multiple pathways can also be created within a circuit. These are called **Parallel Circuits** (they run side-by-side rather than one after the other), as shown in Figure 2-21. If the string of Christmas tree lights were connected using parallel circuits, rather than in a series circuit, then all the bulbs (except the one that just burned out) would continue to shine as they still receive electricity through a parallel pathway.

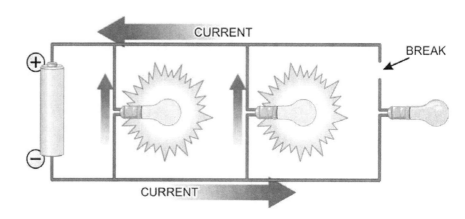

**Figure 2-21:
Parallel Circuit**

ELECTRICAL LOADS

The reason to generate an electric current is to accomplish something—such as creating heat or light, or performing electrical work. Devices are attached to the electrical energy source to perform these activities. Collectively, these devices can be referred to as **Loads**.

Loads

Loads such as light bulbs and fluorescent tubes convert electrical energy into light, while resistive heating elements convert the same electrical flow into heat. Electric motors are designed to convert electrical energy back into mechanical energy. In each case, the load (or loads) placed between the terminals of the voltage source provides some level of **Resistance** to the flow of electrons through the circuit. In an AC circuit the load may also pose a **Reactance** to the changing push being applied. Reactance is the opposition to AC current flow from inductance or capacitance instead of resistance. In a DC circuit the load is strictly resistive. This resistance acts against the current flow being pushed by the voltage as the electrical energy is converted into one of the other energy forms mentioned earlier, as illustrated in Figure 2-22.

Resistance

Reactance

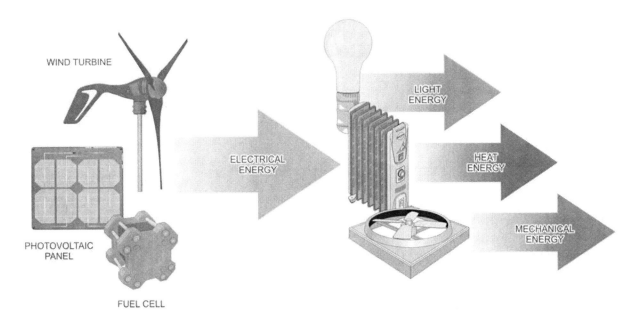

WIND TURBINE

PHOTOVOLTAIC
PANEL

FUEL CELL

ELECTRICAL
ENERGY

LIGHT
ENERGY

HEAT
ENERGY

MECHANICAL
ENERGY

When no external circuit is present, the voltage source pushes against the atoms in the internal wiring, but without a path, no current can flow—you still have voltage (push) but no current (flow). This is referred to as an open circuit. If a complete path is provided through a material whose atoms offer very little resistance to giving up electrons (called conductors), then the electrical push will provide a very heavy flow of electrons through the material between the terminals. If the amount of resistance provided is too low, this is referred to as a **Short Circuit**.

Figure 2-22: Converting Electrical Energy

Short Circuit

Ohm's Law

Electrical load devices typically provide some level of resistance between these extremes. The relationship between voltage, resistance and current flow in a circuit is expressed in a law called **Ohm's Law**. This relationship simply states that the amount of current that flows in a circuit is directly related to the voltage applied and inversely related to the resistance of the load. This is expressed as:

$$I = \frac{V}{R}$$

where I is current in amperes*, V is voltage in volts and R is resistance in **Ohms**.

*An ampere is a measure of how many electrons are moving past a point in one second. One ampere equals 6.24×10 to the 18th electrons passing a single point in one second. That's a lot of electrons hopping down the wire at one time—nobody wants to count that many electrons or keep track of them, so we just refer to them in terms of amperes.

Ohm's Law

Ohms

Load Calculations

The amount of current flowing in a circuit *increases* directly with the amount of push being applied (double the voltage and the current will double as well). The amount of current flowing also *decreases* directly with an increase in resistance (if the push remains constant but the amount of resistance is doubled, the current flow will be cut in half).

For example: If a 6 Vdc battery is connected to a device that has a total resistance of 1000 Ohm (1 kohm), the amount of current that the source would produce should be 0.006 amps (or 6 milliamps—mA). A milliamp is $1/1000^{th}$ of an amp. In electronics you may also encounter current measurements that occur in the 1/1,000,000 (millionth) of an amp and are specified as microamperes (μA)

The Ohm's Law formula demonstrates the relationship between these electrical quantities as follows:

$$I = \frac{V}{R}$$

where:

$$I = \frac{6}{1000}$$

$$I = 0.006 \text{ amp}$$

If the battery is replaced with a 12 Vdc battery, the current flow becomes:

$$I = \frac{12}{1000}$$

$$I = 0.012 \text{ amp (or 12 mA)}$$

Likewise, if the load resistance were increased to 2000 Ohms, the current level pulled from the 12-volt source would be cut in half, as follows:

$$I = \frac{12}{2000}$$

$$I = 0.006 \text{ amp (or 6 mA)}$$

To recap—current *increases* proportionally when voltage *increases* (they are *directly proportional*) and *decreases* proportionally as resistance *increases* (they are *inversely proportional*)

Kirchhoff's Laws

Ohm's Law is used to determine current, voltage, resistance and power relationships in single line configurations. However, there is another set of laws, called **Kirchhoff's Laws** (named after German physicist Gustov Kirchhoff) that can be used to solve complex series, parallel and series/parallel circuits. Kirchhoff explained complex circuit analysis through a current law and a voltage law.

Kirchhoff's Current Law is simple in that it states that the sum of all of the currents entering a point in a circuit must equal the sum of all the currents leaving the point. In other words, the electrons can't just hang around at any point in the circuit. Figure 2-23 illustrates current from a battery entering a connection point that feeds two devices. Each device will pull current from the battery according to the load it places on the supply (determined by Ohm's law).

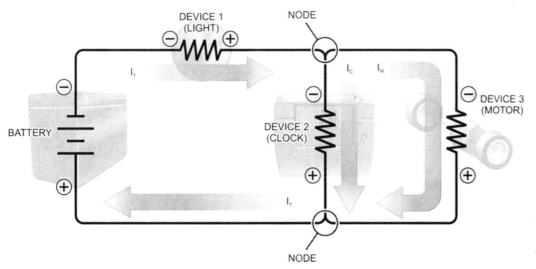

Figure 2-23:
Kirchhoff's
Current Law

This first rule can be expressed with the equation:

$$\Sigma I_{in} = \Sigma I_{out}$$

If the current draw for one device (I1) is 0.5 amps and the draw for the second device (I2) is 5.0 amps, the current entering the connection point (referred to as a node) must equal 5.5 amps. In this example, the current entering the node is the supply current (Is) coming from the battery. The supply current divides into the two branch currents at the node and comes back together at the ground point.

Kirchhoff's second law is his voltage law—**Kirchhoff's Voltage Law**. This law defines the voltage relationships around the current loops of multiple branch circuits. This law states that the algebraic sum of the voltages around a current loop must equal zero.

The second rule (also known as the *loop rule*) is a statement of conservation of energy. The charge within a circuit is not "used up" as current flows through resistors, but potential (voltage) is. Ohm's Law states that the change in potential (ΔV) is equal to the resistance of a material times the current flowing through it ($\Delta V = IR$). The greater the resistance, to more potential is lost.

So as current flows along a closed loop circuit, the sum of all the potential differences (positive or negative voltage drop) must equal zero. This second rule can be expressed in the equation:

$$\Sigma \Delta V = 0$$

To see how this works, polarities must be assigned to all of the devices in each current loop, as illustrated in Figure 2-24. This can be accomplished by assigning negative signs to the end of the device where current enters and a plus sign to the end where is exits the device. Some devices will be voltage drops in the loop while others will be voltage gains in the loop. Devices that are part of multiple loops will be a voltage drop for one loop and a voltage rise in the other loop.

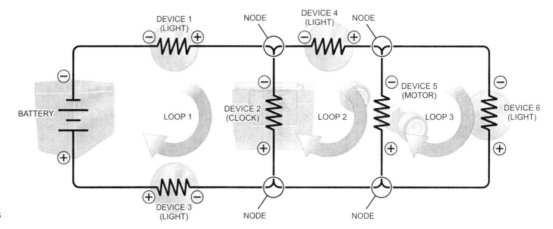

Figure 2-24:
Establishing
Device Polarities

After the polarities have been assigned, equations can be generated for each loop by assigning the polarity and voltage for each device. For the circuit in the figure, the equations generated would be:

Loop 1 (Starting at the bottom of the battery moving clockwise)

$$+Vs - V1 - V2 - V3 = 0$$
$$Vs = V1 + V2 + V3$$

Loop 2 (Starting at the bottom of Device 2 moving clockwise)

$$+V2 - V4 - V5 = 0$$
$$V2 = V4 + V5$$

Loop 3 (Starting at the bottom of Device 5 moving clockwise)

$$+V5 - V6 = 0$$
$$V5 = V6$$

Applying Kirchhoff's Laws

Both of Kirchhoff's laws are used, along with Ohm's law, to solve for all of the currents and voltages in the circuit (without the procedure for reducing resistances). The procedure for doing this is as follows:

1. Assign current flow directions for all of the nodes in the circuit (if the wrong direction is assigned for the currents, the math will still work but the polarity will be negative).

2. Write the current equations for each node, as described above.

3. Assign voltage polarity markings to each device in the circuit based on the direction of current flow assigned through the device.

4. Write a voltage equation for each loop as described above (in a classically drawn schematic diagram, each loop will resemble a window pane). All loop equations must be written going around the loops in the same direction (usually clockwise).

5. Use Ohm's Law to rewrite the entries in each loop equation so that each device voltage is replaced by an equivalent current/resistance statement.

6. Substitute any known values for the circuit devices (such as resistance and battery voltage values) into the equations.

7. Substitute equivalent values for different components back into the equations to reduce the number of variables to the minimum number of variables possible.

8. Solve the simultaneous equations using algebraic processes.

While applying Kirchhoff's laws to solving circuits in the classroom is good theoretical practice, in the "real world", understanding the application of Kirchhoff's Laws enables a technician to troubleshoot problems more efficiently. In particular, they assist in locating bad connections, poorly crimped terminals, and bad ground connections, because these conditions represent an additional component in the circuit.

POWER

Power is defined as "the ability to perform work over a given period of time". Electrical power is expressed in **Watts**, and is governed by the power formula for Ohm's Law:

$$P = V \times I$$

where P is power in watts, I is current in amperes, and V is voltage in volts (in some publications, the symbol E—for electromotive force—is used instead of voltage).

Watts

Difference between Power and Energy

Overall electrical power is measured in watts (W). Technically it is defined as one joule of energy used in one second. There is a difference between energy and power. Power is the amount of energy used over time. So in electrical power measurements, a watt refers to the amount of electrical energy that has flowed during a given period of time (usually an hour).

So, for example, a 60-watt electric light bulb is actually using 60 watts PER HOUR of electricity. A 40-watt light bulb will use the same amount of power in 1.5 hours (60 x 1 = 40 x 1.5). If this 60-watt light bulb is left turned on for five hours, it will consume 300 watt-hours, or more commonly the consumption would be expressed as .3 **Kilowatt-Hours** (measured in thousands of watt-hours).

Kilowatt-Hours

Power Math

One of the most common examples of Ohm's Law to power relationships would be the common 60 Watt candescent light bulb in a typical 120 Vac residential wiring situation. The amount of current drawn by the light bulb can be calculated as follows:

$$P = V \times I$$

where:

$$60 = 120 \times I$$

$$\frac{60}{120} = \frac{(120 \times I)}{120}$$ (dividing both sides of the equation by the same amount)

$$0.5 \, amp = I$$

┌─ **NOTE** ──────────────────────────────
The 60 Watt designation does not address how much light the bulb produces—this specification is measures in lumens and is dependent on the material producing the light energy—only the amount of power consumed by the bulb to produce the light.
└──

Likewise, a 1300 W space heater operating on a 120 Vac line would draw 10.833 amps of current.

$$P = V \times I$$

$$1300 = 120 \times I$$

$$10.833 \, amps = I$$

As with the light bulb example, the 1300 W rating for the space heater does not address how much heat is produced—this quantity is expressed in terms of **British Thermal Units** (BTUs) and is dependent on several design factors of the heater. The wattage rating simply states how much power the heater consumes to generate the heat.

British Thermal Units

In a final example, 1 **Horse Power** (hp) pump motor that operates from a 220 Vac line to pump water to a reservoir does not seem to fit into the Ohms Law power formula. However, there is a direct correlation between horsepower (the rating used to describe motors) and Watts—746 Watts equals 1 hp.

Horse Power

Applying this information to the pump motor scenario gives the following:

$$P = V \times I$$

where:

$$746 \text{ Watts (1 hp)} = 220 \times I$$

$$\frac{746}{220} = \frac{(220 \times I)}{220}$$

$$3.39 \text{ amps} = I$$

The pump motor will draw 3.39 amps of AC current when in operation.

Grounding

When designing a circuit, it is an important safety consideration that the circuit be properly grounded. It is possible for any number of reasons (lightning strikes, trees falling, worn wires, faulty equipment, etc.) for an unwanted electrical charge to find its way onto the circuit. This charge needs to be given a pathway to a reservoir large enough to safely absorb all this extra charge.

The nearest body large enough for this purpose is the earth itself. So every part of the system that could possibly transmit this excess charge must be linked to a common **Ground** (usually an eight foot metal rod driven into the ground).

Ground

Because voltage is actually a difference in potential, it is important that the system use a single ground (or that these grounds be bonded together), since it is possible that rods driven in different locations might have a slightly different electrical potential.

DC Voltage Sources

There are several common sources of DC voltage and current. **Batteries** are easily the most widely recognized examples of **DC Voltage Sources**. Alternative DC sources you will encounter in this course include fuel cells (think of these as hydrogen powered batteries) and photovoltaic cells, or solar cells (think of these as light-powered batteries). Wind turbines may also produce DC voltage and current at its output terminals, but this is only after manipulation of the alternating current it produces naturally.

Batteries

DC Voltage Sources

All of the DC voltage sources mentioned come in many sizes and ratings and produce DC electricity through different processes. For example, batteries produce direct current voltage through a chemical reaction process. The chemicals in the battery react with its terminals when an external path for current flow is provided. The process causes free electrons to gather at the negative (-) terminal of the battery while a depletion of electrons occurs at the positive (+) terminal. This provides the push (-) and pull (+) to create current flow through an external circuit, as illustrated in Figure 2-25.

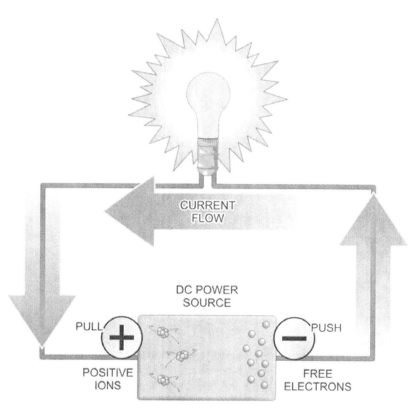

Figure 2-25: Creating DC Current Flow

When an external pathway is provided, the electrons flow from the negative terminal through the external circuit (and the external load) and back into the positive terminal of the battery. If a very low resistance load is placed across the terminals, a large flow of electron current will occur. Larger resistive loads draw lower levels of current flow from the battery, as described by the basic Ohm's Law formula for current, voltage and resistance.

Short Circuit

In cases where a wire or other good conductor is placed across the terminals without a load (referred to as a **Short Circuit** condition), electrons will flow through the circuit and the inside of the battery as quickly as the internal process can generate more free electrons. The acceleration of the process causes the battery to heat up, which in turn can cause it to overheat and possibly explode.

Secondary Cells

Storage Batteries

Some battery types (referred to as **Secondary Cells** or **Storage Batteries**) can be recharged by applying a reverse current to them, as illustrated in Figure 2-26. By applying an external voltage source to the battery at a voltage level *slightly higher* than its terminal voltage, a reverse current is forced to flow back into the battery and the internal chemical process is reversed. Under these circumstances, the battery becomes the load in the circuit instead of the source.

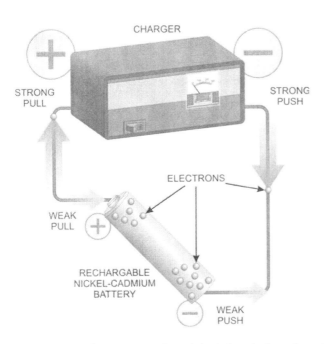

CHARGER

STRONG PULL

STRONG PUSH

ELECTRONS

WEAK PULL

RECHARGABLE NICKEL-CADMIUM BATTERY

WEAK PUSH

Figure 2-26:
Recharging a Battery

Over time, the reverse current flow restores the original chemical configuration inside the battery. The rate at which the battery **Recharges** depends on the chemical configuration and the amount of reverse current flowing through the battery. The amount of reverse current is dependent on the voltage difference between the battery and the recharging source.

The recharging option is not available with all battery types (not all chemical current generating processes can be reversed). Applying a reverse voltage to these batteries (**Primary Cells**) can cause them to overheat and possibly explode.

Recharges

Primary Cells

> ## WARNING
>
> Applying a reverse voltage to non-rechargeable battery types can cause them to overheat and possibly explode.

Parallel and Series Battery Connections

How batteries are wired together, either in parallel or series will have a dramatic impact on the voltage of the electricity they produce. When batteries are connected in series, the voltage of each battery is added to the rest. For example, three 6-volt batteries connected in series will produce an 18-volt electrical current.

The same three 6-volt batteries connected in a parallel circuit will produce a 6-volt electrical flow. However, the amperes (current) will be greater than the series array (remember, the total power generated in both systems are the same, and watts (W) = volts (V) x amps (I). Both wiring configurations, series and parallel are diagramed in Figure 2-27.

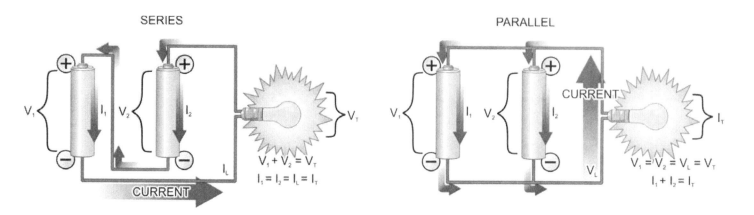

Figure 2-27: Battery Bank in Parallel and Series

LET'S DO THE MATH

Let's take three batteries and connect them together. We can see by the label that these are 6-volt batteries and let's say that the batteries are capable of generating 90 watts of power. First, we need to remember that…

Watts = Volts x Amps

So, if we hook them up in series, we will find that…

90 watts = (6 + 6 + 6) volts x ? amps therefore 90 watts / 18 volts = 5 amps

So if wired in series, the batteries will produce 90 watts of power at 18 volts with a current of 5 amps.

If we wire the same batteries together in parallel, we get a very different result. They still generate 90 watts of power, but the voltage remains at only 6 volts. So our equation is…

90 watts = 6 volts x ? amps therefore 90 watts / 6 volts = 15 amps

So our voltage is less, but the current for the parallel circuit is three times as high.

How Batteries Work

Batteries take advantage of chemical reactions that produce free electrons to produce electricity. As these reactions take place, electrons are moved from one pole of the battery (the positive) to the other (the negative). How quickly this production of electrons takes place depends on the **Internal Resistance** of the battery.

When the two poles of a battery are connected through a circuit, the electrons flow from the negative pole to the positive pole. The electrical charge of the battery decreases as the electrons (energy) flow from negative to positive and the difference is decreased.

Some batteries are able to reverse this process. When electricity is introduced into the battery (from some other energy source) this process is reversed and the chemical process once again concentrates electrons at the negative pole.

Direct and Alternating Currents

There are two ways in which electrical currents are delivered. The easiest to understand is known as **Direct Current (DC)**, which is the form of power generated by a battery, solar panels, lightning and static (to name just a few sources).

In this type of electrical current, the voltage is created (and possibly stored, as in a battery) and once the circuit is created, it flows in one direction at a steady voltage level. For instance, if a 12-volt battery is connected to a circuit, the energy will flow over time, along that circuit at a constant (or close enough to constant) 12-volt level, as shown in Figure 2-28.

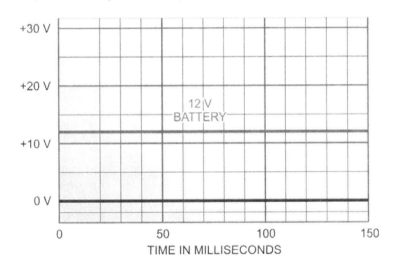

Figure 2-28: Direct Current Voltage Graph

Alternating Current (AC) is the form of electrical current that most people use in their homes, to run electrical appliances and motors. This current does not flow at a constant voltage level, but rather moves in a **Sinusoidal (Sine) Wave** form. The voltage may start at zero, rise to a maximum level (depending on its nominal voltage) fall back to zero, then fall to a corresponding negative maximum level.

An AC circuit might produce a sine wave that rises to +170 volts, then falls to -170 volts, then rises to +170 volts, and so on, as shown in Figure 2-29. The average of these numbers (+170 and -170) will always equal zero. So does the current function at zero volts (which would indicate that there is no power flowing at all)? Clearly this is not the case.

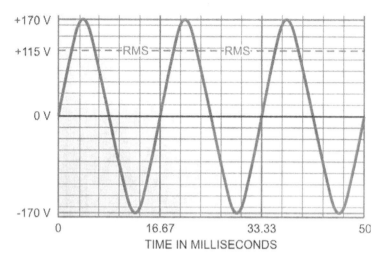

**Figure 2-29:
Alternating
Current Wave**

So AC current is measured using the **Root Mean Square** (**RMS**) which is essentially the voltage that would be carried over a DC circuit from the same power source. So in this example, the current would be said to operate at 115 V (the RMS of the 170 V sine wave), the typical voltage for U.S. residential systems.

Real Power and Apparent Power

The Ohm's Law power relationship described earlier is always true for direct current circuits. However, with alternating current circuits the relationship can be altered by the electrical characteristics of the load. If an AC load is purely resistive, such as an incandescent light bulb, the actual power consumption is easily calculated by $P = V \times I$.

However, not all loads in AC circuits are purely resistive. Some load devices, such as electric motors and transformers (ballasts) in fluorescent light fixtures operate on the principle of **Electromagnetic Induction**. The inductive nature in these loads causes the AC current flow to occur at some time after (lag behind) the application of the voltage to the circuit. The amount of difference between the application of the voltage (the push/pull on the circuit) and the actual flow of current is a value based on the amount of **Inductance** (measured in *henries*) in the device.

Because the values at any given time for current and voltage are at different places in their cycles, as illustrated in Figure 2-30, the simple $P = V \times I$ calculation of power must be modified to include a factor for this difference. This factor is a *cosine* trigonometric function relating the phase shift between the current and voltage waveforms and is referred to as **Power Factor**. In this figure, the phase of the AC current is shown lagging behind the voltage in the circuit.

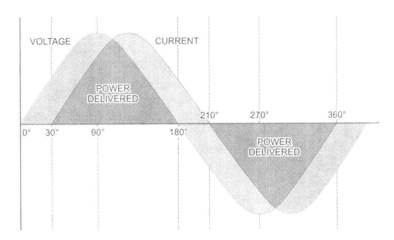

Figure 2-30:
Power Factor

Using the P = V x I power equation on this AC circuit produces an **Apparent Power** calculation that is expressed in terms of **Volt-Amperes (VA)** instead of Watts. However, the **Real Power** (or *true power*) that the circuit consumes is expressed in Watts and is calculated using the following formula:

Real Power (watts) = cosine (phase) x Apparent Power (VA)

As the formula indicates, the real power will varies with the value of the cosine function of the phase difference between the voltage and current waveforms.

Apparent power is the easiest to measure and is obtained by multiplying the rms (root mean square) volts and rms amps. The term "rms" refers to what is obtained by measuring AC voltage with a standard voltmeter and ammeter. The result is expressed as volt-amperes (VA) and not watts. The actual power used by the load is expressed in watts. The important point to remember from this discussion is that some loads in an AC circuit can consume more VA power than real power. Therefore, installers must take the sum of all the VA rating for all devices to be used in a circuit to determine wire size and circuit breaker capacity for the circuit and devices.

Kilowatt-Hours

Utility companies measure energy in terms of the **Kilowatt-Hour (kWh)**. Each kilowatt-hour is equal to one thousand watts of power consumed in one hour. Monthly electric utility bills are based on the base rate charged by the local utility per kilowatt-hour.

Wattage ratings for electrical appliances along with their corresponding costs for an assumed rate of 8 cents per kilowatt-hour are presented in Table 2-2. This cost is probably different in your area—consult your residential power bill or call the local electrical utility company for local rates. Electrical installers use tables like this to determine the load of a given scenarios.

Because some items, such as a bathroom light, will most likely be used for less than 1 hour at a time, this light could be calculated for fractions of a watt-hour usage (i.e., 120-Watt rated light fixture multiplied by 0.25 hours (15 minutes) of usage, would produce a 30 Watt-hours calculated power usage).

Table 2-2:
Residential Electrical
Power Consumption
Estimates @
8 cents/kWh

APPLIANCE	USAGE	RATE
Air cleaner	30 watts per hour	.24 cent per hour (.03 kW/hour x 8 = .24)
Can opener	50 watts per hour	.4 cent per hour (.05 kW/hour x 8 = .4)
Clock	2 watts per hour	.38 cent per hour (.002 kW/hour x 8 x 24 = .384)
Electric heating pad	60 watts per hour	.48 cent per hour (.06 kW/hour x 8 = .48)
Fans (ceiling)	100 watts per hour	.8 cent per hour (.1 kW/hour x 8 = .8)
Fax machine	90 watts per hour	17.28 cents per hour (.09 kW/hour x 8 x 24 = 17.28)
Home computer	200 watts per hour	1.6 cents per hour (.2 kW/hour x 8 = 1.6)
Iron	1100 watts per hour	8.8 cents per hour (1.1 kW/hour x 8 = 8.8)
Microwave	1500 watts per hour	12 cents per hour (1.5 kW/hour x 8 = 12)
Stereo	100 watts per hour	.8 cent per hour (.1 kW/hour x 8 = .8)
Television	150 watts per hour	1.2 cents per hour (.15 kW/hour x 8 = 1.2)
Toaster	1100 watts per hour	.146 cent per hour (1.1 kW/hour x 8/60 = .1467)
Lights	100 watts per hour	.8 cent per hour (.1 kW/hour x 8 = .8)
Oven (electric)	1500 watts per hour	12 cents per hour (1.5 kW/hour x 8 = 12)
Range top stove	300 watts per hour	2.4 cents per hour (.3 kW/hour x 8 = 2.4)
Refrigerator	220 watts per hour	42.2 cents per hour (.22 kW/hour x 8 x 24 = 42.24)

Likewise, a vent fan rated at 125 Watts per hour would use 0.125 kilowatt-hours of power each hour. If the utility company charged 8 cents per kilowatt-hour, it would cost 1 cent per hour to operate the fan. The math works as follows:

125W divided by 1000W per kW equals 0.125 kilowatts

$$\frac{125}{1000} = 0.125 kW$$

0.125kW x 1.0h x 0.08cents/kWh = 1 cent/h

When there is a device, such as a water heater, that is used continuously, the kilowatt-per-hour consumption rate for the device must be multiplied by 24 to determine its power consumption and **Daily Cost of Operation**.

Hertz

The vertical height (amplitude) of a wave is measured in terms of volts (this is the wave's intensity). The frequency of the wave (the time between wave crests) is measured in terms of **Hertz (Hz)**. A hertz is simply the number of times a wave crests each second.

In the United States, most AC electrical power is transmitted at a rate of 60 Hz (meaning that 60 waves are generated each second). This is not the case everywhere in the world. Different countries generate power at different voltages and frequencies, as shown in Table 2-3. It is important to understand that equipment rated for one voltage and frequency may not work with another.

COUNTRY	VOLTAGE	FREQUENCY
United States of America	120 V	60 Hz
Afghanistan	220 V	50 Hz
Aruba	127 V	60 Hz
Belgium	230 V	50 Hz
Fiji	240 V	50 Hz
Canada	120 V	60 Hz
Iraq	230 V	50 Hz
Lebanon	110/220 V	50 Hz
Mexico	127 V	60 Hz
Panama	110 V	60 Hz
United Kingdom	230 V	50 Hz

Table 2-3: Voltages and Hertz Around the World

MAKING ELECTRICAL CONNECTIONS

A common job function of the green technology installer is creating circuitry and making connections to different devices in the system. Incorrect wiring will at best prevent the system from working, and at worst damage equipment or cause injury to personnel. Current levels as low as 0.1 - 0.2 amps can be fatal to humans under certain circumstances. Therefore caution should always be used when working with any electrical circuits or devices.

> ## WARNING
>
> Incorrect wiring will at best cause the system to not work, and at worst damage equipment or cause injury to personnel. Current levels as low as 0. 1-0.2 amps can be fatal to humans under the correct circumstances. Therefore caution should always be used when connecting any type of electrical devices.

Another danger associated with electrical current flow is the possibility of burns or fire related to conductors (wiring and devices that give up electrons easily) over heating. Even though the conductor materials give up electrons more easily than other substances, their electrons do not just fall off the atom—even conductors have some level of resistance in them. Therefore, some energy is given off as heat when current passes through the conductor.

Heat in wiring systems is often a result of too much current flowing through an undersized wire or through a bad connection. One of the keys to minimizing the amount of heat generated in wiring is to use the proper size wiring and the correct external insulation coating. A wire with a larger cross sectional area carries a given amount of current more easily than a smaller wire of the same material. There are simply more atoms across the face of the larger wire to give up the necessary number of electrons. Therefore, less heat is produced for that level of current.

Qualified, licensed electricians must wire up and connect installations that tie into the commercial power system. However, low-voltage, non-grid tied installations can normally be installed, wired and connected by trained personnel.

Electrical Safety

Accidents while working with electricity can (and often do) result in death and/or serious injury. Extreme caution must be taken to keep people and property safe. Each week five workers die in the United States from electrical accidents. Also, numerous injuries result from fires started due to poorly designed or maintained electrical systems.

Injuries due to direct interaction with electricity may include electrical shock and burns. The severity of the shock will depend upon the amount of current, the duration of the exposure as well as the path the current flows through the body.

Low-voltage systems do not mean that there is low risk. Very low currents can paralyze muscles, making it nearly impossible to let go of a wire (prolonging the exposure). They may also cause rapid irregular heartbeats, resulting in death within minutes.

Indirect injuries may also result, including concussions from arcing explosions, eye damage due to arc flash, or falls due to a shock.

Most injuries are the result of either unsafe equipment and/or system installation, unsafe work practices, or unforeseen environmental hazards (such as trees falling on wires). The NEC outlines in detail precautions required in the workplace when working with electricity.

REVIEW QUESTIONS

The following questions test your knowledge of the material presented in this chapter.

1. You have just mounted a 65 kg wind turbine to the top of a 150 meter pole. Unfortunately it fell before you could mount it properly. Assume it takes 10 seconds for the turbine to fall from the top of the tower before smashing into your car, which you unwisely parked directly below. Calculate the kinetic energy generated (in Joules) of the turbine as it totals your car.

2. Explain the four laws of thermodynamics and how they affect passive heating and cooling systems.

3. Define watts, volts and amps (as related to electrical power) and describe their relationship to each other in a mathematical equation.

4. Six 12-volt batteries are connected together in series. How many volts are generated by this battery bank?

5. Define Ohm's Law and its effect on power generation.

6. Discuss how chemical energy differs from electrical energy. From where does chemical energy draw its energy source?

7. What is meant by the term "Absolute Zero"? Why can this temperature never be achieved in nature?

8. Explain the difference between conduction, convection and radiation as it applies to the movement of thermal energy.

9. What is meant by the term "albedo"? Why would a white roof keep a home cooler than a black roof?

10. Explain why only about 51% of the Sun's radiant energy that could potentially be absorbed by the Earth's surface is actually absorbed.

11. Discuss how Power (in terms of mechanical energy) differs from Work.

12. What is a Hertz and how does it differ from a volt?

13. Six 12-volt batteries are connected in series. They are then wired to a light via a circuit. When the circuit is OPEN – how many volts are used by the light bulb (the Load)? Why is this the case?

14. Discuss reflection, absorption, and scattering within the atmosphere and how this impacts the heat of the planet.

15. Explain why sunlight hitting the surface of the Earth at an angle (45 degrees, for example) generates less heat per square meter than does sunlight hitting the earth from directly overhead.

EXAM QUESTIONS

1. The gravitational potential energy of a 5 kg flower pot sitting on a window sill of the fourth floor of an apartment building (12 meters above street level) is:
   a. 60 J
   b. 240 N
   c. 588 J
   d. 3600 N

2. Covalent Bonding is the result of:
   a. An electrical imbalance within the atom
   b. The strong electrical attraction between a proton and a neutron
   c. The random nature of electron orbits
   d. An overlapping or "sharing" of electrons between two atoms

3. The observation that heat will not flow between two objects that are the same temperature is known as the:
   a. Zeroth Law of Thermodynamics
   b. First Law of Thermodynamics
   c. Second Law of Thermodynamics
   d. Third Law of Thermodynamics

4. If during a chemical reaction, heat is given off, the reaction is known as:
   a. Thermal
   b. Radiant
   c. Emitting
   d. Exothermic

5. When radiant energy strikes an object, which of the following will NOT occur?
   a. The energy will be absorbed by the object
   b. The energy will be reflected by the object
   c. The energy will be transmitted through the object
   d. The energy will be reduced by the object

6. Which of the following does not affect the absorption of radiant energy by an object?
   a. Its size
   b. Its temperature
   c. Its temperament
   d. Its color

7. Units of Work are measured in:
   a. Joules
   b. Watts
   c. Newtons
   d. Power

8. Negative charges are _____ positive charges.
   a. covalently bonded to
   b. attracted to
   c. absorbed by
   d. transmitted by

9. Ohm's Law is:
   a. $I = V®$
   b. States that Work can not be created or destroyed
   c. Measures the difference between potential and kinetic energy
   d. Explains convection currents

10. The energy generated by a battery is in the form of:
    a. An open circuit
    b. Direct current
    c. Series connection
    d. Parallel connection

CHAPTER
3

RESIDENTIAL AND COMMERCIAL STRUCTURES

OBJECTIVES

Upon completion of this chapter and its related lab procedures you will be able to perform the following tasks:

1. Identify common structural components of residential and commercial buildings.

2. Describe how different structural components of residential and commercial buildings affect energy consumption by the structure.

3. Explain the importance of an R-value rating in the building and construction industry.

4. List the three main purposes of walls.

5. Differentiate between older and newer interior wall designs.

6. Identify the typical materials used to construct doors.

7. Describe how modern window designs improve the thermal efficiency.

8. Discuss the reasons for overlapping shingles.

9. Explain the main reason for venting an attic.

CHAPTER 3

Residential and Commercial Structures

INTRODUCTION

The main premise of this course is based on the fact that the single greatest source of energy consumption worldwide is related to the operation of residential and commercial buildings. Buildings account for about 40 % of energy consumption worldwide, and approximately 21 % of all greenhouse gas emissions. Therefore, producing more energy efficient buildings represent the greatest overall energy-saving potential for the future.

With this in mind, it is essential that these structures be designed and constructed to be as energy efficient as possible in order to minimize the drain on existing and emerging resources. In addition to making future structures as efficient as possible, the number of existing residential and commercial structures worldwide makes it equally important to make as many of those structures as efficient as possible as well. If not, the growing worldwide population and the number of those people moving into a middle class lifestyle will completely overwhelm the available resources and energy supplies.

BASIC RESIDENTIAL AND COMMERCIAL STRUCTURES

The starting point for maximizing the efficiency of existing and future buildings is to understand the major components and subsystems of residential and commercial structures and the impact they have on material and energy consumption. The remaining sections of this chapter will cover these topics.

Figure 3-1 describes the typical components involved in a stand-alone residential structure.

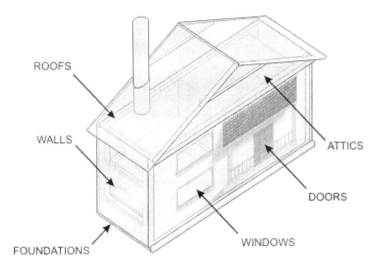

**Figure 3-1:
Residential Structural
Building Components**

Multi-unit residential and commercial buildings employ the same types of components and subsystems as standalone, single-unit residential structures. However the materials and construction techniques are typically quite different. Figure 3-2 shows the components of typical multi-unit residential and commercial buildings.

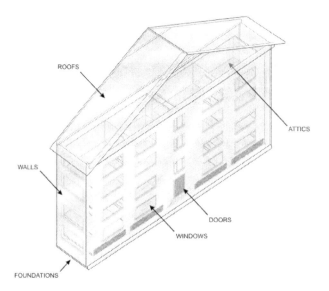

Figure 3-2:
Commercial Structural
Building Components

Foundations

The base of every building of any type is the **Foundation**. The foundation is the portion of the structure that transfers the weight (load) of the structure to the ground. If the foundation is not constructed properly the entire building will be unstable. The preferred material for foundations is typically concrete, although steel and wood are also used in some instances.

There are typically two categories of foundations—**Shallow Foundations** that extend to just below the frost line in the ground, and **Deep Foundations**, which extend deeper into the soil to rest the weight of the structure on a firmer base found further in the ground. In both cases, the foundation is designed to support the weight of the structure above it and prevent it from settling into the soil (or at least limit the settling to an acceptable and consistent amount).

Slab Foundations

The most common types of shallow foundations are **Slab-On-Grade** and **Mat-Slab** foundations. With a slab-on-grade foundation, a slab of concrete is poured into a form on the ground. The slab serves both as a floor and as a support for the structure and rests directly on the ground, leaving no space between the ground and the building, as shown in Figure 3-3.

Foundation

Shallow Foundations

Deep Foundations

Slab-On-Grade

Mat-Slab

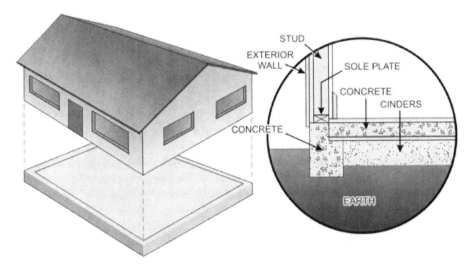

Figure 3-3:
Slab-on-Grade
Foundations

Slab foundations tend to readily pass heat from the building into the soil and return cold into the building when the ground temperature is lower than the building's interior temperature. This represents a large potential for heat loss (and excessive energy consumption) when the temperature outside is cold. Builders often minimized these effects by insulating the interface between the ground and the concrete.

Some slab floor installations also employ active heating methods such as embedded water or electric heaters. Both of these methods involve consuming energy simply to heat the foundation. However, there are passive solar heating options that can be used to heat a concrete floor without consuming generated energy.

Crawl Spaces and Basements

In geographical locations where heavy frost or cold conditions lead to **Frost Heave**, a type of foundation called a **Spread Footing** foundation technique is used. This foundation type provides a stable base around the entire perimeter of a structure (the exterior walls) and typically includes interior spot footings to support raised floor systems, as shown in Figure 3-4. These types of foundations are commonly used in residential structures that include a basement, as well as in a variety of commercial structure types.

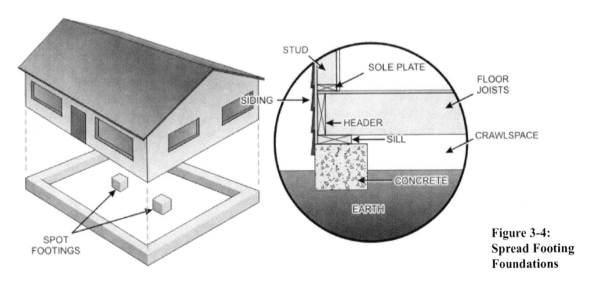

Figure 3-4:
Spread Footing
Foundations

In residential settings where these types of foundations are employed, the building structures are built over a crawlspace or a basement, using wood or steel joists that span the distances between the foundation walls. The walls of the crawl space or basement are typically made of poured concrete or concrete blocks.

If the crawl space or basement is sealed from outside air, it will provide an insulating **Dead-Air Space** between the ground and the raised floor. As long as this cavity of air is prevented from circulating and remains totally sealed, it acts as a form of insulation.

Additional insulating materials may also be applied to the bottom of a raised flooring system to inhibit the exchange of heat between the interior of the structure and the space beneath the raised flooring. The presence of the insulating material greatly increases the insulation value (**R-Value Rating**) of the interface between the crawl space and the inside of the building.

R-value is a term used in the building and construction industry to express the measure of a material's ability to resist thermal changes across a given thickness (the material's heat transfer value divided by the cross sectional area of the material).

R-value in the U.S. is expressed in ft^2 x F/Btu (feet squared times degrees Fahrenheit per British Thermal Units), while other areas of the world express R-value in terms of m^2 x K/W (meters squared times degrees Kelvin per Watt). In both cases, the higher the R-value rating of the material, the better it resists the movement of heat across it.

For example, a well-sealed 2" deep dead air space offers an R-value rating of about 0.8, while applying a fiberglass insulation sheet with the same thickness will boost the rating to about 8.0—a tenfold increase.

Walls

Walls are the vertical structural components of a building. They have three main purposes:

- Supporting ceilings and roofs
- Provide protection from exterior elements
- Separate buildings into rooms

Walls may be constructed from solid materials, such as stones, brick, poured concrete, or logs. However, as shown in Figure 3-5, most walls are typically engineered structures involving several structural elements—stud framing, insulation materials, and internal and external finishing elements. They may include components of other building subsystems such as electrical wiring, plumbing elements and HVAC ducting.

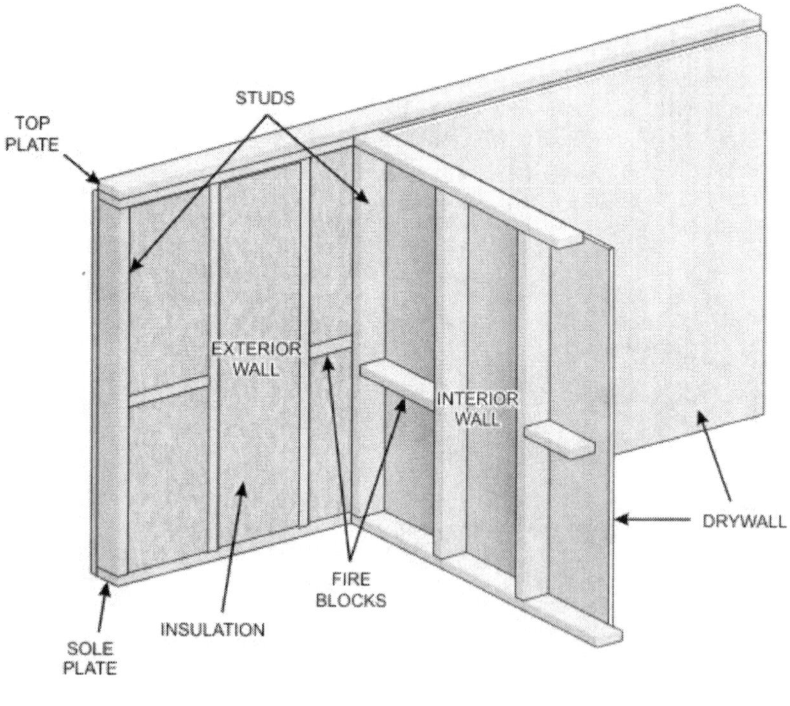

Figure 3-5: Typical Wall Elements

Exterior Walls

Exterior walls form the base for the outer shell of the structure. It generally serves the following functions—supporting the ceiling and roof of the structure, protecting the interior of the structure from the elements of nature, and offering privacy and physical protection for the occupants of the structure. External walls are normally constructed using the components described in the preceding section—framing, insulation materials, and internal and external finishing elements.

The materials and construction of the exterior walls contributes a great deal to the energy efficiency of the building. The insulation value of a wall depends on its thickness, the type of material used to construct it and the insulation methods it employs. The external finishing elements are designed to resist rain, wind, and cold in the winter and to block excess heat in the summer. In addition they must be as leak free as possible. These elements are typically stone, painted wood, concrete, vinyl, aluminum, steel or masonry. In most cases, the finishing element is attached to a layer of sheeting material that connects the finishing element to the framing, as illustrated in Figure 3-6.

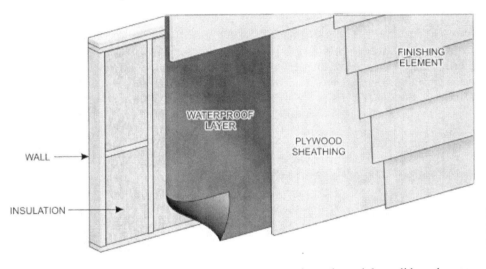

**Figure 3-6:
External Finishing
Elements**

Internal finishing elements, such as plaster, stucco, wood panels, and drywall boards act to help seal the wall as well. These elements attach to the inside of the framing and act to create a dead air space within the wall cavities.

It is common to fill the wall cavities of an exterior wall with an **Insulating Material** that has greater **R-Value** than air. The insulation material is responsible for retarding the movement of heat from warmer areas to cooler areas. Typical insulating materials used in building construction includes: fiberglass, rock wool, loose fill granules, cellulose and plastic foam. Each material offers a different R-value rating that describes how well it retards the movement of heat across a given thickness of the material.

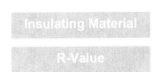

Exterior walls typically feature two types of openings that can significantly affect their thermal efficiency—doors and windows. Other types of wall openings that affect the thermal efficiency of an exterior wall include—wall-mounted air conditioner openings and dryer vents, as well as light switch and receptacle connection boxes

Interior Walls

Load-bearing Walls

Partitions

Interior walls are structures that separate different spaces within the building into rooms, offices, apartments, or suites. Interior walls that support floor, ceiling or roof loads are referred to as **Load-bearing Walls**. Other walls that simply divide space into separate areas are referred to as **Partitions**, or non-load bearing walls.

While interior walls do not have a direct impact on the building's thermal efficiency, they can be used to control the movement of air through the structure and to isolate different sections of the building from others for more efficient heating and cooling operations.

Older residential designs included many interior partitions and doors between rooms. More modern designs tend to include less segmented space, opting instead for open, flowing spaces between rooms. The older designs provided the occupants with the opportunity to only heat those areas of the residence that are in use. Separate heating or cooling sources could be used to control temperature in rooms that are only used occasionally. In addition, the interior walls tended to let enough heat or cooling into the unoccupied space to maintain minimal temperature differentials with the heated/cooled areas of the residence.

Newer designs typically rely on centralized heating and cooling to control the temperature for the entire volume of the residence—including rooms such as formal dining rooms, living rooms, home offices, spare bedrooms, etc. When these areas are automatically part of the heating/cooling operation of the building, a considerable amount of additional energy is expended to heat/cool hundreds of additional square feet of space, as illustrated in Figure 3-7.

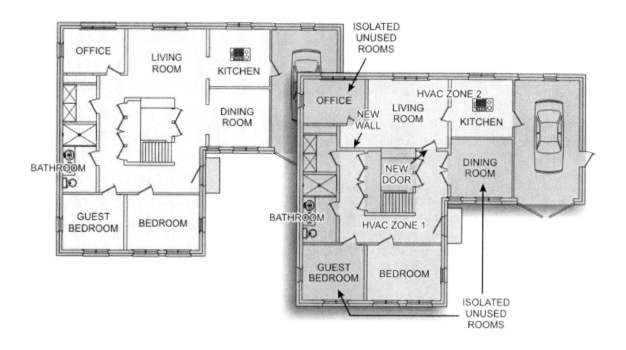

Figure 3-7: Using Interior Walls to Limit Direct Heating/Cooling Requirements

Doors

Doors are openings that control passage through a wall—either between outside and inside, or from room to room. When the movable portion of the door is open, movement through the doorway is enabled (air and light can also pass through the doorway easily when open). When the door is closed it acts as a barrier to movement, airflow, light and noise.

As such, doors can be used to control the atmosphere inside a building or a room. **Exterior Doors** must control the flow of air between the inside and outside of the building, as well as control the loss of heat or cooling through the door itself. **Interior Doors** are also used to control the flow of air through the building or between rooms and can be used to maximize the efficiency of the building's heating and ventilation systems.

Exterior doors typically represent a different R-value than the wall in which they are installed. Their R-value is determined by the type of material used to create the door, whether the door has windows (including their design and total surface area), and how well the door and its supporting framing seal up the opening in the wall. Typical materials used to construct doors include—wood, aluminum, steel, fiberglass and plastics, and glass.

Many exterior door types are solid doors—meaning that the R-value of the door material is the R-value of the door (such as a solid core wooden door). However, other door types include insulation materials within the door to provide greater thermal efficiency than the exterior surfaces of the door—such as a fiberglass door that offers good external resistance to weather elements but needs a good interior insulating material to offer acceptable thermal efficiency.

Other factors that contribute to, or detract from, the door's energy efficiency include—the material used to make the frame the door fits into, the fit between the door and the parts of its frame, and the insulation between the frame and the wall, as illustrated in Figure 3-8. Ideally, all of these factors would be adjusted so that the door offers as much thermal efficiency as the wall it is part of.

Doors

Exterior Doors

Interior Doors

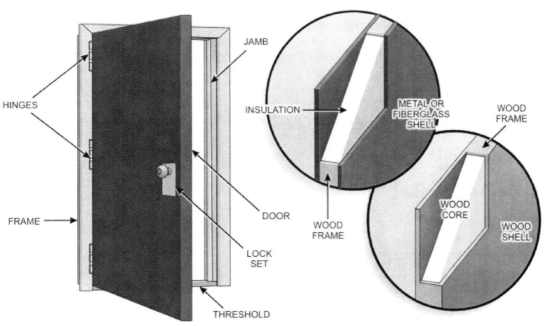

Figure 3-8: Common Exterior Door Components

One common method of increasing a door's thermal efficiency is to install a **Storm Door** over its outside opening. This storm door creates an additional barrier to outside environmental elements, a barrier to air escaping from the interior, and an insulating dead air space between the two doors. These doors are typically lighter than an exterior entry door and often featuring large areas of glass to let sunlight through while blocking air and noise. Because these doors can trap large amounts of heat against the entry door, glass storm doors should not be installed where they are exposed to direct sunlight, as they can damage the main door.

Windows

Windows are see-through openings in walls that provide for the passage of light, air and sound between the spaces on each side of the wall. Windows typically have one or more separate panels of glass or other transparent material that provide for the passage of light and the ability to see through the wall, while at the same time blocking the movement of airflow through the wall. Other window designs include one or more moveable sections that also permit the movement of air and sound through the wall, as illustrated in Figure 3-9.

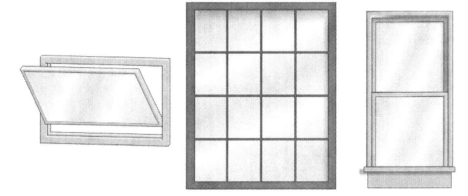

Figure 3-9:
Window Designs

Like walls, windows can be responsible for a great deal of thermal transfer from one side of the wall to the other. Depending on the material and construction methods used in the window, the window can offer quite a range of energy efficiencies. The most common material used for the transparent portions of the window is glass.

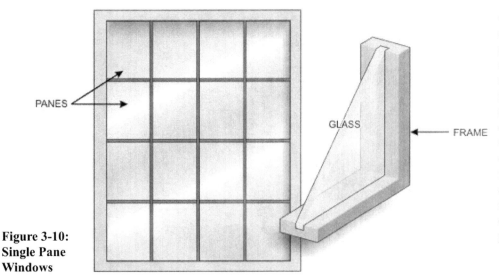

Figure 3-10:
Single Pane
Windows

Older window designs almost exclusively used a single sheet of glass for each pane (the window could be made up of several panes arranged in a frame work), as illustrated in Figure 3-10. With single-pane windows, the thickness of the glass represents most of the thermal efficiency (or inefficiency) of the entire window. Of course, the framing around the window can also be a source of thermal inefficiency, in the same manner as door frames discussed in the preceding section.

Single Pane Windows are found in older buildings and houses. Modern windows typically employ **Multiple Panes** (double or triple) of glass that use a dead air, or gas-filled space between the panes as insulation, as shown in Figure 3-11. **Gas Filled Window Panes** trap argon, xenon or krypton gas between the sheets of glass to increase the thermal efficiency of the window.

Single Pane Windows

Multiple Panes

Gas Filled Window Panes

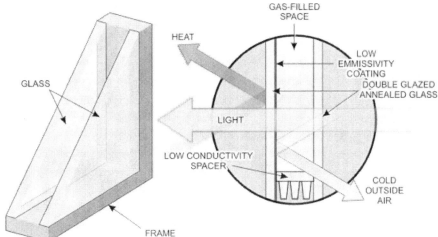

Figure 3-11: Multiple Pane Windows

Double Pane Windows can reduce utility costs by as much as 10% over single pane windows. Many utility companies offer incentive programs to older home owners to get them to replace their single pane windows with more efficient multi-pane windows. Adding storm windows to the outside of the window frame (which also creates a dead air space between the two windows) is another means of creating a more energy efficient window in older homes that are equipped with single pane windows.

Double Pane Windows

As mentioned earlier, framing can also be a cause of poor thermal efficiency associated with windows. If the framing around the window does not seal up well with both the window and the opening in the wall, air can flow freely around the window resulting in excessive heat and cooling losses. Insulation, caulking and weather stripping materials can be used to close off the air flow around the window.

Windows enable the interior area behind it to absorb energy directly from the sun. This is referred to as **Direct Solar Gain**. When the radiant energy from the sun—in the form of sunlight—strikes the objects inside the room, it is converted into thermal energy and warms the space inside. Some of the radiant energy will be absorbed by the objects in the room and released back into the room over a period of time.

Direct Solar Gain

There are several options for controlling and manipulating the thermal affects that windows have on the structure. It is a very common practice to use **Window Treatments** such as curtains or blinds to control the affects of light, provide additional insulation, or ensure privacy for the interior space. The window treatment can be opened during the daylight hours on colder days to allow light into the room to warm it up, and then closed at night to provide additional insulation. On warmer days, the window treatment can be closed to prevent the light from entering the room and heating it up.

Window Treatments

Because window treatments do not provide a seal over the window, convective heat transfers can occur through and around them. This diminishes the insulation properties of the window treatment. For this reason, it is more efficient to employ external shading methods (like those described in the following paragraphs) to reduce heat gain than to use internal window coverings.

The affects of sunlight can also be manipulated through the use of external **Awnings** and **Extended Eves** (*roofing overhangs*), as illustrated in Figure 3-12. As the figure illustrates, these structures make use of the changing elevation of the sun during different seasons. In the winter, when the trajectory of the sun is lower on the horizon, the sunlight can shine directly on southern facing windows (in the northern hemisphere). However, in summer months when the sun is higher in the sky, the direct sunlight is blocked from entering the window, limiting the amount of heat it can generate in the room.

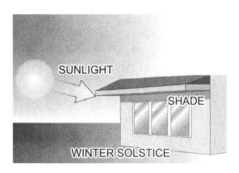 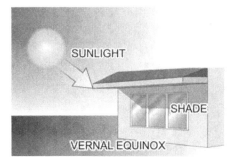 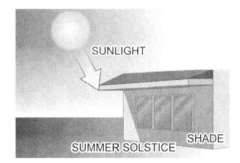

Figure 3-12:
External Passive
Sunlight Controls

It is also possible to interfere with direct sunlight by placing deciduous trees (trees that lose their leaves in winter) in front of the window. In the summer, the leaves on the tree are full and block a significant amount of direct sunlight from entering the window. Conversely, when the leaves drop off in the winter months, a much larger volume of direct sunlight can enter the window and produce heat inside the structure.

Newer window technologies employ advanced methods to respond to the presence of heat and light to control the thermal affects of sunlight on the room. **Photochromic Glass** darkens when exposed to light and **Thermochromic Glass** darkens when it is exposed to increases in temperature. Since these technologies occur automatically, they do not offer the possibility to manipulate the light to our advantage in all cases.

Window Placement in the structure plays a major role in the thermal efficiency of the structure. As mentioned above, windows installed in the southern facing wall (in the northern hemisphere) of a building allows for direct sunlight into the structure that can be manipulated to provide and limit passive heating. However, windows installed in the northern facing wall of the building cannot be used in this manner. These windows can only provide indirect solar gains and actually represent a potential thermal loss.

Industrial and commercial building may have windows mounted at different angles (instead of vertically) that maximize, or minimize, the thermal affects of the sun. These designs use the angled windows to reflect sunlight in summer to reduce heating and glare from the sunlight.

Roofs

The top outer covering of a building structure is the **Roof**. Roofs are designed to protect the structure beneath it from the elements of weather, to tie the walls of the structure together, and to provide ventilation. Most roof designs are based on supplying some type of sloped surface to drain water off the roof. These designs can be **Flat Roofs** set on some angle, or **Pitched Roofs** that use architectural elements to create a steeper sloped design, as illustrated in Figure 3-13.

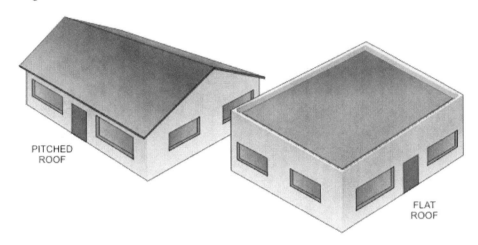

Figure 3-13:
Flat and Pitched Roofs

The roof must include design elements to support the weight of the roof materials and anything else that might be on the roof, such as water puddles, snow, heating and ventilation equipment, etc. The main structural elements in any roof design are **Joists** made of wood, concrete or steel that span the horizontal distances between walls.

With flat roofs, the joists are typically the only structural element of the roof. Even though the roof is flat, it must contain some angle from horizontal to shed water. However, with a pitched (angled) roof additional sloping elements called **Rafters** are included that extend from the **Ridge** of the roof to the **Eave** (from the top of the roof line to the edge of the roof line).

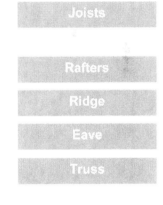

In many roof designs, the joist and rafter combination has been replaced by an engineered **Truss** design. A truss is a structural member composed of triangular connections between horizontal, vertical and sloped members. The pitch of the truss roof trigonometrically changes the way the load rests on the truss members and their supporting walls, as illustrated in Figure 3-14.

The rafters or joists that make up the roof support are typically tied together by sheets of material, such as wooden planks, plywood or metal that run on the top side of the roof. Depending on the type of sheeting used, the roof may employ an additional layer of water/weather proof material to shed rain and snow (it may also be used to manipulate the thermal characteristics of the structure.

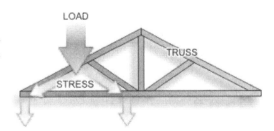

Figure 3-14: Loading Factors on Truss Roofs

The bottom side of the joist may be used as a connection point for **Ceiling** materials. Ceilings are interior surfaces that create the upper boundary of a room and conceal the roof structures above (or the bottom of a floor in the case of a multi-level structure). Figure 3-15 describes the basic components of a roof.

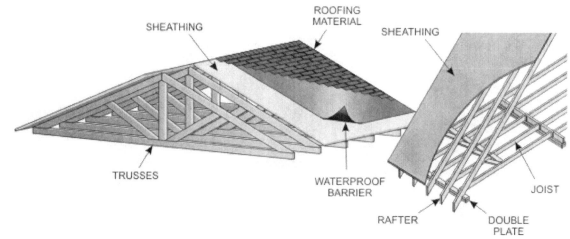

Figure 3-15:
Roof Components

Pitched Roofs are most often covered with a layer of overlapping materials referred to as **Shingles**. The shingles are overlapped in such a manner that the water runs off the roof, preventing it from penetrating the roof and leaking into the spaces below. Common shingles are made of slate, ceramic tile, wood shakes, asphalt, or fiberglass. Other common roofing materials include steel and aluminum panels.

Flat roof designs do not rely on shingles, as their slope angles are typically not sufficient to guarantee that water will run off the roof without backing up under the shingles. Therefore, newer flat roofs employ large roles of rubber or synthetic sheeting materials that are laid down on the roof surface and sealed together to form a watertight barrier across the roof. Older roofs were traditionally sealed with molten tar to make them water proof.

Attics

When a structure employs a pitched roof design, an open space is generally created between the roof and the ceiling. This area is referred to as the **Attic**. In most cases, these areas are unfinished and either neglected or used for storage. However the attic space is particularly important in controlling the temperature of the rooms below it. At a minimum, the attic represents a large dead air space which provides some insulation value between the area below the ceiling and the external temperature of the roof (which is exposed to direct sunlight, snow, rain, cold and other environmental factors).

However, in areas where moist hot air can rise into the attic and meet cold air from the roof, the structure can sustain substantial damage from condensation buildup. For this reason, attic spaces are typically vented to avoid this occurrence. Builders also install **Vapor Barriers** between the attic and the space below it to limit the ability of the air from the structure to rise into the attic area. In addition to installing a vapor barrier, it is common to install insulation material between the ceiling and the open attic space to improve the energy efficiency of the structure. The function of the insulation is to minimize the transfer of heat so that the space below the ceiling retains heat when it's colder outside and stays cooler when it is warmer outside.

REVIEW QUESTIONS

The following questions test your knowledge of the material presented in this chapter:

1. What is the percentage of all greenhouse gas emissions accounted for by buildings?

2. What is the preferred material for constructing a building's foundation?

3. Why do slab foundations suffer from excessive energy consumption?

4. In the construction industry, how is a material's ability to resist thermal change across a given thickness expressed?

5. Differentiate between older and newer residential interior wall designs.

6. What are the two most important functions of an exterior door?

7. Under what circumstances does the R-value of an exterior door material equal the R-value of the door itself?

8. With single-pane windows, what factor determines their thermal efficiency, or inefficiency?

9. How does a flat roof permit the shedding of water during heavy rainfall?

10. Define the word ceiling.

11. What is the most important function of an attic?

12. How do builders limit the ability of the air from the structure to rise into the attic area?

13. Describe what is meant by the term "direct solar gain."

14. Differentiate between photochromic glass and thermochromic glass.

15. What is the name of a wall that divides the indoor space into separate areas, without having to support floor, ceiling, or roof loads?

EXAM QUESTIONS

1. All of the following are legitimate purposes for having walls in a building, except:
   a. defining room separations.
   b. hanging assault weapons for display.
   c. supporting ceilings and roofs.
   d. providing protection from exterior elements.

2. Which of the following does NOT affect the insulation value of a wall?
   a. its thickness
   b. its type of construction material
   c. its insulation method
   d. its color

3. Internal finishing elements include all of the following, except:
   a. wetwall
   b. drywall
   c. plaster
   d. stucco

4. Which of the following would NOT be a suitable insulating material for placement within the cavities of an exterior wall?
   a. plastic foam
   b. fiberglass
   c. wood chips
   d. cellulose

5. R-values for exterior doors are typically determined by all of the following, except:
   a. how long they remain open.
   b. the type of material used to create the door.
   c. whether the door has windows.
   d. quality of the supporting framing seal.

6. Besides the R-value, factors that contribute to, or detract from, a door's energy efficiency includes all of the following, except:
   a. the insulation between the frame and the wall.
   b. the fit between the door and the parts of its frame.
   c. the material used to make the door frame.
   d. the operation of its locking mechanism.

7. When considering the thermal efficiency of a modern multi-pane window, which of the following gases provides the least amount of insulation when used between the panes?
   a. krypton gas
   b. dead air
   c. xenon gas
   d. argon gas

8. Which of the following materials is NOT useful for closing off the air flow around a window?
   a. screening
   b. insulation
   c. weather stripping
   d. caulking

9. Roofs are designed to perform all of the following functions, except:
   a. protect the structure beneath it from weather elements.
   b. tie the walls of the structure together.
   c. to provide ventilation.
   d. direct light into the structure.

10. Roofing shingles are commonly composed of all the following materials, except:
    a. aluminum
    b. slate
    c. glass
    d. asphalt

CHAPTER 4

ENERGY CONSERVATION

OBJECTIVES

Upon completion of this chapter and its related lab procedures you will be able to perform the following tasks:

1. Understand the inefficiencies built into modern energy systems.

2. Discuss the various governmental initiatives and incentives enacted to boost energy efficiency.

3. List the advantages to society and to the individual when energy is conserved.

4. Describe how energy is used within the various sectors of society.

5. Discuss what is involved in a home energy audit, the steps involved and the energy savings that can be realized.

6. Describe two ways to test the integrity of the shell of a residential building.

7. Explain the recommended levels of insulation and how these products are rated.

8. Discuss how windows affect the energy efficiency of a home, potential problem points and how energy-efficient window systems are rated.

9. Understand the difference between venting and infiltration and how the movement of air within a building adds to or detracts from its energy efficiency.

10. List the various heating and cooling options and the advantages and/or disadvantages of each type.

11. Discuss how habits and behaviors can be adjusted to make significant reductions in energy consumption in the typical home.

12. Describe how lighting impacts energy consumption and the various options available to make this function more efficient.

13. List the various options that provide hot water within residential buildings, explaining the advantages and disadvantages of each system.

14. Explain the energy relationship to water and how conservation saves not only water, but fuel as well.

15. Understand and explain the Energy Star program.

16. Discuss phantom loads and their impact on energy consumption.

Energy Conservation

INTRODUCTION

Energy conservation begins with being aware—aware of the world in general and aware of what is being consumed.

In addition to adopting behaviors that are more energy "frugal," various technological solutions exist that can assist in making some tasks more energy efficient. For example, a car that uses one gallon (3.8 liters) of gasoline to travel 40 miles (64 km) performs the same work as a car that travels the same distance but consumes two gallons (7.6 liters) of gasoline—only it does the work more efficiently.

If five people rode in the more fuel-efficient vehicle, as compared to only one, then even more energy savings are realized through changes in behavior. Energy conservation is a combination of energy-efficient technologies and energy-conscious behaviors.

Many people have the mistaken impression that energy conservation implies discomfort and that certain "luxuries" must be "given up." They assume that an energy-efficient lifestyle is by definition an uncomfortable lifestyle. But this simply is not the case. Often the opposite is true—an awareness of one's surroundings and one's impact on that environment can lead to a richer life experience.

If a light is turned off in an empty room—how does that make anyone uncomfortable? If it takes only half the energy to raise the temperature of a room to a certain level—how does that affect the comfort of people within the room?

It takes no more energy (and is much more effective) to hang laundry out to dry on a warm, sunny day than it does to hang it out during a rainstorm. The key to energy conservation (metaphorically speaking) is to be aware of the rain.

WASTE, WASTE, EVERYWHERE WASTE

The modern energy economy is not an efficient system. In fact, scientists conservatively estimate that at least 56% (electric generation is even less efficient) of all the energy produced in the United States is wasted—more than half the oil drilled, the coal mined, the hydroelectric power generated, and the natural gas burned is never used to do work. Some estimates place the percentage of waste even higher.

For example, if coal is burned to generate electric power to light a standard incandescent light bulb—only about 2% of the potential power contained within the coal actually is used to produce light, 98% of this power is wasted.

The first energy loss is at the power generating station. Typical coal-burning power plants operate at about 40% efficiency—meaning that 60% of the coal's energy is lost as heat during the production of electricity.

Moving power from the generating station to the home or business is also a wasteful process. An additional 4% of the original energy contained in the coal (10% of the resulting power is lost in transmission, so 10% of 40% equals 4%) is lost moving the power to the home.

Incandescent light bulbs themselves are very inefficient. So of the remaining 36% of the original energy from the coal, all but 2% of this energy is radiated as heat from the light bulb. As a result of inefficiencies such as these throughout the system, at least 66% of all electricity generated in the U.S. is lost before it ever reaches an appliance. And the energy waste does not end once the power reaches its destination. Conservative estimates suggest that an additional 20% of the electricity, fuel oil and natural gas is wasted in the residential, commercial and industrial use of this power.

The transportation industry has an even worse record of waste. Only about 15% of the energy from gasoline is actually captured to move an internal combustion engine vehicle or run its accessories (such as air conditioning), as shown in Figure 4-1. Most of the loss is in the engine itself—where about 60-65% of the gasoline's energy is lost in the form of heat. Through waste and inefficiencies at every step, 71% or better of the energy used to power the world's vehicles is simply wasted.

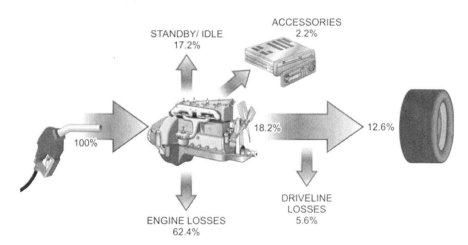

Figure 4-1: Energy Losses in a Gasoline-Powered Vehicle

The Reasons for Waste

Technology is often to blame for much of this waste. For example, the internal combustion engine is a "heat engine" (uses heat to move a piston). The efficiency of this type of engine is limited by physical properties (known as the **Carnot Limit**) to a theoretical maximum of about 50% efficiency. Similar efficiency limitations exist in most modern technologies.

Carnot Limit

Technological limitations are often difficult to overcome, but behavior is much easier to change. A very large portion of the waste within a system is the result of poor design and wasteful behaviors. And until very recently, there was little incentive to change these behaviors. For much of the past 50-60 years, the energy supply has been assumed to be nearly limitless and practically free. There is little social or economic incentive to save gasoline that costs less than a dollar a gallon or to conserve electricity that costs only 8 cents a kilowatt hour.

It was not until the energy price shocks of the 1970s that energy conservation was even a consideration in most U.S. households. The public soon realized that energy efficiency was the first and most effective line of defense against rising prices and diminishing energy supplies. But as energy prices fell in the 1980s and 1990s, conservation efforts largely faded from the public's consciousness.

The Economics of Efficiency

From 1973 (the year of the first oil shock) to 1986, the U.S. economy (**Gross Domestic Product** or **GDP**) grew by 47%. During those 13 years, U.S. levels of energy use remained constant, largely due to energy conservation practices. In fact, industry experts suggest that from 1973 to 1990, U.S. energy efficiency increased by 50%—meaning that one unit of energy in 1990 (a barrel of oil or ton of coal for example) performed the same amount of work as 1.5 units of energy in 1973.

Unfortunately, this frugality was short lived. During the next 13 years (from 1986 – 1999), U.S. energy consumption rose by 26% while the U.S. economy grew at about the same rate as the previous 13 years (a 52% increase in GDP).

Many of the energy efficiency programs implemented by government and changes in consumer behavior did take hold, however, and have had a measurable effect on energy consumption. From 1970 to 2008, the average American cut the amount of energy used each year in half. Energy conservation and energy efficiency have been the single largest source of power over the last 35 years, effectively doubling the nation's fuel supply.

Examples of conservation programs that have proven effective include the CAFÉ standards imposed upon the auto industry as well as the National Appliance Energy Conservation Act designed to increase the efficiency of household appliances.

Corporate Average Fuel Economy Standards

In 1975 the U.S. Federal government passed **Corporate Average Fuel Economy (CAFÉ)** standards requiring that all passenger cars sold in America must obtain an average fuel efficiency of 18 miles per gallon (mpg) by 1978. For the first time, automakers had to consider fuel efficiency in the design of their product—or face the possibility that they could be shut out of the lucrative U.S. auto market. By 1985 the CAFÉ standard had been raised to 27.5 mpg for passenger cars.

But as the result of declining gasoline prices, political pressure from the auto industry, and declining public interest in fuel efficiency, the CAFÉ standard was relaxed for a time, falling to 26 mpg in 1986. In 1990 it was raised to its previous level of 27.5 mpg—where it remained for two decades.

In recent years Congress has once again turned its attention towards fuel efficiency in cars and light trucks. The CAFÉ is set to increase to 30.2 mpg for passenger cars in 2011. The Energy Independence and Security Act of 2007 further requires that U.S. auto manufacturers boost the mileage efficiency of their fleets to 35 mpg by the year 2020.

In 1973 there were 102 million cars on U.S. roads, driving an average of 9,600 miles (15,450 km) per year. By 2004 the number of cars had grown to 150 million and driving distances had increased to an average of 12,000 miles (19,300 km) each year. If average U.S. fuel efficiency for autos had not improved since 1973, U.S. drivers would be using more than twice the gasoline currently pumped into their cars each year, as shown in Figure 4-2.

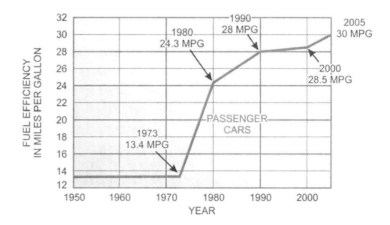

Figure 4-2:
Improving Fuel
Economies for U.S. Cars

Appliance and Equipment Efficiency Standards

In 1987, U.S. President Ronald Regan signed into law the **National Appliance Energy Conservation Act (NAECA)** which established, for the first time, national energy efficiency standards for an array of appliances (such as dishwashers, toasters, etc.). A number of laws have since been put in place that establish or raise energy efficiency requirements for appliances, lighting, and commercial and residential heating/cooling systems.

The effect of these regulations has been dramatic. It is estimated that efficiency standards for appliances alone have reduced the amount of electricity used in the U.S. by about 2.5%—over 88 billion kWh of power saved in 2000 alone.

Advantages of Energy Conservation

While energy conservation is certainly good for the environment and may even be good for the economy (certainly it is not detrimental), it also holds many benefits for individual consumers. These include:

- Saving money. On average, every dollar spent on energy conservation results in $5 in actual energy savings.

- Better housing financing. Many lenders offer lower mortgage rates and larger loan amounts for homes that are energy efficient. The rationale (other than encouraging efficiency) is that money not spent on energy is money the homeowner will have available to service a larger mortgage.

- Less maintenance. Energy efficient homes place less of a strain on heating and cooling systems, resulting in longer life for the unit and reduced operating costs.

- Quick and easy. Energy conservation methods can usually be implemented very quickly and typically require little formal training to implement.

- Free or inexpensive. Savings can be achieved with very little expense (or no expense at all). It costs nothing to turn off lights or turn down the heat in rooms that are not in use.

- Less greenhouse gas emissions. The less energy consumed, the lower the level of greenhouse gases emitted into the atmosphere.

- Higher home value. Studies indicate that energy-efficient homes are easier to sell and bring a higher price than inefficient models. For every $1 decrease in energy costs achieved through efficiency, the average sale price of the home increases by nearly $21.

HOW ENERGY IS USED

Before the waste within a system can be addressed and eliminated, it is important to first understand where and how that energy is being used. As shown in Figure 4-3, energy use is typically divided between the transportation, industrial (which includes agriculture), commercial (offices and stores), and residential market segments.

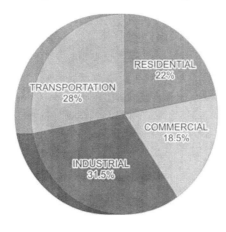

**Figure 4-3:
Carving up the U.S.
Energy Pie**

Industrial Energy

The industrial and manufacturing portion of the U.S. economy uses the largest share of the energy "pie". This sector accounts for over 31% of the energy consumed, producing the food, chemicals, clothing, paper and computers used each and every day by society.

The largest sub-component of this energy use is in refining petroleum (for gasoline and diesel) and generating electricity, as shown in Table 4-1. The manufacture of chemicals (for agriculture as well as other uses) accounts for another one-quarter the energy used by the industrial sector of the economy.

Table 4-1: Energy Consumed within Industrial Sector of the U.S. Economy (1998)

Petroleum and Coal Products	30.76%
Chemicals	25.48%
Metals & Fabricated Metal Products	12.63%
Paper & Printing	11.96%
Food	4.39%
Glass/Cement Products	4.11%
Wood Products	2.51%
Transportation Equipment	2.07%
Plastics and Rubber Products	1.38%
Textile Mills	1.08%
Machinery	0.91%
Computer and Electronic Products	0.86%
Miscellaneous	0.81%
Electrical Equip., Appliances, & Components	0.60%
Beverage and Tobacco Products	0.45%
Total	**100.00%**

While consumer behavior cannot often impact the energy efficiency within the industrial sector directly, it can have a dramatic "indirect" effect. In recent years consumers have become more environmentally conscious in their purchases, demanding that the products they buy be produced as sustainable as possible.

Manufacturers have responded, changing material sources, improving processes and reducing packaging. They have also responded with extensive marketing strategies that promote the environmental advantages of their product.

According to a 2008 survey:

- 43% of companies plan to increase spending on "green" marketing practices.

- 82% of consumers are focused on buying green products and services.

- 7 out of 10 consumers pay attention to company practices regarding the environment.

While much of this advertising is simply "**Greenwashing**" (questionable or unsubstantiated environmentally positive claims attributed to their products) many manufacturers have made great strides in the energy efficiencies of their production processes and/or the components used in manufacturing the products. Since 1973 the U.S. industrial sector has grown 60%, while energy consumption within this sector has grown only 15%. For example, in 1973 a ream of office paper required the energy equivalent of 3.7 gallons (14 liters) of gasoline to produce. By 2008, energy efficiencies in production reduced the amount of energy required to the equivalent of 2 gallons (7.6 liters) of gas.

While energy consumption within the industrial sector is highly dependent upon economic activity (higher economic output generally translates into increased energy consumption), this sector of the U.S. energy market is predicted to increase only by about 4% over the next 20 years. Declines in chemical production will be offset by increased energy for fuel refining—particularly in the manufacture of biofuels.

SCIENCE NOTE: GREENWASHING

As people become more conscious about the environment and waste, suddenly folks that yesterday would gladly dump a bucket of toxic waste on their grandmother's petunias are out there trying to tell the world they are "green."

You should know that there is nobody (not the government, not private organizations) out there deciding what is green and what is not green. It is the latest "new and improved" of the marketing world. It can mean anything to anyone—so most of the time it really means nothin' to nobody.

So before you take anyone's word for it that a product is green, ask some questions. Greenpeace, an environmental group, calls these the "CARE" questions.

Is the green thing advertised part of the company's Core (see, that's the "C" in CARE) business, or just a side business they got into to try to make them look good so you won't complain that they just blew up the mountain down the road?

The "A" is for Advertising. Are they just telling you they are green, using their ads to justify why they should just continue business as usual? Then we get to "R" for Research. Are they putting their money where their mouth is, trying to find ways to reduce pollution or use fewer resources?

And finally, there is "E" for Environmental Lobbying. Is the company saying they are green in their ads while pushing for laws that makes it easier for them to pollute?

I know what you're thinking, it's not easy being a consumer. But one sure fire way to be just a bit greener is just don't buy that thing that you were going to buy but you really don't need. Save money and the planet by not buying stuff. See how simple conservation can be?

Energy in Agriculture

A very large portion of the energy consumed within the industrial sector of the economy is used to produce, transport, package and process the food society eats. As much as 19% of the fossil fuels burned in the U.S. are estimated to be used in the production of food (7% for production, 7% for processing/packaging, 5% for distribution and preparation). That doesn't even consider the energy needed to dispose of the waste and packaging produced.

The industrial agriculture system that has evolved within the U.S. during the past 50 years is extremely energy intensive. For example:

- Heavy dependence on fossil fuel-based fertilizers

- Pesticides

- Large centralized processing facilities

- Larger and larger equipment using more fuel

- Long distances from farm to dinner table (an average distance food travels before reaching American consumers is 1800 miles, spending 7-14 days in transit) contributes to making the food industry highly dependent upon fossil fuels.

Research indicates that two units of fossil fuel are required to produce one unit of food energy under the current food production system. Low cost food produced within this system requires low energy prices. In recent years, increases in fuel costs have quickly been reflected in rapid increases in the cost of food.

SCIENCE NOTE: FOOD

Since World War II, the food industry in the U.S. has undergone an amazing transformation. The family farm is a fading memory. Today's farms are large agribusinesses, usually focused on growing one or two commodity crops. Thousand-acre corn farms produce a lot of corn, but at a cost of about 2 units of fossil fuel for every unit (calorie) of food energy produced.

Producing beef consumes even more energy. It takes about 54 units of energy to produce one unit of food energy from beef. It also requires a lot of water—over 5200 gallons (that's almost 20,000 liters) of water by some estimates to produce just one pound of hamburger. Large meat-producing facilities generate more greenhouse gases than a large city. So what can we do?

Many people are moving towards a more local food economy. They argue that there is no reason to buy a carrot that has traveled over 1800 miles (that's the average now in the U.S.) when you can grow one in your own back yard or buy it at the local farmer's market. Corn that is grown organically produces 5.79 units of energy for every unit it consumes. Grass fed beef production uses a lot fewer resources than cattle "finished" in large feed lots.

Energy for Transportation

About 28% of all the energy used in U.S. is directly consumed in moving people and goods from one place to another. Of this fuel, 62% is in the form of gasoline (including ethanol), 24% is diesel, 8% is jet fuel and about 2% is compressed natural gas.

In 2005 there were approximately 297 million people living in the United States. That same year, there were over 239 million vehicles (cars, trucks and buses) in the nation—nearly one for every man, woman and child.

Just as with cars, other forms of transportation have increased their fuel efficiencies in recent years. Since 1973 the aviation industry has seen the price of jet fuel increase ten-fold. They have responded by dramatically increasing the efficiency of their fleet. In 1978 airplanes averaged just 15 passenger miles (miles traveled per passenger carried) per gallon (3.7 liters) of jet fuel. By 2004 the average fuel efficiency of the U.S. fleet of commercial airplanes had increased to 40 passenger miles (64 km) per gallon (increasing fuel efficiency by more than 160%).

The nation's fleet of large trucks has also improved its fuel efficiency. In 1977 the average tractor-trailer in the U.S. got only 4.8 mpg (2 km/liter). By 2005 that number had improved to around 10 mpg (4.25 km/liter).

Despite increases in fuel efficiencies, the transportation sector continues to consume more and more fuel as worldwide demand grows even faster. Since 1973 the number of passengers flying on airplanes has more than doubled. In 2004 more than 600 million passengers flew, that number is expected to increase to 1 billion by 2010.

Researchers project that by the year 2030, the number of vehicles worldwide will more than double. New vehicle registrations in China, for example, have increased dramatically in recent years, as shown in Figure 4-4. In 2009, China surpassed the U.S. as the world's largest auto market, purchasing 2.7 million vehicles in the first quarter of that year (compared to 2.2 million sold in the U.S.).

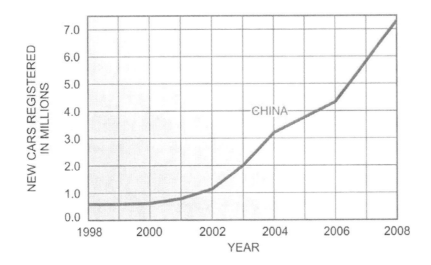

**Figure 4-4:
New Car Registrations in China**

Residential Energy Use

When discussing energy conservation, most attention is generally focused on the residential sector of the market (which accounts for about 22% of the energy consumed in the U.S.). And certainly there are many savings to be made in this sector. The average American consumes nearly twice the amount of energy each year than do residents in other industrialized nations.

Much of this energy is consumed within the home. Most household energy is used in heating and cooling the structure, as shown in Figure 4-5, but a substantial portion is also used to run appliances, heat water and provide light.

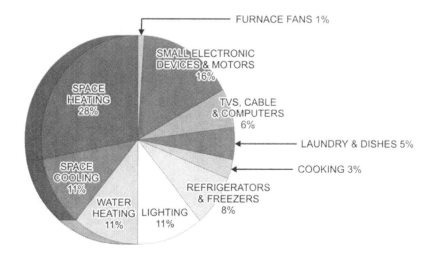

Figure 4-5:
Energy Uses Within the Home

Home Energy Audit

While energy-use statistics may be helpful in setting energy-saving priorities, individual household's energy use will vary significantly. So a good place to start in reducing the amount of energy consumed within a specific home is to conduct a **Home-Energy Audit**.

There are many professional firms that specialize in conducting residential energy audits (many states have licensing programs for this profession), or homeowners can perform these evaluations themselves. Typically an audit includes:

- Checking the building shell for leaks and drafts. Depending on the age and construction of the building, energy savings achieved through reducing heat and cooling loss can be as great as 30%.

- Evaluating insulation levels. Even a tightly sealed home will conduct heat through the shell of the building. Insulation reduces this energy loss and increases the level of comfort within the structure.

- Inspecting the heating/cooling system. Older or poorly maintained equipment can greatly increase energy costs. Nearly 40% of a household's energy expense is consumed in the heating and cooling of the building. Special attention should be paid to make sure these units are operating at optimal levels.

- Change lighting. Providing light within a home accounts for about 10% of the energy consumed. Energy efficient bulbs, automatic switches or changes in habits can greatly reduce this expense.

- Upgrade water heating system. Consuming about the same amount of energy as lighting, water heaters are another area where waste can be eliminated. Heat levels can be adjusted, timers installed, insulation added or the unit can even be replaced with a more energy-efficient model.

- Switching to other appliances. Electrical appliances used within the home consume a significant portion of energy. Evaluate the use and efficiency of these items and consider eliminating or replacing ones that are little used or inefficient.

SCIENCE NOTE: WHAT IS YOUR CARBON FOOTPRINT?

Everywhere we turn it seems someone is talking about "**Carbon Footprint**" — how to reduce it, or providing some tool that helps calculate it. But they never seem to tell you what it means or why you should care.

A carbon footprint is a term that pins a number on each of us, saying that we are each responsible for releasing so many pounds (or tons or kilograms) of carbon dioxide into the atmosphere just because we exist. Supposedly, the "footprint" of greenhouse gas that we contribute by simply living on this planet.

For example, the average American generates 20 tons of CO_2 every year. Try to imagine CO_2 as it floats in air (drifting up into the atmosphere) — so how does it weigh anything, let alone 20 tons?

The **Union of Concerned Scientists** say that a gallon of gasoline gives off 24 pounds of CO_2 when it's burned. A gallon of gas only weighs about 6 lbs—so where did the other 18 lbs come from?

Carbon Footprint

Union of Concerned Scientists

The Building Shell

Because the heating and cooling of the structure accounts for such a significant portion of the total energy used within a home, it is logical to focus first on making sure that this energy does not simply escape out into the atmosphere.

Most professional home energy auditors will test the **Integrity of the Shell** (the exterior walls, roof and foundation) of the home in several ways.

Integrity of the Shell

Visual Inspection

An audit should include a complete visual inspection of the building, going throughout the structure, determining if:

- There is adequate insulation in the attic.

- There are any obvious cracks or holes in the walls or roof.

- The windows are insulated (double-paned) and tightly sealed.

- Fireplace dampers are open or leaky.

Blower Door Units

While visual inspection will identify the most blatant problems, professional energy auditors will often use a **Blower Door Unit** to determine how drafty the structure is and then locate the source of these problems.

A blower door unit is attached to an exterior door, as illustrated in Figure 4-6. The home is then sealed (windows, doors and vents closed, etc). The fan is started, pushing air from inside the home outdoors. The air that is removed from the home is replaced with air entering through gaps, leaks and holes in the shell of the building. The blower door unit measures the amount of air being drawn into the home (and then out via the fan).

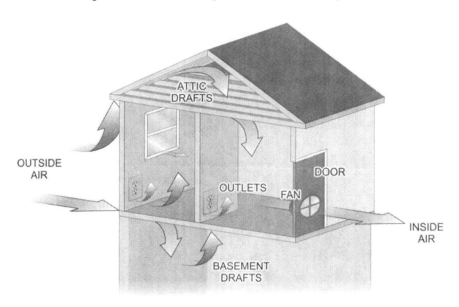

Figure 4-6:
Blower Door Test

A well-sealed home will allow a flow of between 500 to 1,500 cubic feet (14.2 to 42.5 cubic meters) of air per minute. Many U.S. homes built prior to 1970 typically provide much higher readings of between $6,500 - 8,500 \text{ ft}^3$ (185-240 m^3) per minute.

While the unit is running, smoke sticks are often used to help find leaks. When these sticks are held near the exterior wall, any leak will push the smoke into the interior of the room. Once identified, these leaks and cracks can then be filled (typically with a latex caulk).

Infrared Cameras

Another method to determine how heat might be escaping from a building is to use an **Infrared Camera**. An infrared camera displays variations in heat, rather than light. Photos of the shell of the building reveal areas where heat is escaping (or entering, depending on the relative temperature of indoor versus outdoor air).

These units are especially good at identifying where insulation may be missing within the wall, as they measure heat losses due to **Conduction** and **Radiation** (energy flowing through the material) as well as **Convection** (energy passing through gaps and holes in the exterior of the building).

Infrared Camera

Conduction

Radiation

Convection

Common Problem Spots

Heated or cooled air leaking from a building can account for as much as 30% of the energy losses of a typical home. Locations where these leaks commonly occur include:

- Plumbing penetrations through insulated ceilings or floors
- Fireplace dampers
- Around windows and doors
- Attic access hatches
- Chimney penetrations
- Recessed lights and fans
- Wiring penetrations through insulated walls, floors and ceilings
- Electrical outlets and switches on exterior walls
- Around cabinets and closets
- The junction of the walls and floor

Wind Barriers

In areas that experience a significant amount of wind, external barriers will assist in lowering energy consumption. Even the best constructed homes allow outside air to infiltrate the shell. This inflow of air can be increased dramatically with the added force of wind.

A wind and water barrier installed outside the building (typically under the siding) will reduce the effects of forced air penetrating the structure. Wind breaks (rows of trees or a wall) placed on the prevailing-wind side of the home can also help reduce this problem.

Insulation

In addition to leaks in the shell, inadequate insulation accounts for the largest preventable source of energy loss within a typical home. In addition to saving money and energy, a well-insulated home is more comfortable as it maintains a more uniform temperature throughout the house.

The amount and type of insulation best suited for a building is dependent upon a number of factors. These include:

- The climate where the building is located.

- The space available for insulation.

- The accessibility of the space where the insulation will be installed.

- The price and availability of the insulation material.

Types of Insulation

Insulation is available in a number of forms. Common forms include:

- Blankets, in the form of batts or rolls. This flexible insulation is made from mineral fibers, including fiberglass or rock wool. They are typically sold in widths designed to fit standard spacings of wall studs and attic or floor joists.

- Blown-in loose-fill insulation. This insulation is made of cellulose (typically treated recycled newsprint), fiberglass, or rock wool in the form of loose fibers or fiber pellets, and can be blown into wall cavities or open cavities between floor joists. It can also be mixed with an adhesive or foam and applied to open wall cavities, as demonstrated in Figure 4-7. Adding adhesives avoids settling of the material within the wall cavity over time.

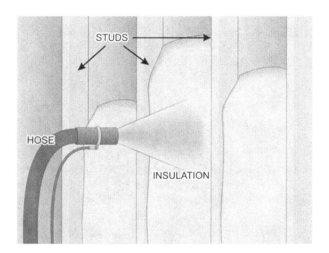

Figure 4-7:
Blown-In Insulation

- Foam insulation. Polyisocyanurate and polyurethane foam insulation is usually installed by a professional, using specialized equipment. It comes in two forms: open-cell and closed-cell. Open-celled foam allows water vapor to move through the material more easily than closed-cell foam. Open-celled foams also usually have lower insulating properties for a given thickness. This product is often used to insulate open, irregular or hard to reach surfaces.

- Rigid insulation. Often used around foundations or pipes, this form of insulation is made from fibrous materials or plastic foams. As the name indicates, the material is rigid with few heat-loss paths.

- Reflective insulation or **Radiant Barriers**. When a single reflective surface is facing an open space, such as an uninsulated attic or cellar, it is called a radiant barrier. This reflective surface prevents heat from radiating through the shell of the building. Aluminum foils with a variety of backings such as kraft paper, plastic film, polyethylene bubbles, or cardboard are often used in addition to or as part of other insulation systems.

R-Values

Insulation is rated in terms of how well it resists the transfer of thermal energy. The measurement of a specific product's effectiveness in blocking heat transfer is called its **R-Value (RSI-Value** is the metric equivalent). The higher the R-value, the better the product will be at retaining heat within a building.

Much of the insulating value of a product stems from its ability to trap air within its structure. As a result, insulation that is compacted (the air squeezed out) is generally less effective than looser fill.

Moisture can also affect the R-value of insulation. Moisture can enter the system from the exterior of the building (through holes or leaks) or from sources of moisture located inside the building (water pipes, bathrooms, cooking, etc). Just as with air infiltration, moisture leaks should be caulked, repaired and/or filled to prevent damage to the structure as well as a reduction in insulation effectiveness.

Moisture moves throughout the home in a process known as **Diffusion**. Just as thermal energy moves from an area of high heat to lower heat (higher concentration to lower), moisture too will move from an area of high concentration (such as a humid bathroom or kitchen) to an area of lower concentration. As colder air generally holds less moisture than does warmer air—this moisture diffusion often results in moisture moving towards colder portions of the home. When the moist warm air strikes a cooler surface, **Condensation** may occur, causing moisture to form on walls and windows.

The addition of insulation will affect how moisture moves throughout the house. It may prevent, or redirect the air flow. Unintended condensation can occur, resulting in moisture problems or damage. A properly installed **Ventilation System** will help avoid some of the problems created by moisture in a home.

In the United States, residential homes are typically constructed using 2x4 or 2x6 wooden wall studs. Batt or roll insulation designed to fit within these wall cavities will provide insulation levels up to R-15 for 2x4 walls and up to R-21 for walls constructed using 2x6s.

Radiant Barriers

R-Value

RSI-Value

Diffusion

Condensation

Ventilation System

The amount of insulation required is dependent upon the location of the home. The Department of Energy has divided the U.S. into 8 zones, as illustrated in Figure 4-8, in determining their recommendations for insulation levels. Table 4-2 indicates the recommended minimum insulation levels for the various U.S. zones for wood-framed homes. Additional insulation will provide even more energy savings.

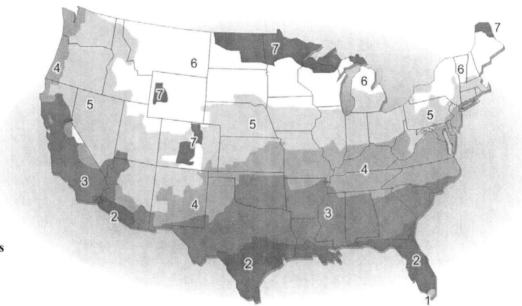

Figure 4-8: U.S. Zones for Insulation Recommendations

Table 4-2: Minimum U.S. Recommended Insulation Levels

ZONE	ATTIC	CATHEDRAL CEILING	WALL CAVITY	FLOOR
1	R30 (RSI 5.0)	R22 (RSI 3.9)	R13 (RSI 2.2)	R13 (RSI 2.2)
2	R30 (RSI 5.0)	R22 (RSI 3.9)	R13 (RSI 2.2)	R13 (RSI 2.2)
3	R30 (RSI 5.0)	R22 (RSI 3.9)	R13 (RSI 2.2)	R25 (RSI 4.4)
4	R38 (RSI 6.7)	R30 (RSI 5.0)	R13 (RSI 2.2)	R25 (RSI 4.4)
5	R38 (RSI 6.7)	R30 (RSI 5.0)	R13 (RSI 2.2)	R25 (RSI 4.4)
6	R49 (RSI 8.6)	R30 (RSI 5.0)	R13 (RSI 2.2)	R25 (RSI 4.4)
7	R49 (RSI 8.6)	R30 (RSI 5.0)	R13 (RSI 2.2)	R25 (RSI 4.4)
8	R49 (RSI 8.6)	R30 (RSI 5.0)	R13 (RSI 2.2)	R25 (RSI 4.4)

R-Value vs. Actual Effective R-Value

Product performance tests to determine R-value are conducted under ideal conditions, at 70°F (21°C) with no air movement and low humidity. These conditions are rarely present in the "real world"—so the actual (or effective) R-value of a home may be significantly lower than the rated R-value of the product installed.

In addition to moisture and moving air, other factors may be present that lower the actual insulating performance of the home. For example, insulation that is compressed may have a lower effective R-value.

Another common insulation problem is referred to as **Thermal Bridging**. This is common when insulation is placed between wooden studs in a wall or floor. The wood has a lower insulating value than does the insulation, so heat can transfer through the wooden board at a faster rate than the insulation-filled cavity.

Windows

Windows are an especially vulnerable part of the shell of a building. Energy passes through and around windows in a number of ways, as illustrated in Figure 4-9. These include:

- Non-solar heat losses and gains (the **Insulating Value** of the window)

- Solar heat gains in the form of radiation;

- Airflow, both intentional (**Ventilation**) and unintentional (**Infiltration**)

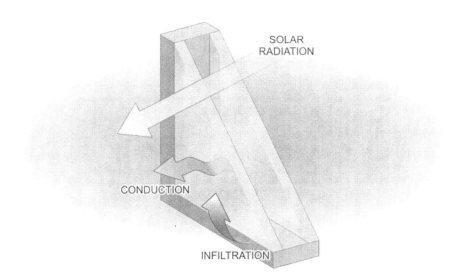

**Figure 4-9:
Ways Windows
Lose Energy**

Insulating Value of Windows

During winter months, heat will move through windows to the outside (traveling from an area of high energy density to lower density through convection, conduction and radiation). Heat will enter the home through windows during the summer months.

The effects of non-solar heat losses are typically greater during winter months, since the difference between inside and outside temperatures is usually greater during these months. As a rule, the greater the temperature differential, the greater the non-solar heat loss.

The insulation effectiveness of a window is called its **U-Factor** (or sometimes referred to as its **U-Value**). The lower the U-factor of a particular window, the better it is at resisting non-solar heat loss (or gain). The U-factor is determined by the **National Fenestration Rating Council (NFRC)**, a nonprofit, public/private organization created by the window, door, and skylight industry (the word **Fenestration** comes from Latin, meaning to design and place windows in a building).

Any window certified by the NFRC will display a label such as shown in Figure 4-10. These labels allow consumers to compare, not only U-factors, but also:

- Solar heat gain

- Visible light transmittance

- Air leakage

- Resistance to condensation

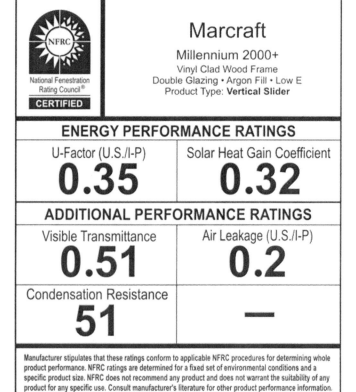

Figure 4-10: NFRC Window Label

LET'S DO THE MATH

Since we are really talking about the same thing (insulation value) when we talk about U-factors for windows and R-values for insulation—you might think they could make up their minds and give them the same number… but that would be too easy.

However, there is a way to figure all this out. The U-factor of a window is simply the inverse of the R-value that is used in North America to measure insulation effectiveness. So, you can simply use the equation U-factor = 1/R-value to figure out how well the window is insulated (compared to the wall).

For example, if we have a window with a U-factor of .35, we can determine the R-value using basic math:

    1/R-value = .35 (U-factor)
    1 = .35 * R-value
    1/.35 = R-value
    R-value = 2.86

If your walls have an R-value of 13 (for example), you can see that the window will certainly be a weak spot in the building.

There was a time when nearly all windows consisted of a single pane of glass. The insulating effectiveness of such a window was minimal. Double paned (or **Double Glazed**) windows were introduced, consisting of two panes of glass with trapped air between. This system proved much more effective in resisting heat loss.

Manufacturers soon found that gases such as argon, krypton, sulfur hexafluoride, and even carbon dioxide offered better insulating properties than trapped air. Krypton, for example, is twice as dense as argon (which is 38% more dense than air), making it a better insulator.

Most manufacturers offer products that incorporate a low emission (**Low-E**) coating that further lowers heat loss. A low-E coating is a microscopically thin metal or metallic oxide coating deposited on a glazing surface. This coating limits radiative heat flow between the panes of glass by reflecting heat back towards its source.

The relative impact on the insulating value of these various refinements to window design can be seen in Table 4-3.

Table 4-3: U-factor for Various Window Systems

GLAZING TYPE	TYPICAL U-FACTOR	RELATIVE R-VALUE
Single glass	Not rated	1.00
Double glass, ½ inch air space	0.48	2.08
Double glass, ½ inch air space, low-E	0.38	2.63
Double glass, ½ inch argon gas, low-E	0.34	2.94
Triple glass, ½ inch argon gas, low-E	0.23	4.35
Quadruple glass, ¼ inch krypton gas, low-E	0.22	4.55

Solar Heat Gain

Heat Gain Coefficient
(SHGC)

Solar radiation entering a home through a window includes both heat and light. The **Solar Heat Gain Coefficient (SHGC)** indicates how well a window blocks the heat portion of this energy from entering the home through the window. The SHGC is expressed as a number between 1 and 0. The lower the number, the less heat the system transmits.

Homes that rely on heat gain (passive solar heating) through windows should incorporate windows with a high SHGC. In areas where interior cooling is of primary concern (such as in tropical or sub-tropical environment), windows with a very low SHCG should be selected.

Visible Transmittance

Visible Transmittance
(VT)

The primary purpose for installing a window is to allow light to enter the building. The **Visible Transmittance (VT)** rating of a window is expressed as a number between 1 and 0—indicating how effective the window is in transmitting visible light. The higher the number, the more light that will enter the home through the window. Homes seeking to increase energy effectiveness through daylighting should use windows with a higher VT.

Air Leakage

Air Leakage (AL)

Even the most energy-efficient window system will permit some air to infiltrate around the edges of the unit. The NFRC rates windows as to their **Air Leakage (AL)** with a rating that is determined by measuring the cubic feet of air passing through a square foot of window area each minute.

AL rates for modern window systems typically fall between 0.1 and 0.3. An AL rating of 0.2 (meaning that 0.2 cubic feet of air passes through the window system each minute for each square foot of surface area) or less is recommended for energy-efficient homes.

Condensation Rating

Warmer air typically contains more moisture (humidity) than does cooler air. If the warm air in a home comes in contact with a cool surface (such as a window), condensation may occur. If left unchecked, this moisture can damage the window system.

Condensation
Resistance (CR)

The NFRC provides a **Condensation Resistance (CR)** rating for window systems as well (although not all windows are rated for condensation since this is a voluntary part of the rating system). The CR is expressed as a number between 1 and 100. The higher the number, the better the window system is at resisting condensation.

Other Considerations

Energy efficiency can also be influenced by the material used to construct the frame of the window. Wood composites, fiberglass and vinyl frames reduce heat transfer, resulting in a more energy-efficient system.

It is also recommended that windows with "warm edges" be used if at all possible. Warm edges are created when insulated spacers are placed between the panes of glass and the frame. These not only help hold the panes in place at the proper distance from each other, but they reduce the amount of energy conducted from the window to the frame—a significant source of heat loss.

Ventilation

The movement of air through a building can have a dramatic impact, not only on the health of the occupants, but on the amount of energy needed to heat or cool the structure. As a building is made more weather-tight, the amount of unplanned air that enters (air infiltration) is usually greatly reduced.

This reduction in air flow increases the energy efficiency of the building, but can also lead to unintended problems such as moisture issues and/or increased indoor air pollution due to a lack of outdoor air infiltration.

Moving Air Within the Home

Hot air rises. So in a typical home, warmer air will naturally tend to move towards the ceilings or upper floors of the building (known as the **Stack Effect**). **Ceiling Fans** are an effective way within a room to keep the air "mixed," avoiding a situation where warm heated air concentrates above the living space.

Ceiling fans also help in cooling a room by creating a low-level wind chill effect. Moving air makes the actual air temperature "feel" cooler. During the summer months, turning the thermostat up just a couple of degrees can save as much as 14% of the energy used for air conditioning. Moving air, even at these slightly higher temperatures, will feel just as comfortable.

About two-thirds of the homes in the U.S. use a **Forced-Air Duct System** to move heated or cooled air throughout the building. Typically these duct systems are a major source of air infiltration. Properly sealed ductwork can reduce heating and cooling costs by as much as 20%. Leaky ductwork running through an uninsulated attic, for example, may be heating a great deal of what is effectively outdoor air.

Leaky ductwork not only allows heated air to escape into areas that do not require heating, resulting in higher energy costs, but will also increase the wear and tear on the heating system. Air entering and leaving the system through leaky ducts causes the unit to move more air than it was designed to handle, straining the system.

Moving Air In and Out of the Home

A healthy building requires a constant inflow and outflow of air. If this flow is unintended, it is referred to as infiltration. The intended flow of air is referred to as ventilation. An example of a simple ventilation system is a kitchen exhaust fan that removes hot moist air from above the stove and vents it to the outdoors.

Many homes, however, incorporate large ventilation systems, rather than just exhaust fans in the kitchen and bathrooms. Complete ventilation systems are designed to move more air than a simple exhaust fan. These functions include:

- Remove stale air containing water vapor, carbon dioxide, airborne chemicals and other pollutants to outside the home.

- Bring in fresh outside air, which presumably contains fewer pollutants.

- Distribute the outside air throughout the house.

Simple ventilation systems employ an exhaust fan that pulls air from within the building and vents it to the outdoors. Systems such as the one illustrated in Figure 4-11 place the building under a slight negative air pressure, so outside air naturally flows into the house through vents or open windows.

Figure 4-11:
Exhaust-Only
Ventilation System

One downside to these systems can be found in homes that also have a fireplace or wood stove. The negative air pressure within the home may result in a back-draft, where air flows into the home through the flue or chimney, bringing smoke into the living space.

Many ventilation systems try to balance the air flow by using two fans: one for exhaust and another for fresh air. This balanced air flow can be difficult to achieve, however, especially in homes that have a forced air heating system. Highly engineered duct design and careful installation are required. Even then, a well **Balanced Air System** can be disrupted by someone opening or closing a door or window.

Balanced Air System

Air vented to the outdoors, either passively (through convection) or actively (using a fan) will result in heated or cooled air escaping the building. To avoid this, many systems employ a **Heat-Recovery Ventilator (HRV)** to capture some of this lost heat.

Heat-Recovery Ventilator (HRV)

The most common type of HRV is an **Air-to-Air Heat Exchanger**. This unit transfers heat from the outgoing air to the fresh air being drawn into the home. A balanced air system is required for this type of unit.

Air-to-Air Heat Exchanger

Another type of HRV is an **Exhaust Air Heat Pump**. These units transfer heat from the outgoing air into the hot water tank. After much of the heat contained in the air is used to heat the water, it is then allowed to vent to the outside.

Exhaust Air Heat Pump

Heating and Cooling Units

In 1992 the U.S. Department of Energy determined that all furnaces sold in America must have an **Annual Fuel Utilization Efficiency (AFUE)** rating of at least 78% in an effort to boost the fuel efficiency of these high-energy appliances. This means that 78% of the energy used (be it electric, gas, or oil) must be converted into usable heat.

Units installed prior to 1992 typically had efficiency ratings of only 65% or below. Replacing older systems with more efficient newer units is a very effective way of reducing energy use for heating and cooling a home.

In selecting a heating/cooling unit, there are several factors that should be considered. These include:

- Fuel type: Various systems can be fueled with electricity, natural gas, propane, or fuel oil.

- Unit efficiency: AFUE ratings typically range from 78% to as high as 99%.

- Unit size: The size of the furnace or air conditioner required will be determined by the size of the living area of the home, installed insulation values, air infiltration, number of windows, etc. Bigger is not necessarily better, as units sized too large for the structure will not cycle at peak efficiency. System sizes should be determined using a **Manual J** (available from the **Air Conditioning Contractors of America**) or an equivalent calculating tool.

Heat Pumps

An energy-efficient alternative to the traditional furnace or boiler may be found by installing a **Heat Pump**. Heat pumps are remarkably efficient, producing as much as 4.5 times the heat energy (an amazing efficiency rating of about 450%) than the electrical energy they consume.

There are two basic types of heat pumps: air-source and ground-source. **Air-Source Heat Pumps** generally do not perform well in areas with extended periods of sub-freezing temperatures. In warmer climates, however, they are an efficient energy source for both heating and cooling.

Heat pumps are very efficient because they move existing heat rather than create it. In an air-source heat pump, the unit gathers heat from the outside air, concentrates it, then uses it to heat the home. In warmer months, the system operates in reverse, drawing warm air from within the home, cooling it, then returning it to the house.

Ground-Source Heat Pumps, also called **Geothermal Heat Pumps**, draw heat energy from the earth, rather than the air. A ground-source heat pump is shown in Figure 4-12. These systems are effective in colder climates (where air-source models are impractical) and can reach efficiencies of up to 600% on the coldest winter days.

Annual Fuel Utilization Efficiency (AFUE)

Manual J

Air Conditioning Contractors of America

Heat Pump

Air-Source Heat Pumps

Ground-Source Heat Pumps

Geothermal Heat Pumps

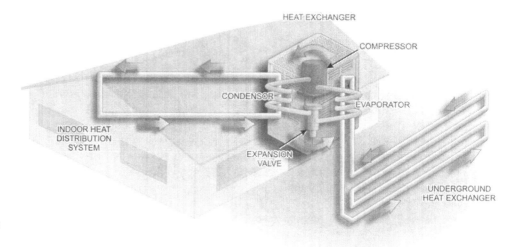

Figure 4-12:
Ground-Source
Heat Pump System

Behaviors

Changes in habits and simple actions can save a significant amount of the energy that is used to heat or cool a residential home. These include:

- Unblock vents and registers. Modern air-handling systems are highly engineered and designed for maximum efficiency. Move furniture (or baskets of dirty laundry) from in front of heating vents to allow for proper air flow.

- Monitoring thermostat settings. By lowering thermostat settings a few degrees in the winter, and raising the temperature setting a few degrees in the summer, a significant amount of energy can be saved. For each degree adjusted, energy use can be cut 3-5%. Table 4-4 outlines suggested settings in a typical home. Note that winter temperatures are lowered at night (when people are sleeping) and during the day (when at work or at school).

- Dressing for the weather. The primary purpose of heating or cooling the home is to provide a comfortable environment for the occupants. Wearing heavier (or layered) clothing in cooler temperatures, and lighter clothing in warm months reduces the need for artificial temperature control.

- Closing windows and doors. After spending a considerable amount of time and money weather-proofing the home, leaving windows and doors open when the heating or cooling system is in operation cancels the effort.

- Blocking off unused rooms. If portions of the home are not in use, keep them closed off from the primary heating and cooling system.

- The right timing for cooking and laundry. On hot days, time cooking and laundry activities to take place during the cooler part of the day (mornings or evenings). These activities produce heat inside the home which the air conditioning system must increase production to counteract.

- Opening and closing curtains and blinds. During cool months, open the drapes or blinds to allow the passive solar energy of the sun to assist in warming the home. Then close them at night to assist in keeping the heat within the building. During warmer months, closing curtains and blinds may reduce the need for air conditioning.

- Maintaining the system. Check and replace all filters as recommended by the manufacturer and periodically check the unit to make sure it is operating at peak levels.

TIME	SETPOINT TEMPERATURE (HEAT)	SETPOINT TEMPERATURE (COOL)
Wake	< 70°F (<21°C)	>78°F (>25.5°C)
Day	Lower by 8°F (4.5°C)	Raise by 7°F (4°C)
Evening	< 70°F (<21°C)	>78°F (>25.5°C)
Sleep	Lower by 8°F (4.5°C)	Raise by 4°F (2°C)

Table 4-4: Recommended Thermostat Adjustments

Controls

There are many products on the market that will help homeowners save energy by automatically controlling the heating and cooling systems:

- **Programmable Thermostats** are available for almost all heating and cooling systems. These can be set to raise or lower temperatures to predetermined set points at specific times each day. Units of this type typically pay for themselves in energy savings within a year of installation.

- **Automatic Vent Dampers** close the flue at the furnace or boiler when the burner shuts off. These systems can not only cut fuel consumption by 3-15%, but also may prevent combustible gases from entering the home if the furnace malfunctions.

- **Remote Energy Monitoring Systems** allow users to connect to their home's energy system while away (via the Internet) and adjust temperature settings based on changing weather conditions. At a minimum, such monitoring systems create an awareness of how much energy is being consumed. Users can then adjust behaviors to reduce energy consumption. Studies show that continuous feedback on energy use can lead to reductions of 5 to 15%.

Lighting

Lighting accounts for about 10% of a typical U.S. home's energy use, and about 20% of the amount of electricity used. The traditional light bulb of choice, since the days of Edison, has been the **Incandescent Light Bulb**. These bulbs are very inefficient, producing only about 15 lumens of light per watt of electricity used (90-95% of the energy used is given off as heat, rather than light).

Australia was the first nation to ban incandescent light bulbs, phasing them out by 2010. Provisions in the U.S. Energy Independence and Security Act of 2007 will phase out most incandescent light bulbs in the U.S. by 2014, requiring that light bulbs marketed after that date be at least 30% more efficient.

One of the quickest, least expensive, and easiest ways to save electricity is to change out inefficient light bulbs and lighting fixtures.

Compact Florescent Bulbs

Compact florescent light bulbs (CFLs) are about 75% more efficient than traditional incandescent light bulbs, and last about 10 times longer. In recent years the price of CFLs has fallen dramatically, making them an extremely cost-effective way to save energy within the home.

If every U.S. home installed just one CFL, the reduction in greenhouse gas emissions would be equal to the annual output of CO_2 from 800,000 automobiles.

LET'S DO THE MATH

Some people have argued that CFLs actually cause more environmental damage than good—since they contain mercury that, if released, will pollute the environment. This mercury can get into the water system, concentrate in fish—and be a real problem.

Typical CFLs do contain about 4 milligrams (mg) of mercury, although newer models have cut mercury levels in half. So, in order to reduce the possibility of mercury pollution, you really should recycle those CFLs (you can often do that at the retailer where you bought the bulb). If the bulb is kept intact, no mercury can get out. But even if the CFL is broken in a landfill, only about 14% (.6 mg) of the mercury is actually released, the remainder stays bonded to the inside of the glass bulb.

According to the Environmental Protection Agency (EPA), U.S. industry releases 104 metric tons of mercury into the atmosphere each year. The majority of these emissions are from coal-powered electric power plants. So it is the using of electricity, not the bulb itself that is the main problem.

Over the life of a typical incandescent light bulb, 5.8 mg of mercury is released into the atmosphere—that is if the electricity used to power the bulb comes from a coal-powered plant. Since a CFL consumes less than one-quarter the power, only about 1.2 mg of mercury would be released to power that bulb. Then, if you drop the bulb another .6 mg of mercury escapes.

So let's do the math. With a normal incandescent light bulb and a coal-powered power plant—we KNOW that 5.8 mg of mercury will go out into the atmosphere. With a CFL, we KNOW that 1.2 mg will be released, but that amount might be as high as 1.8 mg (if the bulb is shattered).

T8 Florescent Lights

In commercial and industrial applications, newer **T8 Florescent Light Bulbs** offer significant advantages over the more traditional T12 units. As illustrated in Figure 4-13, the T8 models are easily identified by their smaller diameter (one inch or 25.4 millimeters). Even smaller, fuel efficient T5 light bulbs are also available.

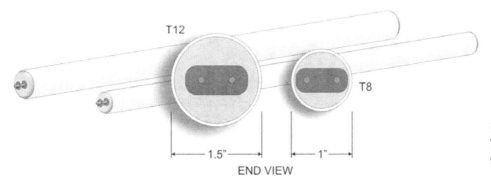

Figure 4-13:
T12/T8 Florescent Tube Comparison

The name of these bulbs reflect the shape (T for tubular) and the diameter (in 1/8 inches—so a T5 is 5/8 inch in diameter, a T8 is 8/8 inch—or one inch—in diameter, etc).

These newer models of tubular florescent lights provide higher levels of illumination while consuming about 20% less energy.

Light Emitting Diodes (LEDs)

One of the most recent developments in residential lighting is the use of **Light Emitting Diodes (LEDs)**. LEDs have long been used in electronic applications, and are now finding their way into household lighting. Typical LED units combine a number of small filament-less bulbs such as illustrated in Figure 4-14.

Figure 4-14:
LED Light Bulb

LEDs are typically more expensive than comparable compact florescent bulbs, and have about the same energy efficiency (watts to lumens). One advantage LEDs do have over CFLs is in longevity. The life of a CFL can be reduced through constant on/off cycling (turning the light on and off in an effort to save electricity). LEDs do not have the same problem. As a result, LEDs can last 5-10 times longer than a CFL.

LEDs are also less sensitive to low temperatures (CFLs may produce less light in very low temperatures) making them a good choice for outdoor applications such as traffic lights or signage.

Motion Sensors

Turning off lights in unoccupied rooms is an obvious way to reduce energy costs without any reduction in comfort or functionality. However, human nature being what it is, unnecessary lights are inevitably left on.

Automatic Occupancy Sensors are available that "feel" the presence (or absence) of a human in the room and turn on or off the lighting as needed. Most detectors sense whether a person is present or not based on passive infrared and/or ultrasonics.

Passive Infrared (PIR) Sensors respond to sudden changes in background heat energy by detecting the appearance of heat energy at a wavelength emitted by humans. If that heat energy is present, the lights are turned on. If it is not there, the lights are switched off.

Ultrasonic Sensors use a quartz crystal that radiates high-frequency (25-40 kHz) sound waves undetectable by the human ear. These sound waves bounce off of objects, surfaces and people. When the waves bounce back to the sensor, their frequency is measured. Motion is detected in the room when there is a slight shift in frequency (the **Doppler Effect**).

Motion sensors can be adjusted with longer or shorter time delays (the time between when the sensor decides the room is unoccupied and when it shuts off the light). The shorter the delay, the greater the energy savings, but very short delays may result in frequent on/off cycles, reducing the life of the light bulbs in the room.

Many sensors can also be adjusted for light sensitivity—determining whether daylighting (light entering through windows or skylights) is sufficient and no additional lighting is required, even when the room is occupied.

Automatic sensors can reduce lighting costs by as much as 45%. This is especially helpful in commercial buildings where lighting accounts for a very large portion of the building's electrical costs (as much as 50%).

Hot Water

The heating of water used in the home typically contributes as much to energy costs as does lighting. Just as with lighting, most of this energy is simply wasted in household hot water systems. As indicated in Figure 4-15, less than half the energy used to heat water actually reaches the occupant in the form of hot water.

Automatic Occupancy Sensors

Passive Infrared (PIR) Sensors

Ultrasonic Sensors

Doppler Effect

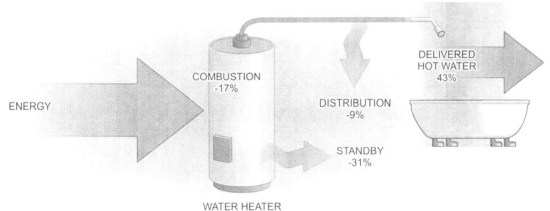

ENERGY

COMBUSTION
-17%

DISTRIBUTION
-9%

STANDBY
-31%

WATER HEATER

DELIVERED
HOT WATER
43%

**Figure 4-15:
Hot Water Heater
Efficiency**

The efficiency of hot water storage tanks is rated as to the unit's **Energy Factor (EF)**. This rating is based on an assumed daily usage of 64 gallons (242 liters), regardless of the tank size. The EF is expressed as a factor of how much hot water is available based on the amount of energy consumed (its efficiency). Larger tanks have a larger external surface, providing a greater opportunity for heat loss. As a result, smaller tanks typically have a greater EF than do larger tanks. How the unit is powered will also impact how efficiently it creates hot water.

Energy Factor (EF)

Fuel Choice

In selecting a hot water heating system, one of the first choices a homeowner must make is deciding which fuel to use in powering the unit. Typical options include electricity, natural gas, or propane (and perhaps fuel oil, although not all fuel choices are available in all areas).

Energy-efficient gas hot water storage tanks have an EF of .62 or higher. Energy-efficient electric units will have a higher efficiency rating, closer to .95. Even though the efficiency of an electric unit may be better, the annual operating cost of an electric unit may still be significantly higher than natural gas or propane. As seen in Table 4-5, the annual cost of operating an electric hot water storage unit can be as much as three times the cost of a comparable natural gas unit.

**Table 4-5: Annual Operating Cost
Comparisons**

NATURAL GAS		PROPANE		ELECTRIC	
Price per Therm	Annual Cost	Price per Gallon	Annual Cost	Price per Kilowatt-Hour	Annual Cost
$0.50	$136	$0.95	$283	$0.08	$390
$0.60	$163	$1.05	$313	$0.10	$488
$0.70	$190	$1.15	$343	$0.12	$585

For safety, as well as for energy efficiency reasons, fuel-burning water heaters should be installed with **Sealed Combustion** (direct-vented). In sealed combustion systems, outside air is vented directly to the water heater and exhaust gases are vented directly outside, keeping fuel combustion totally separate from the internal house air.

Demand or Tankless Water Heaters

A second consideration regarding how hot water will be created and delivered within the home is the type of system installed. Traditional systems heat water and store it in a large holding tank for later use.

Demand (also called **Tankless** or **Instantaneous**) **Water Heaters** do not heat and then store water. They operate by heating water only as it is needed (water flowing through the unit is heated). On-demand tankless units are available in electric or gas models.

Advantages of Demand Water Heaters

Tankless systems offer some significant advantages over traditional storage tank units. These include:

- Energy efficiency. Because there is no storage tank, there is no standby loss of heat within the tank. By minimizing these losses, energy consumption of a tankless system is 10-30% less than a comparable storage-tank system.

- Unlimited hot water. Since hot water is heated as needed, the "tank" never runs out. Storage-tank systems are limited in the amount of hot water they can provide at any one time (limited by the size of the tank).

- Smaller size. Without the need for a large storage tank, these systems can be installed in areas that have limited space available.

Disadvantages of Demand Water Heaters

But there are disadvantages to these systems as well. Including:

- Price. Demand water heaters are typically more expensive to purchase and install than a comparable storage-tank system.

- Less hot water. While the flow of hot water may be theoretically "limitless", the amount of hot water flowing will be limited by the energy available to heat it. Electric demand water heaters are designed to raise the temperature of water by about 60°F (33°C). So water temperatures must start at 60-70°F (15-20°C) in order to raise the water temperature to the 120-130°F (49-54°C) recommended for most hot water heaters. In winter months, initial water temperatures are typically much lower than this, resulting in either less hot water available or the need to provide a large electrical current (larger models may require 40-60 amps at 220 volts) to meet the demand.

Water Conservation

Regardless of the fuel used or the type of unit installed, there are simple steps that can be taken to conserve both water and fuel. The average American uses about 112 gallons (425 liters) of water for indoor use each day (how this water is used is displayed in Figure 4-16). This compares with average daily water consumption in Europe of around 37 gallons (140 liters) and only about 21 gallons (80 liters) used each day by a person living in China.

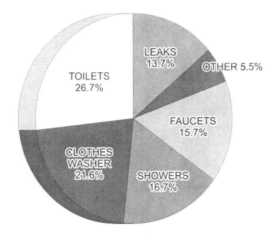

**Figure 4-16:
Average Daily U.S.
Indoor Water Use**

SCIENCE NOTE: THE WATER-ENERGY RELATIONSHIP

Water (not only hot water) uses up a tremendous amount of energy. When water is wasted, energy is wasted. So if you're really worried about saving energy—then use less water (you should anyway, but that's another story).

To supply water to the home, it must be pumped, diverted or in some way extracted from its source (like a lake, river, well or even the ocean). It then has to be collected, and somehow shipped from the source: treated, and then distributed to the home.

But the energy needed to provide water doesn't end there. After we use the water—it goes somewhere in the form of waste water and/or sewage. This waste water has to be collected, transported and treated again. At that point, it is either recycled, or discharged back into the environment. And every step of the way it takes energy.

In fact, in 2005 the State of California estimated that it took up 19 percent of the state's electricity use, 30% of natural gas and over 88 billion gallons of diesel fuel each year just to provide water to residents.

So think about it, that's not just a glass of water you're drinking—there's a whole bunch of fossil fuel and money in there too.

Methods to Conserve Water

The average resident in the U.S. consumes more than three times the amount of water daily as do residents in most other nations around the world. Methods exist that can reduce this rate of consumption. Some of these include:

- Installing water saving features in the home. Low-flush toilets, low-flow faucets and other water saving devices can save as much as 30% of the water used within the home.

- Fixing leaky pipes. Nearly 14% of the water used within homes simply drips away from leaks in faulty pipes and fixtures. One dripping faucet can waste as much as 48 gallons (182 liters) of water each week. Fixing these problems can eliminate a significant source of waste.

- Being aware of the water being used. Shorter showers, turning off water faucets when not in use, washing only full loads of laundry, and other methods of saving water are simply a function of being aware of water as a valuable resource and using it wisely.

Reducing Hot Water Costs

The amount of hot water used or wasted within the home can be reduced in a number of simple and inexpensive ways. These include:

- Lowering the temperature. Set water heater thermostats to no more than 120°F (49°C). Higher temperatures are typically unnecessary and consume a larger amount of energy. Reducing the setting from 140°F (60°C) will cut water-heating costs by 6-10%

- Installing a timer. If hot water use is limited to certain times during the day (mornings or evenings, for example), install a timer that heats water to only be available during those times.

- Insulating the tank and water pipes. Insulating blankets are available that will reduce the heat loss from the unit. An R-19 insulating blanket is recommended. Also, wrap exposed pipes in foam insulation designed for this purpose. A well-insulated tank will save an additional 4-9% on water heating costs.

- Using laundry magnets. Specially designed (coated in rubber or plastic) magnets work well for normal laundry and require no detergent. The magnets lift the dirt from the clothes in a way that makes it necessary to use only the rinse and spin portion of the washing cycle…saving a lot of water, and energy.

Appliances and Electronics

The appliances in a typical North American home (including a washer/dryer, refrigerator, and stove) account for about one-third of the energy consumed within that household. Products ranging from electric toothbrushes to electric blankets to microwave ovens consume—and perhaps more importantly, waste—huge amounts of fuel each year.

The amount of electricity used by older appliances can be determined using an **Electronic Energy Meter**. Plug the meter into an outlet, then plug the appliance into the meter. As the appliance is operated, the meter will indicate the amount of energy used. Many units allow utility rates to be programmed in, calculating the annual (or hourly) cost of operating that appliance.

Energy Star

For new appliances, this calculation has been done for the consumer. In 1992, the U.S. Environmental Protection Agency (EPA) created a voluntary energy efficiency program for computers called **Energy Star**. The government established guidelines against which computers were rated, then authorized labels that manufacturers used to promote their efficient models.

Since that time, the program has expanded to include 35 product categories, rating products as varied as refrigerators to toasters to furnaces to lighted exit signs. Energy Star labels, such as illustrated in Figure 4-17, indicate how energy efficient a specific appliance is when compared to similar available models. The label will also indicate the estimated annual energy cost of powering the appliance.

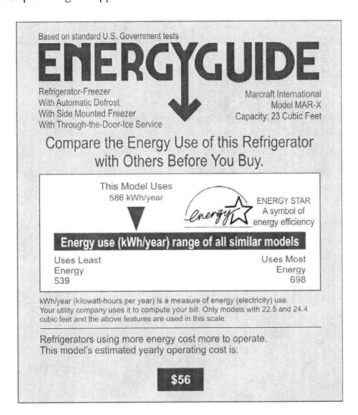

Figure 4-17: Energy Star Label

Since 1992, more than 15,000 organizations have participated in the Energy Star rating program. Program partners include manufacturers, retailers, builders, businesses and utilities. More than 2.5 billion Energy Star labeled products have been purchased since the program began.

It is estimated that in 2007 alone, consumers saved over $16 billion (and reduced greenhouse gas emissions by 40 million metric tons) on utility bills due to more efficient Energy Star rated appliances (based on a comparison with pre-1992 models). Energy Star rated appliances are on average about 30% more efficient than non-rated models.

Many builders have incorporated the Energy Star program into the design of their new buildings. Residential and commercial buildings that comply with the program's guidelines and incorporate Energy Star rated appliances can receive an Energy Star rating for the entire building. As with individual appliances, Energy Star rated homes use about 30% less energy than non-rated homes. There are currently over one-million homes in the U.S. that have received the Energy Star rating.

Phantom Loads

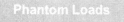

As electronics have been incorporated into many household appliances, increasingly these units draw energy even when the appliance is turned off. Known as **Phantom Loads**, or **Vampire Power**, or simply **Standby Power**—this constant drain of electricity can be quite significant.

For example, a television set may draw 10-15 watts of energy to enable the "instant on" feature or to maintain in memory programmed information. While this power requirement is low, it is constant… 24-hours a day, 365 days a year. In fact, a typical microwave oven in the home uses more power each year in "standby mode" than it does while cooking (because the oven is cooking only a few minutes each day).

The many tiny red (or yellow or orange) LED lights glowing on various appliances or electronic devices are an indication of this energy being used to maintain the unit while it is turned "off". Approximately 22 % of the energy used in appliances, and 10% of the total electricity used in a typical home powers appliances and electronics that are NOT in use.

Electronic Power Supplies

More and more electronic devices incorporate electronic power supplies, or "wall packs" designed to convert AC household current to DC needed to operate the product. These familiar black boxes that attach to the outlet (as seen in Figure 4-18) consume electricity whether the appliance is on or off.

Figure 4-18:
Electronic Power Supply

Products such as laptop computers may incorporate the power supply within the cord (rather than at the outlet) and other appliances such as stereos or televisions may incorporate them within the body of the appliance itself. There are over 2.5 billion power supplies in use within the U.S., consuming an estimated 2% of all the electricity produced each year.

Addressing Phantom Loads

In recent years many nations have passed laws prohibiting or limiting the power used in standby mode (limiting it to one watt or less). In 2007, for example, the State of California began limiting external standby power to 0.5 watts or less.

Individuals can also limit the effects of phantom loads. One simple technique is to plug electronic devices (such as televisions, DVD players, stereos or microwave ovens) into **Power Strips** that can be easily turned off when the appliance is not in use. An added benefit to this practice is that many power strips also incorporate surge protection that will protect appliances from damaging voltage spikes.

Power Strips

Appliances that require a dedicated outlet (draw too much power for a power strip to handle) can be plugged into switched outlets or simply unplugged when not in use.

High Energy Consuming Appliances

Purchasing the most energy-efficient appliance (Energy Star) is a logical step in conserving energy within the home. How these appliances are used will also impact the amount of fuel consumed by the typical household.

Refrigeration

Refrigerators and freezers consume about 8% of the power used in a typical home. Side-by-side models use about 10-30% more power than units with the freezer either on the top or bottom (for similar size models). Features such as in-the-door ice/water dispensers will also add to the energy inefficiency of the model.

Ways to conserve energy in the storage of food include:

- Checking the door seals of the unit to make sure they have not deteriorated over time. Gaps and cracks in the seals allow the cold air to escape (adding to the units fuel costs).

- Setting the temperature of the refrigerator to between 36-38°F (2-3°C) and the freezer to between 0-5°F (-18 to -15°C). Temperatures 10°F (5.5°C) lower than recommended range will add about 25% to the cost of food storage.

- Keeping the unit out of the sunlight. Locating the unit in a cooler location (out of the sun or away from heaters and dishwashers) will lower the cost of cooling food.

- Defrosting the unit. The buildup of ice on the coils will require the compressor to run longer to maintain cool temperature.

- Cooling foods to room temperature. Allow hot foods to cool before putting them into the refrigerator or freezer.

- Filling the freezer. A full freezer uses less energy than an empty or nearly empty unit.

- Cleaning the coils on the back or underneath the unit once a month.

Laundry and Dishes

Washing and drying laundry and/or dishes accounts for about 5% of a typical home's energy use. Newer Energy Star dishwashers are 25-60% more efficient than older or non-rated models. They also use considerably less water (about 3-10 gallons per cycle).

Front-end loading clothes-washing machines are typically much more efficient than top-loading models. Energy Star rated units will save significant energy as well as water (about 18 gallons/ 68 liters per load).

Clothes dryers use 2-4 times the amount of energy as a clothes washer, and about twice the amount of energy consumed by a new refrigerator. There is no Energy Star rating for dryers.

Once again, behaviors can play a major role in lowering energy consumption. These include:

- Wash only full loads. The same energy and water is consumed in washing half a load as a full load.

- Air dry laundry whenever possible. Free-standing clothes dryers and clothes pins are a compact and inexpensive way to dry clothes without electricity.

- Keep filters clean.

- Turn down temperature settings. Warm or cold water wash cycles will reduce the amount of energy consumed. Rinse cycles should always be set to cold.

Cooking

Cooking consumes about 3% of the residential energy fuel budget. The greediest appliance in this category is the stove/oven—whether electric or natural gas. But other units such as microwaves, toaster ovens, crock pots or other more specialized cooking appliances also add to this energy-use mix. Matching the appliance with the task (small items cooked in a toaster oven rather than a conventional oven, for example) is a good way to save energy.

Convection ovens typically consume about 20% less energy than conventional ovens, as air circulating around the food provides a more even (and efficient) heat distribution requiring less cooking time. For small food portions, microwave ovens can save as much as 70% of the energy that would be used to heat the item in a conventional oven.

Selecting the proper method of cooking a particular item (small portions heated in the microwave, for example) can save a significant amount of energy. Table 4-6 provides a comparison of the costs associated with using different appliances to prepare a meal.

Table 4-6: Energy Cost of Cooking

APPLIANCE	TEMPERATURE	TIME	ENERGY	Cost*
Electric Oven	350°F / 177°C	60 minutes	2.0 kWh	20 cents
Gas Oven	350°F / 177°C	60 minutes	.11 therm	13 cents
Convection Oven – Electric	325°F / 163°C	45 minutes	1.4 kWh	14 cents
Frying Pan	420°F / 215°C	60 minutes	.9 kWh	9 cents
Toaster Oven	425°F / 218°C	50 minutes	.9 kWh	9 cents
Crockpot	200°F / 93°C	7 hours	.7 kWh	7 cents
Microwave Oven	"High"	15 minutes	.38 kWh	4 cents
Solar Oven	220°F / 105°C	5 hours	Free	Free

Costs calculated at 10 cents per kWh, and $1.20 per therm for gas.

SCIENCE NOTE: SOLAR OVENS

If you really want to be energy efficient when you cook, just make yourself a simple solar oven and cook your meals outdoors in the summertime. There are simple solar ovens made from nothing more than a couple of cardboard boxes, some aluminum foil, a bit of newspaper and a piece of glass or an oven cooking bag.

You can buy commercially manufactured solar ovens that heat to even higher temperatures, but even a homemade oven like this will heat to about 220°F (105°C) when placed in the sun. Even on a cloudy day, the temperature inside the box reaches about 120°F (49°C).

Cooking outside also lets you take the heat out of the kitchen, so you are not paying to heat the house (by cooking) and cool it at the same time.

The solar oven cooks your food like a slow cooker—it won't burn the food (so you can leave it in the oven and forget about it)—and best of all it's free. No fossil fuels—no electricity—no natural gas—just good old-fashioned sun power.

Energy Efficiency Incentives

The *American Recover and Reinvestment Tax Act of 2009* expands or creates a number of governmental incentives for consumers to improve the energy efficiency of their homes. It provides for a tax credit (reduction in taxes paid) of up to $1500 for improvements to the home's shell (windows, insulation, sealing) as well as the heating and cooling systems. This credit is based on 30% of the cost of materials (labor is not included).

A number of states offer additional incentive programs (tax credits, grants, rebates) to promote energy efficiency. For example, the State of Kentucky offers up to an additional $250 tax credit (limited to 30% of the cost of the product) to homeowners within that state when they install energy efficient windows.

Many utility companies offer energy efficiency incentives to their customers as well. Major utility companies have a stated goal of reducing electricity use nationwide by 5.5% by the year 2015. As generating capacities reach capacity, peak load power purchases as well as construction of new production facilities pose significant costs to operating utilities. They have found that every dollar spent on consumer energy efficiency saves the utility company $2-$3 by delaying the need for construction of additional generating capacity.

These programs are varied and locally specific. For example, a Michigan utility company will pay customers $50 to replace in inefficient refrigerators, which they will pick up for free. Other power companies distribute free compact florescent light bulbs, and still others will provide rebates of several hundred dollars to customers installing tankless hot water heaters.

REVIEW QUESTIONS

The following questions test your knowledge of the material presented in this chapter.

1. Discuss how behaviors as well as technology can combine to result in energy conservation.

2. Compare U.S. economic growth from 1973-1986 and U.S. growth between 1986-1999 and show the relationship between energy consumption and economic expansion.

3. List four benefits to owners when they implement energy conservation measures within the home.

4. Define "greenwashing" and how it may adversely affect energy conservation initiatives.

5. Discuss the ways in which industrial food production is fuel dependent. Identify possible production methods that are less energy-intense.

6. List the steps involved in a home energy audit and the energy savings that can be realized from each change.

7. Discuss the difference between R-Value and Actual Effective R-Value, and what factors affect this difference.

8. List the five attributes commonly rated by the NFRC for window systems.

9. What is a low-E window and how does this technology compare to a radiant barrier?

10. Explain the purpose of a simple whole-house ventilation system and how it might affect the operation of a wood-burning stove in a residence.

11. How do balanced air systems work and what are the advantages and disadvantages of such systems?

12. Explain why a heat pump may be a more energy-efficient alternative to a natural gas forced air furnace.

13. Discuss the various lighting options and the advantages and disadvantages of the various technologies.

14. What are the advantages and disadvantages of demand hot water heaters?

15. Discuss the Energy Star program and its impact on energy consumption in the U.S.

EXAM QUESTIONS

1. How much energy is lost to heat in a typical internal combustion engine?
   a. 10-15%
   b. 30-35%
   c. 60-65%
   d. 80-85%

2. The U.S. fuel efficiency standard that applies to passenger cars and light trucks is called the:
   a. NAFTA (North American Fuel & Transport Agreement)
   b. GDP (Gasoline and Diesel Program)
   c. NAECA (National Automotive Efficiency and Conservation Act)
   d. CAFÉ (Corporate Average Fuel Economy)

3. Which of the following market segments currently consumes the most energy each year in the United States?
   a. Transportation
   b. Industrial
   c. Commercial
   d. Residential

4. A complete inspection of a home to determine where energy savings can be made is typically referred to as:
   a. a home-energy audit
   b. an energy-assistance program
   c. a load-management system
   d. an annual fuel utilization efficiency (AFUE)

5. A single reflective surface on insulation that faces an open space is called:
   a. a radiant barrier
   b. an R-value enhancement membrane
   c. a closed-cell fill
   d. a space blanket

6. The process by which moisture moves throughout a home is called:
   a. diffusion
   b. infiltration
   c. ventilation
   d. humidification

7. The insulating effectiveness of window systems is indicated by its:
   a. R-value
   b. RSI-value
   c. I factor
   d. U-factor

8. The tendency of hot air to rise towards ceilings or to the upper floors of a building is known as the:
   a. thermal elevation property
   b. stack effect
   c. condensation resistance
   d. radiant barrier

9. Furnaces sold in the U.S. must be rated as to their:
   a. Annual Fuel Utilization Efficiency (AFUE)
   b. Capacity and Fuel Efficiency (CAFÉ)
   c. Heat Recovery Index (HRI)
   d. Utility System Savings Ratio (USSR)

10. How much of the total power consumed by the average U.S. home is lost to phantom loads?
    a. 3.5%
    b. 10%
    c. 40%
    d. 60%

CHAPTER 5

PASSIVE SOLAR SYSTEMS

OBJECTIVES

Upon completion of this chapter and its related lab procedures you will be able to perform the following tasks:

1. Explain the difference between active and passive systems.

2. Give several examples of passive daylighting systems.

3. Understand how to determine the location of the sun (throughout the year) for a given site.

4. Discuss what is meant by a Sun Chart and how to read one.

5. Discuss the properties of thermal mass, specific heat capacity, thermal lag and thermal storage capacity of building materials and their effect on passive solar heating.

6. Explain the difference between direct, indirect and isolated passive solar systems within buildings.

7. Understand passive solar cooling and ways to incorporate these systems into a residential home.

Passive Solar Systems

INTRODUCTION

By harnessing the light and heat from the sun, amazing energy savings can be realized within most structures. Unfortunately, many existing buildings (and even a shameful number of newer buildings) have ignored this almost free energy source during the design and construction phases of the project. However, passive solar energy should not be overlooked when conducting an energy audit.

What is solar energy? **Solar energy** is energy from the sun. But in a very real way, almost all energy comes from the sun in one way or another. Fossil fuels (such as coal) are simply stored plant and animal matter, converted over millions of years into concentrated fuels that may be burned. Their original energy came from, you guessed it, the sun. Winds, water currents, even wood burned in a campfire—all are the result of converted energy from the sun. So the term needs to be defined a bit more narrowly.

The Solar Energy referred to in this chapter is restricted to the radiant light and heat energy that currently strikes the earth from the sun. A person standing in the sun will feel the heat and see the light energy from the sun. Heat and light can be concentrated, stored and used to make lives more comfortable in a variety of ways. This energy can also be converted into electricity through the use of **Photovoltaics** (using solar panels).

The sun produces a tremendous amount of energy. It is estimated that in one hour enough radiant energy hits the earth from the sun to power all the needs of human civilization for an entire year. If a plot of land 100-miles square covered in solar panels was used to harness the electrical energy from the sun, even if the process used was only 10% efficient (meaning that only one tenth of the energy was actually converted into electricity), this solar array could provide enough energy to supply all the electrical needs of the United States.

ACTIVE VERSUS PASSIVE SYSTEMS

Solar energy systems are often described as either **Active Solar** or **Passive Solar**. These are very simple concepts, but can be confusing since different people often define them differently. And as with most simple concepts, the more they are examined, the less simple they appear to be.

Let's assume that if energy is added into a system from some outside electrical source, it is an **Active System**. If no added electrical energy is required, then it is a **Passive System**.

A window that allows the sun to shine into a room is an example of a very simple **Passive Solar System**. The window allows the heat and light from the sun to passively (it just happens) create warmth and natural light within the room.

Solar energy

Photovoltaics

Active Solar

Passive Solar

Active System

Passive System

Passive Solar System

Suppose a curtain is then placed over the window to regulate the amount of sunlight allowed into the room. If this curtain is opened and closed by hand, this is still a passive system (even though human energy is technically added into the system). But if the curtain is closed automatically (with an electrical system) based on the temperature in the room or the time of day—then this becomes an active system. See how this definition can become a bit fuzzy?

Passive Solar

Passive Solar Energy

It is possible to utilize the sun's energy without converting it into electricity. In fact, it is done all the time. If no outside energy (such as that supplied by a mechanical or electrical device) is used to convert the energy of the sun into useful heat, light, or electrical energy—this is referred to as **Passive Solar Energy**.

Infrared Radiation

Visible Radiation

The radiant energy of the sun can be felt as heat (**Infrared Radiation**) and as light (**Visible Radiation**), or some combination of the two. Imagine resting on a blanket at the beach. The warmth of the sun and the intense light are clear examples of the energy contained in the sun's rays. No outside energy source is required. Sunbathing might be considered enjoying passive solar energy at its most basic.

There are many ways to capture this energy and utilize it. Take light for example.

Active Solar

An **Active Solar** power system might use a solar collector array (solar panels linked together) to change the radiant energy (light) of the sun into electrical energy. Then, this energy could be transferred over an electrical circuit to a light bulb inside of a house. Within this light bulb, the electrical energy is once again converted into light.

Or simply cut a hole in the wall and allow the light to shine in. A window is a very basic example of a passive solar energy system.

Using the light from the sun is just one way to passively (without any external energy) harness the free energy from the sun. Passive solar systems can also concentrate and trap heat inside the building. Water can be heated or, by using the heat energy of the sun and the principle of convection, air can be moved around within a building for heating and cooling purposes.

Daylighting

Daylighting

The process of creating buildings or other living spaces that use as much natural light (light directly from the sun) as possible, is called **Daylighting**. People have been doing this since the dawn of time, but as fossil fuels become more scarce (and more expensive), natural lighting is a cost-effective way to reduce active energy consumption.

A window is a very basic form of daylighting. But often it is difficult to put windows everywhere they might be desired (for example, in a large building, the rooms in the middle just don't have any outside walls—so windows are impractical.) So how is natural light directed to where it is needed? In order to perform this task efficiently, an understanding of the relative positions of the earth and sun is required.

Where is the Sun?

On different places on the Earth and at different times of the year, the sun's light energy (sunshine) hits the earth in different ways.

It has long been known that the Earth revolves around the sun. It takes it a year (well, actually 365 ¼ days—which is why a day is added in February every four years) for the Earth to make one complete journey around the sun.

And while it travels through space, the Earth is tilted at a 23.44 degree angle in relation to the Sun, as shown in Figure 5-1. This angle does not change as the Earth makes its journey around the Sun. This tilt is very important in understanding how the sun's light changes in a given place on the globe at different times of the year. Its effect on the earth's surface is so profound that the tilt of earth's axis is the major factor in creating seasonal (such as winter and summer) cycles.

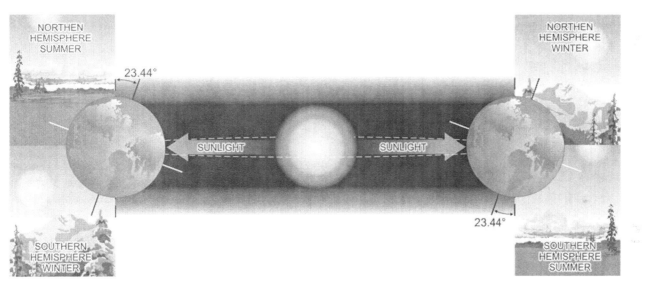

The earth spins on this tilted axis (an imaginary line connecting the north pole with the south pole). It takes 24 hours for the earth to spin completely around—a natural event known as a **Day**. As the earth spins in relation to the sun, half of the earth is always facing towards the sun, and half is always facing away (in darkness—or to be very technical—**Night**).

But because the earth is tilted, not every place on the planet receives 12 hours of light and 12 hours of darkness each and every day. Nearer the equator, the amount of daylight does not vary much from this 12-hour time period. But closer to the poles, the amount of time the sun shines on any given day can vary dramatically—depending on the time of the year.

Figure 5-1: Winter/ Summer Diagram

You would think that on the spring and autumn equinox, the days all over the globe would be exactly 12 hours long. After all, the sun is hitting every part of the planet for the same amount of time. But it turns out that this is not really the case.

As we know, the earth is a round sphere. So, if we were to draw circles on the globe (like the equator and the tropic of cancer and the arctic circle, and so forth), each circle is just a bit smaller in circumference as we move north or south from the equator. Eventually we could draw a tiny circle around the north or south pole.

So on the equinox as the sun starts to rise, it will peak up over the horizon just a little bit earlier the further north or south you go. It takes longer then for the sun to rise and set the further from the poles you go. It also appears to move horizontally along the horizon as it does so.

Therefore, on the spring and autumn equinox, the day will actually be 12 hours and eight minutes (or so) long at latitudes of around 30 degrees north or south. At 60 degrees north, the day will actually be around 12 hours and 16 minutes long.

Spring Equinox

Northern Hemisphere

Summer Solstice

On the **Spring Equinox** (March 21st) every place on the planet will have almost exactly 12 hours of sunlight and 12 hours of darkness. In the **Northern Hemisphere** (the half of the earth north of the equator) the amount of time each day when the sunlight hits the surface of the earth will gradually increase each day after the spring equinox, eventually reaching a maximum on the **Summer Solstice** (June 20th).

This increase is more dramatic the further north one travels. Taking just one step north from the equator— the change in the amount of daylight would be so small as to not be noticed. But at the north pole (to use the extreme example), the amount of time the sun shines (ignoring clouds and rain for the moment) will increase dramatically. So dramatically, in fact, that in only three months (from the spring equinox to the summer solstice) the amount of daylight increases from 12 hours to 24 hours.

In the **Southern Hemisphere**, of course, this process is reversed. Beginning on March 21st the days get shorter— until on the summer solstice the South Pole would experience 24-hours of darkness.

In addition to the amount of sunlight received each day, it is very important to understand that the angle with which the sunlight strikes the earth will change as well. It is possible to create a three dimensional representation of the sun's track across the sky, such as the one in Figure 5-2, for any location on earth and for any given day.

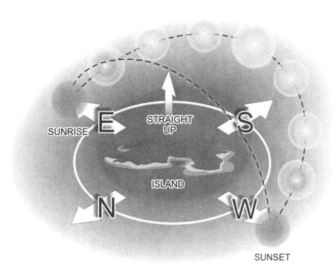

Figure 5-2: Sun Chart

Southern Hemisphere

Angle of the Sun

For those living on the equator, figuring out the angle of the sun on the spring or autumnal equinox is a relatively easy task. On these days the sun appears to rise due east. It tracks for six hours in a perfect 90 degree arch, and can be located directly overhead at solar noon. The sun then continues due west and sets six hours later (a perfect 12-hour day).

But due to the angle and shape of the earth, this track in the sky changes the further it is measured from the equator and towards the poles (the greater the **Latitude**, the more pronounced the angle of the sun).

On any given day at any given moment, there is only one location on earth that is pointing directly at the sun. Latitudes north or south of this location will find that the sun appears to track in the sky in the direction of this focal point (in the northern hemisphere, this will be in a southerly direction). The higher the latitude, the lower in the sky the sun will appear to track.

Trying to calculate where the sun might appear at any time and at any place on the planet would be a tremendous amount of work. For each location, the sun would appear to track a unique path across the sky. In order to harness the full power of the sun for any given location, it is necessary to know where the sun will track for that particular location.

Fortunately, there are tools that will do these calculations. By entering a given location's latitude (how far north or south the location is from the equator), and the time of year, these systems will automatically calculate the location of the sun for each minute of the day. The locations are plotted on a 2-dimensional diagram that represents the track the sun will take, as shown in Figure 5-3. This diagram is called a **Sun Chart**.

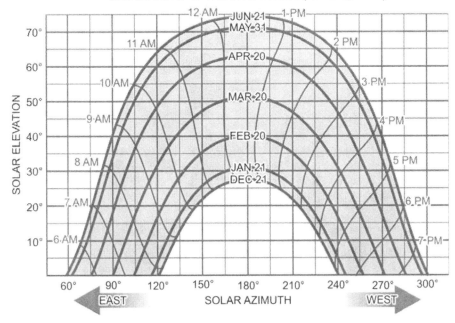

Figure 5-3:
Sun Chart at 40
Degrees North

Reflected Light

One way to bring more light into a building in the northern hemisphere is to place as many windows on the southern side of the building as is practical. Windows placed on the northern side will bring in almost no light—and will probably loose a great deal of heat in the winter.

Before the days of electrical (or artificial) lights, people often gathered more light through the available windows with the use of **Reflectors**. In fact, as early as the 1850's companies such as the Chappuis Light Factory touted the cost savings of natural light over lighting the workplace with fossil fuels.

A common light reflector was called a **Light Shelf**, which consisted of a light-colored or reflective surface (like a mirror) that could be adjusted to reflect additional light through the window, as illustrated in Figure 5-4. Often this light was focused toward a white (or light colored) ceiling, giving the room a brighter feel without producing an irritating glare.

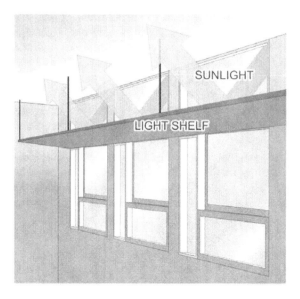

**Figure 5-4:
Light Shelf**

But as the popularity of electrical lighting increased, this practice of natural lighting fell out of fashion.

Skylights

More common today than a light shelf, is a **Skylight**, another passive form of daylighting. In its simplest form, a skylight is little more than a window built into a roof—allowing light to enter the room from above, as shown in Figure 5-5. Skylights are commonly used in larger buildings to bring natural light to interior spaces.

**Figure 5-5: A Properly
Installed Skylight**

Poorly designed skylights may lead to a few problems. Skylights are essentially a hole in the roof of a building, so if they are not properly installed, they tend to leak when it rains.

Skylights will also affect the temperature within the room. Depending on how they are designed, they may increase heat in the summer (remember, sunlight contains not only light energy, but heat energy) or they might allow heat to escape in the winter months.

Light Tubes

An alternative to skylights designed to bring natural light into interior spaces within a building is a **Light Tube** (often referred to by many other names such as a light pipe, sun pipe, sun scoop, solar tube, or tubular skylight).

A light tube is essentially a rigid or flexible metal tube, coated on the inside with a highly reflective material (like a mirror). On the outside of the building, this tube is connected to a clear dome (of glass or plastic). Sunlight enters the tube through this round dome and is then reflected down the tube, bringing natural light into the room through an opening in the ceiling, as shown in Figure 5-6. Often **Light Diffusers** are attached to the opening in the ceiling to keep down the glare from the sunlight.

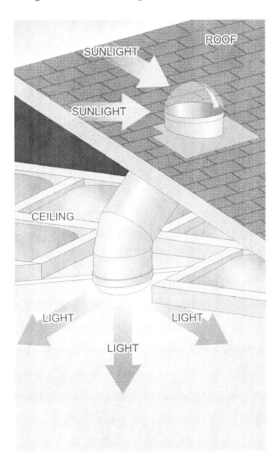

**Figure 5-6:
A Proper Modern
Light Tube**

Light tubes have several advantages over a traditional skylight. First, since the surface area is smaller (in relation to the amount of light it transmits) less heat is transferred into the tube. This may be especially important in summer months or in warmer climates since the room being lit will not receive as much unwanted thermal energy.

Also, light tubes can usually be installed in existing buildings without having to make any structural changes to the roof. Skylights are typically relatively large, so rafters or other structural components of the roof may need to be moved or altered in order to install them. This can greatly increase the cost of the installation.

Also, due to their design and smaller size, light tubes are much less likely than skylights to leak.

Clerestory Windows

Clerestory Windows

On taller buildings or in rooms with high ceilings **Clerestory Windows** (pronounced clear-story) are another daylighting alternative. These are relatively short horizontal windows that are located up near the ceiling. These windows allow natural light into a room near the ceiling, where it can be reflected into the room (usually by a white or light-colored ceiling surface), reducing the need for artificial light during the day.

Some architects incorporate this idea in order to bring light into a room when the roof pitches overlap. By incorporating clerestory windows into these split-section roofs, such as the design illustrated in Figure 5-7, the designer adds natural light to the room while maintaining an attractive exterior design.

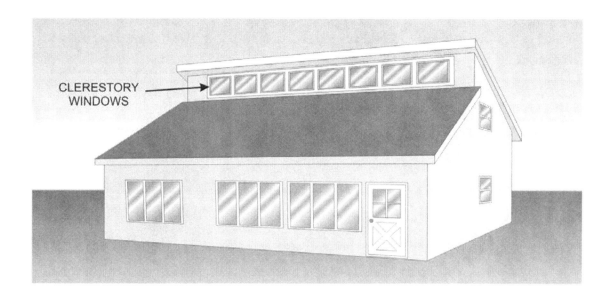

CLERESTORY WINDOWS

Figure 5-7: Clerestory Windows

And if there are nosy neighbors, clerestory windows may be a particularly good idea. A building may be designed with plenty of windows, allowing in large amounts of sunlight. But if the blinds are drawn or the curtains pulled because people keep looking in—then the windows are not helping much to bring in light or radiant heat. Clerestory windows are placed high enough that this loss of privacy is rarely a problem.

SCIENCE NOTE:
HOW LIGHT IS MEASURED

Everything gets to be measured, and light is no different. When we talk about how to measure light, we are really talking about a bunch of different things.

For example, if we have a light bulb we can try to measure how much light it gives off (**Luminous Flux**) or how bright (**Luminous Intensity**) it is. Or we might just want to know how light the room will be (**Illuminance**) if we turn on the light. So we have different ways (of course, one would be way too easy) of measuring this.

Scientists decided that the amount of light given off at the source (like the sun, a light bulb or a candle) would be measured in **Lumens** (lm). They came up with a really complicated way of deciding what a lumen is—but an easy way to figure it is that the flame of a candle gives off about 12 lumens. Or, if you don't have any candles handy, figure a normal 60-watt light bulb gives off about 890 lumens.

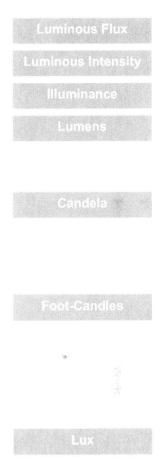

When we want to know how bright a light is, we measure that in terms of **Candela** (cd). The flame of one candle is about one candela. Easy enough. So light two candles and they are shining with two candela of brightness. One hundred candles are equal to 100 candela, and so on.

But when we are talking about light, usually we are talking about how bright the room will be lit. We want to know if it will be bright enough to read a book, or see to cook dinner. So we need a way to measure the amount of light in terms of **Foot-Candles** (fc). This idea is also pretty easy to understand, although just a little bit weird.

One foot candle is really just the amount of light that would strike the inside surface of a ball with a one-foot radius if you put one candle (one candela) inside it. Or a more logical way of looking at it is this is the amount of light one lumen would shine on a square foot of flat surface.

But since most people in the world use the metric system (instead of inches and feet), they (the people who decide these things) decided to measure this illuminance in **Lux** (which is the amount of light one lumen shines on a square meter instead of a square foot). So usually we figure one foot-candle equals about 10 lux (even though the true measurement is closer to 10.76 lux).

So what does all this mean in the real world? Well, it means we can measure how light a place is. So standing outside in bright daylight, the light will measure at about 1,000 foot-candles (10,750 lux). An overcast day might only be around 100 fc (1075 lux). They have found that offices or classrooms should be lit to about 25 fc (250 lux), supermarkets are lit to about 75 fc (750 lux) and so on.

Passive Solar Heating

Sunlight is a form of radiant energy that contains both heat (infrared radiation) and light (visible radiation). With proper building design, much of this passive heat can be captured and used to decrease the amount of fossil fuel-generated energy.

Both heat and light are actually **Photons** that travel across distances at the same speed—the speed of light—186,282 miles (300,000 kilometers) per *second*. But as they travel, these photons vibrate in a wave pattern. Visible light (the light that can be seen by the human eye) vibrates at a higher frequency (shorter gaps between the peaks of the waves, as shown in Figure 5-8) and heat vibrates at a lower frequency (longer gaps).

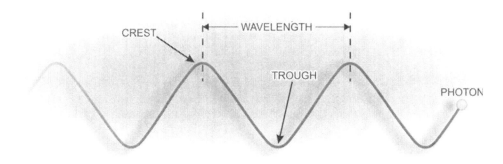

Figure 5-8: Wavelength

Electromagnetic waves can range dramatically in size. A single radio wave can measure the size of the nucleus of an atom. These **Wavelengths** are measured in **Angstroms** (denoted with the symbol Å). This unit of measurement is only one ten-billionth of a meter in length, or about the size of a single atom. Size comparisons of wavelengths within the electromagnetic spectrum are shown in Figure 5-9.

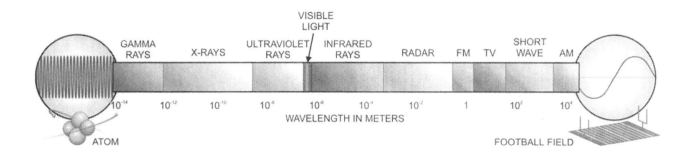

Figure 5-9: Electromagnetic Spectrum with Size Comparisons

Wavelengths can vary dramatically, from as large as a football field to as small as a sub-atomic particle. And depending on their wavelength and frequency, they can behave very differently. Radio waves are pretty long, unless of course we are talking about short-wave radio, which is shorter than some radio waves, but still longer than light waves and even cooler things like gamma rays and infrared.

Remember, waves hitting an object can either bounce off, be absorbed, or go right through an object. Depending on the waves, they will behave quite differently. That's why a radio wave might go right through a wall (so we can listen to our favorite tunes), but light waves will not.

It's obvious that we can use infrared (heat) waves to warm up food, but who would ever think of cooking a meal using radio waves, or x-rays? Well, you never know. Microwaves were used in radar systems during World War II. A scientist named Percy LeBaron Spencer working on a similar system noticed that his candy bar kept melting when he was around the machine. And that was how the microwave oven was invented. Who knows what might be next?

When sunlight hits an object, its radiant energy is either reflected off that object, or absorbed by that object, or transmitted through that object. Some of that reflected energy will be in the form of thermal energy, and some will be in the form of light energy. The energy that is absorbed is typically absorbed as thermal (heat) energy. Photons from the light energy are absorbed by whatever they hit, and the vibration slows down—converting to heat.

The radiant energy absorbed and stored during the day, may then radiate out from the material at a later time. Figure 5-10 shows a very common day/night heating cycle, where the radiant energy of the sun is absorbed during the day and then released at night to keep the room at a comfortable temperature as the air cools.

Figure 5-10: House Heated by Sun During Day and Night

Every kitten knows that if she sleeps near a sunny window on a cold day, the light energy of the sun will warm her body. This is known as **Direct Solar Gain**. When sun strikes an object, its light energy converts to heat energy and some of that energy is absorbed by the object. As this energy conversion takes place, the object gets warmer.

SCIENCE NOTE: WHY BLACK OBJECTS ABSORB MORE HEAT THAN WHITE OBJECTS

We now understand that light energy converts to heat when it is absorbed by an object. So it would make sense that if less light is absorbed by an object, it will heat up less than a similar object that absorbs more of the radiant energy.

We also know that the radiant energy of the sun covers a pretty big electromagnetic spectrum. All the way from radio waves to gamma rays. Well, somewhere in the middle is a tiny portion of this spectrum we call visible light (the stuff we can see). Even this little bit of the spectrum can be broken down further. We see visible light as white, but that is just when all the various visible colors (literally the colors of the rainbow) are combined.

Every object that we see contains some sort of pigment. It is the physical properties of that pigment that makes things appear to be different colors. For example, grass appears to be green (assuming it isn't dead like the grass in our back yard) because it absorbs all the visible light except the green part. That part is reflected back as light—so the object appears to be green.

If an object appears to be white, that means almost all the visible light radiation is being reflected back (so it is not being absorbed). If an object appears black, almost all the visible light is being absorbed. The darker the color, the more light is being absorbed and converted into heat. As a result, things that appear darker to us will (by their very nature) absorb more heat.

Some materials allow light energy to pass through, but block the slower waves of heat energy. A window is a good example of such a material. In fact, if you can see through a solid object (like glass or clear plastic) it is allowing the visible light to pass through.

Importantly, a material such as glass also blocks much of the heat energy from passing through. Some materials are better than others at doing this, and engineers have come up with techniques to do an even better job of it, such as insulated glass shown in Figure 5-11.

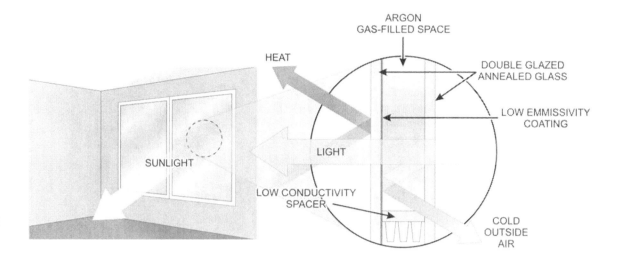

Figure 5-11: How Insulated Glass Works

Insulated glass windows allow light in, and keep ambient heat (heat in the air, not in the light) out. But more importantly (when it comes to passive solar heating), the window also keeps ambient heat in. Light waves are allowed through the glass and into the room. The gas trapped between the layers of glass serves as an effective insulator, preventing heat from conducting through the surface.

As light energy continues to flow in, it will be converted to heat energy by striking an object (like the floor or the kitten). In fact, if the room is very well insulated it will get warmer and warmer. This is known as the **Greenhouse Effect**.

Greenhouse Effect

The greenhouse effect can heat up, not only a room or a kitten, but an entire planet. Think of the atmosphere as a giant round window and the Earth as the room in which you live. When everything is working perfectly, the window (in this case, the atmosphere) is open. All of the energy that hits the earth from the sun is balanced by the energy that escapes out into space (or flows out the window).

By adding gasses (such as carbon dioxide and methane) into the atmosphere that allow radiant energy in but block heat energy from escaping (called **Greenhouse Gases**), the room (in this case, the Earth) will get warmer and warmer. The Earth has seen a steady rise of these gas emissions, as shown in Figure 5-12, that have led to concerns of their effect on global warming.

Greenhouse Gases

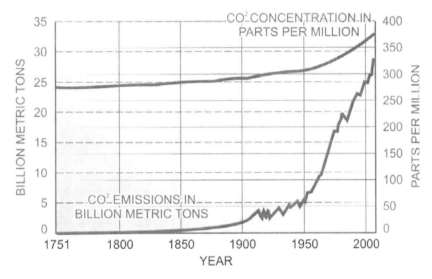

Figure 5-12: Global Carbon Emissions Graph

There are a lot of theories about why the atmosphere of the Earth is filling up with more and more greenhouse gases, but one source which humans can control is through the burning of fossil fuels. Every time a car is started, an airplane flies or the furnace kicks on, just a little bit more of these greenhouse gases are released into the atmosphere.

A **Solar Oven** (or solar cooker) takes advantage of this greenhouse effect to cook food using only the rays of the sun. As shown in Figure 5-13, a simple cardboard box, a plastic cover and some reflective foil creates an environment in which light energy within the box is converted to heat—but then not allowed to escape. As more light is converted to heat within the box, temperatures rise. A small home-made solar oven can reach temperatures in excess of 220°F (105°C).

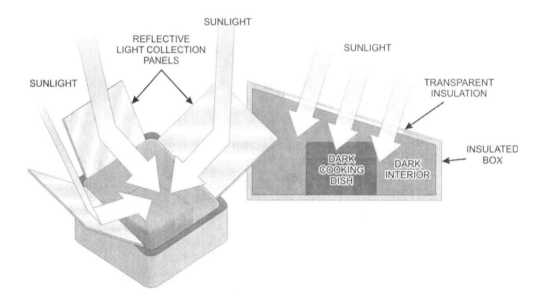

Figure 5-13: A Solar Oven

SCIENCE FACT: SOLAR FURNACES

This passive solar stuff isn't just for wimps. You can do some pretty destructive things by just using the power of the sun.

For instance, legend has it that a couple thousand years ago a Greek scientist named Archimedes managed to defeat the Roman navy by burning them out of the water just by using the power of the sun. They say he used "burning glass", which they figure was just a bunch of mirrors that concentrated and directed the sun's rays onto those poor wooden ships.

Now whether that's true or not, in 1970 some scientists did build the world's largest solar furnace in the mountains of France, as shown in Figure 5-14. This thing, using just the sun's rays, can generate a heat ray that exceeds 5,430°F (3,000 °C).

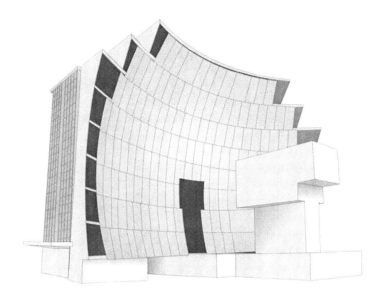

Figure 5-14:
Solar Furnace

Thermal Mass

Not too far below the earth's surface (in most places only a few feet) the stored heat energy is relatively constant. The heat is stored within the **Thermal Mass** of the earth.

In fact, the soil located several meters below the surface is usually the same temperature as the average outside air temperature in any given location. It is too far down to heat up much during the summer and also too far down to cool very much during the winter. This is why the air in caves feels cool during the summer. The air in the same cave during the winter will feel warmer than the outside air.

So, for example, in New York City the average air temperature for the entire year is about 55°F (13°C). So a home in N.Y. buried a few meters below the surface of the earth (or having several meters of earth piled up around it) will remain 55°F (13°C) all year long—regardless of the outside temperature. This may not be a very comfortable living temperature, but it certainly is much less expensive to heat to a comfortable level from 55°F (13°C) than it is to heat to the same temperature from, say, 0°F (-18°C) on a cold winter's day.

It is important to remember that energy (in this case heat energy) always tries to move from a place where it is concentrated (warmer) to a place where it is less concentrated (cooler).

So, for example, the floor or walls of a room will continue to absorb the heat from the converted sunlight until they are the same temperature as the air within the room. Some of this absorbed energy will be stored as potential energy, and some will be kinetic. The potential energy stored in the material is like money in the bank. The moment the surface of the floor is warmer than the surrounding air, some of that heat energy will try to leave the floor (where it is more concentrated) into the air (where it is less concentrated).

The effect of thermal mass when incorporated into a building is to level out exterior temperature fluctuations, assisting in keeping the inside temperature within the **Comfort Zone**. As shown in Figure 5-15, the comfort zone is the range of temperature at which most humans feel comfortable. While this range may vary dramatically from person to person, and based on environmental factors such as humidity, air flow, etc—the range is typically thought to be between 65°F (18°C) and 80°F (27°C).

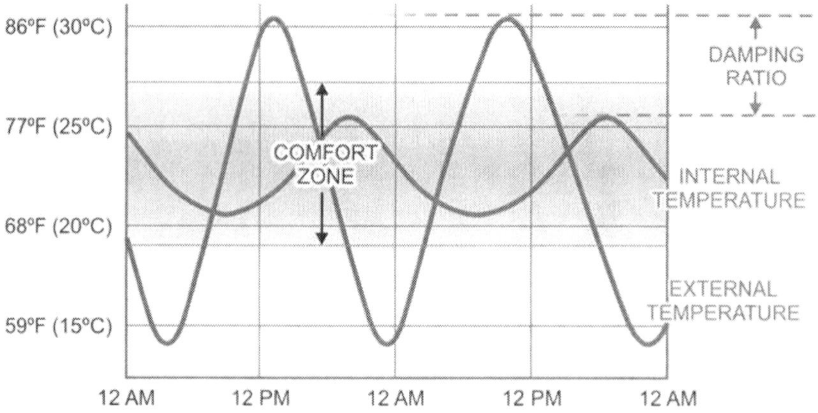

Figure 5-15:
Comfort Zone
Diagram

Damping Ratio

Quantum Physics

The thermal mass of the material moderates temperature fluctuations, keeping them within this comfort range inside the building. How well it performs this task, and how well it reduces the extremes in temperature, is known as the material's **Damping Ratio**.

But some materials are better at absorbing heat energy than others. To illustrate how this works, let's examine what happens when a piece of metal is placed next to a block of wood and left out in the sun. An hour later the block of wood is still relatively cool, but the metal may be too hot to touch. The metal has absorbed more heat energy than the wood. Yet they both received exactly the same amount of heat and light energy from the sun. Different materials absorb heat differently.

Black Body Radiation

Sometimes the simplest questions prove to be the most profound. Back in 1704, Sir Isaac Newton wondered, *Do not all fix'd Bodies, when heated beyond a certain degree, emit Light and shine; and is not this Emission perform'd by the vibrating motion of its parts?*

In other words, doesn't everything emit heat and light? Well, this simple question led to hundreds of years of scientific discussion and ultimately prompted the evolution of **Quantum Physics**.

It has long been observed that some materials absorb energy better than others. And also, some materials emit energy (heat and light) better than others.

The result of the discussion that Newton prompted is a general agreement that **a body emits radiation at a given temperature and frequency *exactly* as well as it absorbs the same radiation.**

This concept can have profound implications in the design of heating systems. It is clear that charcoal absorbs more radiant energy than does snow. So if an engineer designs a system to absorb heat, it would not be constructed out of snow.

It is theoretically possible that a perfect material exists (a black body) that absorbs all radiant energy that touches it. This material will also (at a given temperature) emit ALL the absorbed energy. In essence, the perfect thermal battery.

Specific Heat Capacity

The amount of heat energy that it takes to raise the temperature of a quantity of material by 1°C (also known as one **Kelvin**) is called the **Specific Heat Capacity** of that material. The higher the specific heat capacity number associated with a material, the more energy it takes to raise the temperature of that object.

For example, air (the air you breathe) in a room has a specific heat capacity of 1.012. A cup of water has a specific heat capacity of 4.1813. So it would take a little more than four times the amount of energy to raise the temperature of the water by 1°C than to raise the temperature of the same amount of air. Additional specific heat capacity ratings for common building materials can be found in Table 5-1.

MATERIAL	SPECIFIC HEAT CAPACITY
Air (typical room conditions)	1.01
Asphalt	0.92
Brick	0.84
Concrete	0.88
Glass (silica)	0.84
Gypsum	1.09
Sand	0.835
Soil	0.80
Water	**4.1813**
Wood	0.42

Table 5-1:
Common Building
Materials Specific Heat
Capacity

These numbers also assume that the materials compared are at the same temperature to begin with. So, in this example, it would take four times the amount of energy to raise the temperature of one gram of water from 30°C (86°F) to 31°C (88°F) than it would to raise the temperature of one gram of air from 30°C (86°F) to 31°C (88°F).

This is why the water in an unheated swimming pool usually feels cooler than the air around it. The air heats up at a rate four times faster than the water.

Thermal Storage Capacity

Several factors other than the specific heat capacity of a material will affect how much heat an object will radiate in this way. One critical factor in all this is just how much of the material is actually heated (its mass).

Obviously it takes less energy to heat a cup of water by one degree than it does to heat an entire swimming pool. So the amount of energy stored in a swimming pool will be much greater than the amount of heat energy stored in a cup of water.

For this reason, the heat capacity (as opposed to the specific heat capacity) of a material must take into account the mass of that material. The relative **Thermal Storage Capacity** of a material is in this way adjusted for the material's mass. But the mass of a material is only half the equation.

Another factor affecting this equation is the **Density** of the material. The density of a material is defined as its mass is divided by its volume. While it is not exactly correct, we can think of mass (as it applies to thermal mass) as the weight of the material and **Volume** is the amount of space it takes up.

$$\rho = \frac{m}{V}$$

where:

ρ is the density
m is the mass
V is the volume

For example, given 100 lbs (45.5 kg) of popcorn and 100 lbs (45.5 kg) of bricks, the popcorn will take up much more space than the bricks. Therefore the popcorn is less dense than the bricks.

Table 5-2: Thermal Storage Capacity of Common (and Uncommon) Building Materials

Generally speaking, the more dense the material, the better it is for thermal mass. So when specific heat capacity, mass and density are factored in, materials can be compared with respect to their relative thermal storage capacity. Various thermal storage capacity ratings for common building materials are listed in Table 5-2.

MATERIAL	THERMAL CAPACITY
Water	4186
Concrete Block	2000
Sandstone	1800
Compressed Earth Blocks	1740
Brick	1360
Plasterboard	800
Wood Flooring	780
Carpet	260

One common material with a very high thermal capacity is water. This is one reason why systems such as roof ponds and water walls (walls that store or contain large amounts of water) are effective in moderating daily temperature fluctuations. Water, however, presents some unique building concerns (such as leaks and freezing) that often make it an impractical choice, despite its very high thermal capacity.

Once a material has been selected, a designer can impact the thermal storage capacity of a structure by increasing its mass. Most commonly this is done by increasing the thickness of the walls.

And finally, the **Reflectivity** of the material must be considered. Darker, coarse objects will reflect less radiant energy than will light, shiny objects. The goal when incorporating thermal mass into a design is for the material to absorb as much heat energy as possible. Dark materials with a rough surface will absorb more energy than will light materials.

A dark wall located on the equator side of the building will absorb a tremendous amount of heat energy on a sunny day, as shown in Figure 5-16. This stored energy radiates through the wall, heating the interior space. However, if the sun is not shining, the same wall will radiate heat out of the building. Also, it may take several hours for the sun to warm the wall enough to begin to heat the interior.

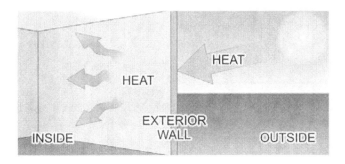 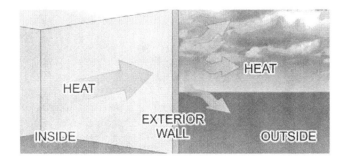

Figure 5-16: Standard Exterior Wall—with Day/Night Heat Cycle

Thermal Lag

Just as different materials absorb heat energy at different rates, they also release this energy differently.

The amount of time it takes for an amount of heat energy that is absorbed into an object to radiate back out from that object is called the **Thermal Lag**. This lag is an important factor when selecting a material to use in a thermal mass heating system.

Assume a room is to be heated using direct solar radiation and thermal mass. During the day, the thermal mass of the room will absorb heat from the sun. If the sun set at 9 pm and the room immediately began to cool, the heat energy stored in the thermal mass during the day will begin to radiate out. If the thermal lag for material that absorbed the heat is only five minutes, by 9:05 pm all the energy absorbed during the day would have been released. It might get very warm for five minutes, but quickly the room will cool down to whatever the outside temperature is. Obviously this heating system is not very effective.

But, if the thermal lag were 10 hours, the stored energy would be released slowly all night long, releasing the last bit of stored heat energy at 7 am, just as the sun rises to start the warming process all over again. The thermal lag characteristics of common materials are shown in Table 5-3.

Table 5-3: Relative
Thermal Lag of
Materials

MATERIAL	THICKNESS	TIME LAG (HOURS)
Adobe	10 inches (250 mm)	9.2
Compressed Earth Blocks	10 inches (250 mm)	10.5
Concrete	10 inches (250 mm)	6.9
Double Brick	8.75 inches (220 mm)	6.2
Rammed Earth	10 inches (250 mm)	10.3
Sandy Loam	40 inches (1000 mm)	30 days

Conductivity

The **Conductivity** of the material will greatly influence the rate at which absorbed heat is released. As with specific heat capacity, different materials have a different rate of conductivity. The higher the conductivity, the faster the absorbed heat energy will radiate out of the material. The conductivity of common building materials is listed in Table 5-4.

Table 5-4: The Relative Conductivity of Materials

MATERIAL	CONDUCTIVITY
Water	1.9
Concrete Block	1.8
Sandstone	1.6
Compressed Earth Blocks	1.1
Brick	0.72
Plasterboard	0.17
Wood Flooring	0.14
Carpet	0.07

There are other factors, however, that will also affect how quickly absorbed heat radiates from a material. These include:

- How quickly the surrounding temperature cools.

- If the air around the object is moving, and just how fast it is moving (every child knows that if something is too hot to eat, just blow on it and it will cool down more quickly).

- The surface texture of the material. Smooth materials have less surface touching the air than do rough or bumpy materials—so they tend to cool more slowly.

- The thickness of material. The thicker it is, the slower it will cool.

Thermal Cycle

Thermal Cycle

If a home is designed properly, this **Thermal Cycle** of storing heat energy in the thermal mass of the building during the day and releasing it at night, will help to even out the temperatures inside the house from day to night. This is especially helpful in climates (such as a desert) where the temperature varies dramatically from day to night. It also works well in less extreme conditions.

A year can also be thought of as a very long day. The heat cycle of day and night is simply extended to a heat cycle of summer and winter. During the summer months, the thermal mass absorbs more heat than it radiates out, gradually warming. It becomes a "heat battery", storing heat energy until the surrounding air becomes cooler for a long period of time (winter). It will release much of that energy each night, but not all.

Then, during the winter months, the thermal mass of the building will release more energy than it absorbs. In this way, the home will actually generate a small amount of the energy it absorbed during the summer back out during the winter.

SCIENCE NOTE: UNDERGROUND HOUSES

Those cave men had it made. Caves are like the perfect place to live. Cool in the summer, warm in the winter, paint a couple of mastodons on the wall—and home-sweet-home. Maybe just a bit dark and damp, however.

So why not build your house underground, with just a bit of it poking up (for sunlight and such)? That way, the temperature in the winter stays pretty mild (never getting below the average annual outside temperature) and in the summer you have free air conditioning.

Not as crazy as you might think. Some people are now building underground homes using old automobile tires (like the Earthship™ in Figure 5-17) to contain the rammed earth used to construct the walls. This is taking thermal mass to the extreme.

But people are funny. They like things they are used to. Early settlers in America first built homes by using caves or digging out hollows into the hillside. They would then build a front on the home (facing south to get sunshine and warmth). These homes were warm and cozy—but the neighbors all decided that they were not "British" enough. They wanted homes like they were used to back in England.

So after a time, everyone was required to abandon the cave homes and build themselves a "proper" house made of stone or wood. Problem was, it was a lot colder in America than these folks were used to back home. They even built huge fireplaces inside where they could sit (literally inside the fireplace) because otherwise the ink would freeze as they tried to write letters telling their friends back home how warm and cozy things were in *The Colonies*.

Figure 5-17: Earthship™—Underground Home Designed by Michael Reynolds

Direct, Indirect and Isolated Solar Gain

If the thermal energy that is absorbed directly into an object and stored in it radiates directly out into the area to be heated, this is called **Direct Solar Gain**. In other words, the room or object is gaining energy directly from the sun. A window that allows sunshine into a room is a good example of this, as illustrated in Figure 5-18. The radiant energy of the sun converts from light to heat and warms the room. In addition, some of the heat energy is absorbed by the thermal mass of the walls and floor. When that stored heat energy radiates out (as the air cools), it directly heats the room.

**Figure 5-18:
Direct Solar Gain**

If, as in Figure 5-19, there is thermal mass between the sun and the area to be heated, the area will still realize some of the advantages of solar gain. This gain is not realized directly (through direct sunlight) so it is referred to as **Indirect Solar Gain**. An un-insulated exterior wall that faces the sun is an example of indirect solar gain. As the sun strikes it, the wall will absorb thermal energy (how much depends on the factors discussed earlier). Much of that energy will radiate back out of the house, but some will radiate through the wall and heat the interior of the room.

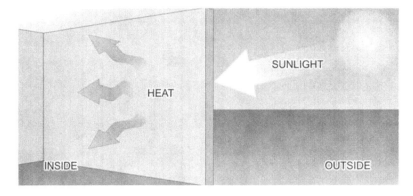

**Figure 5-19:
Indirect Solar Gain**

The heat radiated outward could also be captured by enclosing the wall in some sort of glass container (such as a greenhouse). The air within the greenhouse will heat through direct solar gain, and the adjacent home will heat through indirect solar gain.

Think back to the solar oven. This solar oven is just a box (a bigger box might be called, say, a greenhouse). If the solar oven (or greenhouse) is insulated well, the air will be trapped within that space. The glass top allows sunlight to enter the box, but the glass also prevents heat (or most of the heat, anyway) from escaping.

Over time, the direct solar gain continues to heat the inside of the box until the temperature is hot enough to cook food. In fact, a well-constructed solar oven made of cardboard will reach temperatures in excess of 220°F (104°C).

If this box were a greenhouse, it would not be very practical to allow the air to heat up to the same level as an oven. If the building is designed it in a way to allow the convection of that heat energy to move into the house, this passive system could be quite effective in heating a larger space within the home (to a comfortable temperature). As shown in Figure 5-20, this form of passive system takes advantage of **Isolated Solar Gain**.

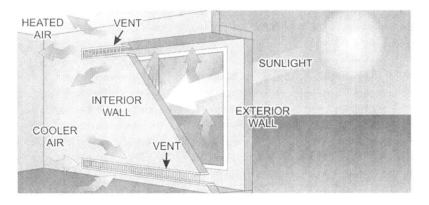

Figure 5-20:
Isolated Solar Gain

An example of such an isolated system is called a **Trombe Wall**. The Trombe wall is named after the French inventor, Felix Trombe, who reintroduced the concept back in 1964, although Edward Morse had patented the concept back in 1881 (nothing new under the sun).

This design magnifies the effect of direct solar gain, concentrating the heat into a masonry wall by use of a glass enclosure. The glass prevents much of the concentrated heat energy from simply radiating back into the exterior air.

In addition, modified Trombe walls typically incorporate vents that allow warm air to enter the building and cooler air to be drawn in from within the building, creating a passively circulated heat cycle, as shown in Figure 5-21. In this way, a Trombe wall takes advantage of the principles of direct solar gain, as well as indirect solar gain to passively heat a home.

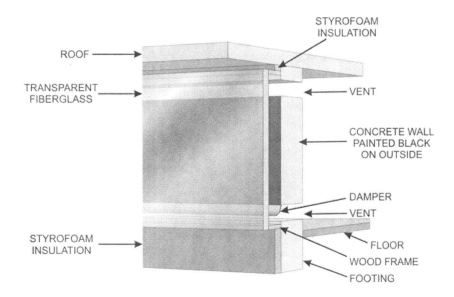

Figure 5-21:
Trombe Wall

One disadvantage of such a system is that in order for it to work, it requires a large windowless area on the equator side of the building. This space might just as effectively (and less expensively) incorporate a window to accomplish almost as much direct solar gain. Also, during extended periods of no sunshine, the Trombe wall may radiate out a considerable amount of thermal heat from the building.

Sun Room

An insulated greenhouse, conservatory or **Sun Room** on the equator side of the building is a more common method of incorporating isolated solar gain into a building's design, as shown in Figure 5-22. A sun room is simply a Trombe Wall where the trapped air space is expanded and used as a room. Such a space overcomes several of the disadvantages of the Trombe Wall.

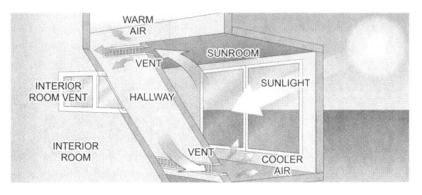

Figure 5-22:
Sun Space

Sun Rooms allow occupants to take advantage of any exterior views, and create additional living space. Also, the larger air space is less likely to allow a significant amount of thermal radiation to escape during extended periods of cloudy weather.

However, without proper venting, rooms such as these can become quite warm, examples reaching 180°F (82°C) when the outside temperature is 0°F (-18°C). Also, if airflow between the main living space and the sun room is not properly controlled, heat gained during the day will quickly be lost at night (or on cloudy days).

Designers and engineers have used the concepts of thermal mass, convection and thermal lag to create a variety of passive heating and cooling systems over the years. Another example is **Water Walls**, that replace the masonry wall mass with a wall of water—taking advantage of the superior thermal lag qualities of water.

Water Walls

Roof Pond

Other designers have placed similar systems on top of the home, creating a **Roof Pond**, like the one pictured in Figure 5-23, on top of the building to passively heat and cool the home.

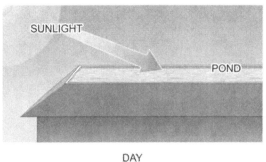
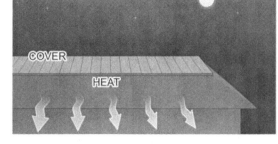

Figure 5-23:
Roof Pond

DAY

NIGHT

SCIENCE NOTE: ROOF PONDS

What could be cooler than having a pond on your roof? Or maybe we should say what could be hotter? Some people actually heat their homes by putting a pond on top of their house. Here's how it works.

These "ponds" are actually a bit more like a raised swimming pool. During sunny days, the water absorbs a lot of the sun's heat. Then, at night or on cloudy days, you go up top and cover it up. The warm water kind of radiates heat down through the ceiling, keeping the place warm. The water also insulates the house.

In some desert countries, they actually use this system in reverse to keep the house cool. During the day they keep the pond covered, so the water stays cool (and helps to cool the house). Then they uncover it at night, so that any heat that was absorbed is then radiated out.

Of course, certain concerns immediately spring to mind. Like, what happens when the thing springs a leak? Nothing like having a swimming pool come flowing down through the ceiling while you are watching TV.

Also, that water must weigh a ton (or many many tons). The home would really have to be over built to support that much weight.

It is possible to use the thermodynamic properties of convection to move warm air from one part of the home to another, cooler area. This process could be accelerated by using a fan to move the air more quickly—but once there is outside energy added into the system (the electricity to power the fan) it is no longer a passive system—but an **Active Solar Thermal System**.

Systems that rely on the movement of heat through convection can be modified to allow this heat flow to occur in one direction only. Such a system incorporates a **Thermal Diode**, similar to that shown in Figure 5-24. This thermal diode could be as simple as a damper or flap that opens when air flows in one direction, but closes when the air flows in the opposite direction (a passive system). Or it could be electronically controlled (an active system).

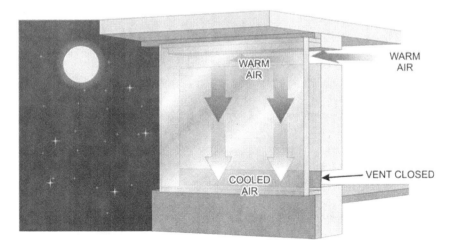

Figure 5-24:
Thermal Diode System
Diagram

Air is not the only material that transfers energy through convection. Liquids are also subject to the principles of convection. Since these liquids typically have a higher specific heat capacity than air, it will generally take longer for the absorbed heat to radiate out.

The passive thermal diode in a liquid system such as a roof pond is the insulated cover that is added or removed to accommodate the desired direction of heat flow. Thermal diode systems can be physical systems (such as the insulated cover) or they can be chemical. Solar ponds are an example of a system that very effectively employs a chemically-based thermal diode system to generate tremendous amounts of heat.

SCIENCE NOTE: SOLAR PONDS

This is just about the coolest idea yet. You can actually generate a huge amount of heat with nothing more than salt water and sunshine. This effect was first noticed in Transylvania in the early 1900s. They discovered that in naturally occurring salt-water lakes, the water at the bottom of the pond was hotter than the water at the top. A lot hotter.

So why is this? Well, it turns out that water with salt in it is more dense than water that doesn't have salt. So the salty water sinks to the bottom of the pond. After a while, you end up with a layer of water near the bottom that is very very salty. The water at the top has almost no salt in it at all. And in the middle is a layer of water that varies between salty and not salty (the closer to the bottom layer, the saltier it becomes).

Now, in a normal pond (without the salt), sunlight comes in and warms up the water. Some of the light energy goes right through the water up above (because water is clear like glass), and is converted to heat when it hits the bottom. The warm water in the bottom rises up through convection, and of course it all mixes together until the pond has a pretty uniform temperature.

But in these salty ponds, like the one in Figure 5-25, the warmer water in the bottom is too heavy to rise up and mix with the lighter, less salty water. So it just sits there, getting hotter and hotter. The bottom layer in some ponds gets so hot it could boil—well, water. The bottoms of some of these ponds have been measured at 212°F (100°C).

And it stays hot for a long time. In fact, they found in a solar pond in Texas that even when the top of the pond was covered with ice, the bottom layer was still 154°F. That is cool and hot at the same time.

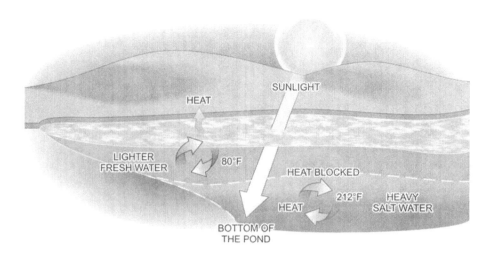

Figure 5-25:
Solar Pond

Passive Solar Cooling

Just as the energy from the sun can be used to heat a building, the sun's energy can also be used to cool it. This can be accomplished in several ways. **Natural Cooling** is perhaps the easiest and should be the first option. In warmer climates, or during summer months, this can be every bit as important as heating a home is in the winter.

There are three ways that passive solar heat can enter a building:

- Through direct solar gain, such as sunlight entering through windows and skylights.

- Through indirect solar gain, such as by radiating through exterior walls (heat transfer).

- Through infiltration (just as warm air can leak out of a poorly insulated home in the winter, warm air can "leak" in during the summer).

Shading

The easiest way to prevent direct solar gain (sunshine) from getting inside a building during the summer is to block it before it enters. An awning over windows on the southern side of a building (the northern side in the southern hemisphere) is an effective passive way of cooling the interior of a structure. Properly sized, these awnings block direct solar gain during the summer months when the sun tracks higher in the sky, but allow direct solar gain during winter months, as shown in Figure 5-26.

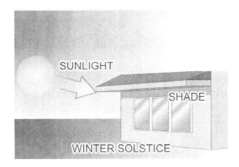 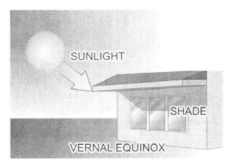 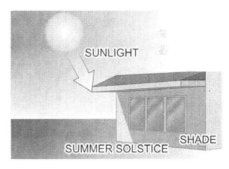

The sun's rays can be blocked in other ways as well. This could be accomplished simply by closing the curtains or blinds on the window—although this will usually prove to be ineffective in keeping the building cool. While the blinds are blocking the light from entering the room, the heat energy is simply collected behind the curtain (still inside the room). If the blinds were on the outside of the building, they would keep out more of the heat—but it is not a very convenient way to manage solar radiation. Fortunately there are passive systems available that will accomplish the same goal, such as chemically changing the window's characteristics from clear to opaque under preset conditions.

Figure 5-26: Sizing Awnings

SCIENCE NOTE: SMART GLASS

About 30 percent of all the heating and cooling loads in a typical house are due to windows. In the winter, a lot of energy leaves the building through poorly designed windows. In the summer, the opposite is true. Huge amounts of heat enter in the form of sunlight.

If we could find a way of solving this problem, we could actually save about 6% of the energy consumed in the United States each year.

So, how could you keep the rays of the sun from coming in through the glass without putting curtains outside?

Well, maybe the answer can be found in your sunglasses. For many years we have been able to buy sunglasses that turn darker the brighter the sun. When indoors they are, well, clear as glass. But go out in the bright sunshine and they quickly turn dark. Since we can do this for sunglasses, why not for windows?

It turns out that these kind of windows are actually available. **Photochromic** (sensitive to light) and **Thermochromic** (sensitive to heat) glass are passive systems, since they darken automatically. But we probably want to control this process. For instance, we would want the window to allow light inside on a cold winter's day and only block the light when it gets too warm inside.

There are now active systems available that will lighten and darken with the flip of a switch. Typical insulated windows contain gases between the layers of glass to help in preventing the transfer of heat (in and out of the building). These active **Electrochromic** windows have several layers inside that keep different gases separated. When a tiny current of electricity is introduced, the gases mix and the window turns dark. Flip the switch, the window becomes clear once again.

Of course, these new windows have not been widely adopted, largely because of their cost. Currently they cost about two to three times as much as a standard window. But if you consider the cost of energy—you will soon find that these are a bargain.

Photochromic

Thermochromic

Electrochromic

In many parts of the world, an effective way to block the sun's rays is by planting deciduous trees. Figure 5-27 shows how the leaves from the trees serve as an effective sun screen in the summer months. But in the winter the leaves fall from the trees, allowing sunlight in during the colder months when it will then help to passively heat the building.

Figure 5-27: Trees in Front of a Window

SUMMER

SUNLIGHT

WINTER

Convective Cooling

Another method of cooling a home is to use convection. Since hot air is less dense than cool air, it rises (or more exactly is displaced by cooler, more dense air). An efficient building design will take advantage of this natural process by allowing the warm air to escape near the ceiling and draw in cooler air from near the floor. Natural convection creates an air flow.

There are two ways of increasing the effectiveness of **Convective Cooling**. The first is to simply bring in cooler air. The second method is to increase the flow rate of the air through the building. The cooling effect of this increased airflow can be quite dramatic.

If the outside air temperature is 10°F (5.5°C) cooler than the indoor temperature, a vent that allows in 500 square feet of air per minute will provide 5,400 Btu's of cooling each hour, as shown in Table 5-5. If the flow rate is doubled to 1,000 square feet per minute, the cooling effect is also doubled, passively generating 10,800 Btu's of cooling.

Convective Cooling

AIRFLOW (V)	DIFFERENCE IN TEMPERATURES, (ΔT) BETWEEN OUTSIDE AND INSIDE AIR			
	5°F	10°F	15°F	20°F
100 cfm	*0.5	1.1	1.6	2.2
500 cfm	2.7	5.4	8.1	10.0
1000 cfm	5.4	10.8	16.2	21.6
2000 cfm	10.8	21.6	32.4	43.2

Table 5-5: Airflow Effect on Cooling

*In thousands of Btu's per hour.

Increasing Air Flow

The flow of the convection current can be increased or assisted in several ways. A mechanical device (such as an energy-efficient attic fan) can be utilized for this purpose. But an electrical device introduced into the system changes it from a passive system to an active system (and of course consumes electricity).

A fan, however, may not be necessary to increase the flow of air. Figure 5-28 demonstrates that there are many passive cooling systems that take advantage of prevailing winds to magnify the airflow. In areas with predictable wind flow patterns, these systems can be quite effective in keeping a building cool.

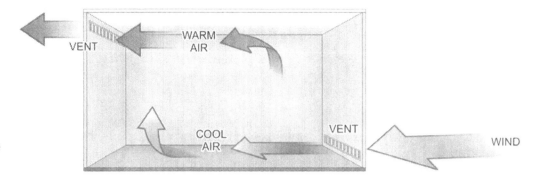

Figure 5-28: Wind Assisted Convective Cooling

Another method of increasing the air flow is known as a **Thermal Chimney** (or sometimes called a solar chimney). Similar in concept to a Trombe Wall (which is used for heating), a thermal chimney takes advantage of convection to draw warm air from inside a building. The "super" heated air rises quickly within the thermal chimney, pulling air from within the building. The warm air leaving the building is then replaced with cooler air drawn in from another source, as depicted in Figure 5-29.

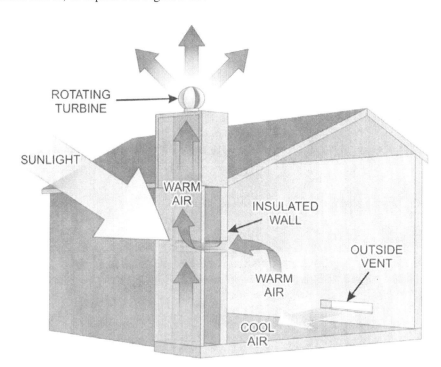

Figure 5-29: Thermal Chimney

Thermal chimneys can be constructed in a long narrow configuration, just like a standard chimney, or the concept could be incorporated into an attached greenhouse or sun room, as shown in Figure 5-30.

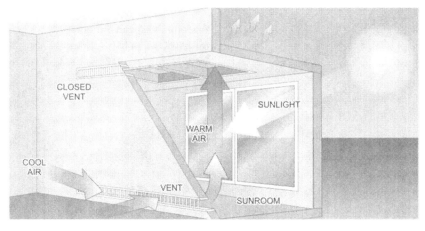

Before the age of air conditioning, building designers routinely incorporated these cooling concepts into the design of buildings. A good example of utilizing awnings, convective cooling, prevailing winds and thermal chimneys can be seen in the design of a traditional Florida "Cracker" style home, as shown in Figure 5-31.

In addition to convective cooling, these homes were typically raised above the ground to allow air flow beneath, but also to remove the effect of the warm thermal mass of the earth from adding heat within the structure.

Figure 5-30: Sun Room Thermal Chimney

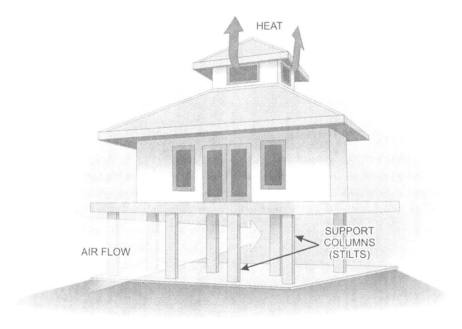

Figure 5-31: Florida Cracker Home

Introducing Cooler Air

The cooling effect of convection may be enhanced, not only through increased air flow, but also by lowering the temperature of the air that is brought into the structure. The greater the difference in air temperature between the warm inside air and the cooler outside air, the more effective convection will be in cooling the building.

Outside air is usually drawn in from a point as near the ground as possible (warm air rises, so lower air will be just a bit cooler). The thermal mass of the earth itself can be utilized to get even cooler air.

Walk into a cave in the summer and the air feels quite cool. The same cave will feel relatively warm in the winter. The temperature of the cave has not changed. What has changed is how it feels in relation to the outside air temperature.

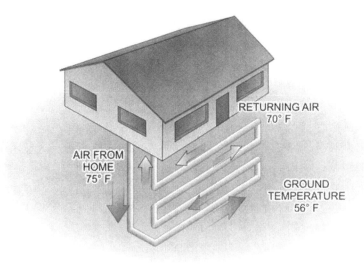

Below the frost line (the surface of the earth that freezes and thaws), the temperature of the earth remains near the average annual temperature for any given location. This thermal mass can assist in keeping a home warm in the winter, but it can also be used to keep a home cooler in the summer.

Air drawn through buried pipes is cooled by the surrounding earth (or in some systems, the pipes are placed in the cool waters of a nearby pond or stream). A buried pipe system that lowers the air temperature by even 5°F (3°C) can have a significant impact on the cooling capacity of a passive convection cooling system, as shown in Figure 5-32.

Figure 5-32: Buried Pipe Cooling System

Evaporative Cooling

When a person perspires, the sweat evaporates. It takes energy for this to occur, reducing the temperature of the skin (and the air immediately surrounding it). This effect is greater in hot, dry environments where the air can absorb more moisture and there is a greater difference between the air's **Wet Bulb Temperature** (the coolest the air could become if totally saturated with moisture) and its **Dry Bulb Temperature** (the current air temperature at the current humidity).

SCIENCE NOTE: SWAMP COOLERS

For thousands of years, people have understood that the air can be cooled by passing it over (or through) water. In ancient Persia (modern day Iran), they used a wind catcher (called a *Bâd gir*) to cool the air inside buildings in that hot dry climate.

Wind shafts on the roof caught air and channeled it over water. This cooler air was then directed inside to cool the building.

A modern day variation of this process can be found in an **Evaporative (Swamp) Cooler**, available from many commercial manufacturers. These coolers operate by blowing air (usually with an electric fan) over wet pads. An efficient swamp cooler operating in low humidity can cool air by 20 to 25°F (11 to 13°C).

The following questions test your knowledge of the material presented in this chapter.

1. Discuss the difference between an active system and a passive system.

2. Explain how the angle of the Earth in relation to the Sun affects the angle of sunlight at a given location on the Earth's surface throughout the year.

3. List three passive Daylighting systems. What are the advantages of each?

4. Define direct solar gain, indirect solar gain, and isolated solar gain and give examples of architectural features that incorporate these principles.

5. Discuss what is meant by Thermal Mass. How can this be used in homes to increase heating and cooling efficiency?

6. Explain why the specific heat capacity of a material would impact its effectiveness as a building material.

7. How does the heat capacity of a material differ from its specific heat capacity?

8. Why is the thermal lag characteristic of a material important when constructing a building to use thermal mass as a heat source?

9. What is a Trombe Wall and what passive solar principle(s) does it incorporate in its operation?

10. How does a roof pond help keep a home cool in the summer and warm in the winter?

11. Give three examples of passive cooling systems. What are the advantages of these systems over active systems such as air conditioning?

12. Discuss two ways to passively increase the airflow within a building.

13. How do swamp coolers work?

14. Explain how solar ponds store energy. How could this be used to provide heat within a building?

15. What factors affect the thermal storage capacity of an object or building material?

EXAM QUESTIONS

1. If the same object is placed in the sun at two different locations, which of the following does NOT affect the amount of solar radiation that object will absorb?
    a. the angle of the sun
    b. the temperature of the air as compared with the temperature of the object
    c. atmospheric conditions
    d. its thermal storage capacity

2. Light is typically measured in:
   a. lumens
   b. cubic meter candles
   c. Coulombs
   d. photon radiance

3. If the specific heat capacity, thermal storage capacity and thermal lag properties of a material were the ONLY criteria used, which of the following materials would make the most effective building material from a passive heating and cooling perspective?
   a. air
   b. water
   c. concrete
   d. wood

4. The angle of the Sun in relation to the Earth's surface increases as:
   a. temperature increases
   b. latitude increase
   c. altitude increases
   d. atmospheric pressure increase

5. A tool used to describe the location of the Sun throughout the year for a given location is:
   a. an altimeter
   b. a light diffuser
   c. a solstice
   d. a sun chart

6. A passive lighting system that is often used when roof pitches overlap to bring light in through the wall near the ceiling is call a:
   a. Clerestory Window
   b. Split-Section Light Tube
   c. Light Shelf
   d. Full-Spectrum Skylight

7. How well the thermal mass of a material reduces temperature extremes is known as its:
   a. absorption factor
   b. black body radiation
   c. damping ration
   d. specific heat capacity

8. Which of the following is an example of incorporating thermal mass into the design of a home as a passive heating and cooling system?
   a. A concrete home built over a waterfall (such as Frank Lloyd Wright's Falling Water)
   b. A large air mass contained within a structure (such as Buckminster Fuller's geodesic dome)
   c. A buried home (such as Michael Reynold's Earthship design)
   d. A modular pre-fab building incorporating insulated panels (such as Liam Neilson's containerized bungalows)

9. Which of the following is NOT a passive solar energy system?
   a. a light tube
   b. a very thick rammed earth wall on the north side of a room
   c. a stand-alone photovoltaic system
   d. a solar batch heater solar thermal system

10. A window that darkens when exposed to bright sunlight is:
    a. photovoltaic
    b. photochromic
    c. photogenic
    d. photothermic

CHAPTER 6

GREEN BUILDING

OBJECTIVES

Upon completion of this chapter and its related lab procedures you will be able to perform the following tasks:

1. Understand what qualities constitute a green building.

2. List and relate the advantages of sustainable construction.

3. Identify the barriers that restrict the expansion of green construction.

4. Discuss the various sustainable construction and design philosophies and their impact on architectural design.

5. Define many of the terms commonly used in the sustainable building industry.

6. Discuss the history of green building certification and the role it has played in the expansion of the industry.

7. List in detail what features are evaluated in a LEED-certified building, and what LEED programs are available.

8. Identify and list the various issues associated with green design.

9. Discuss how the land, landscaping, building shape and size, and the selection of materials affect the energy efficiency of a building.

10. Understand what is meant by a heat island and how the design of a building can affect the temperature of the surrounding community.

11. Discuss the life cycle evaluation process.

12. Discuss what is meant by a closed-loop materials strategy.

13. Give examples of biobased products and how they may be used in building construction.

14. Discuss the effect building design and construction materials can have on the health of the building's occupants.

15. Discuss various indoor comfort issues and how green design addresses these issues.

16. Understand the economic factors involved in green construction and design and how these calculations are made.

17. Discuss how green buildings fit into the broader concept of intelligent communities.

Green Building

INTRODUCTION

Green building is about more than just constructing an energy-efficient structure. It is concerned with creating a comfortable living or working space where the occupants have a **Sustainable** relationship with their community, their environment, as well as the resources of the planet upon which they live.

The building industry is extremely large and uses a lot of resources. How it goes about its business affects a great many people as well as the planet's resources. Construction accounts for about 8% of the annual U.S. gross domestic product (GDP) and consumes about 40% of all the raw materials generated nationwide.

The buildings created hold a lot of people and things. By some estimates, over 90% of everything produced resides in a building in one form or another (either as part of the building itself or a product stored or used within the building).

GREEN BUILDINGS

Green buildings come in many shapes and sizes. They include residential, commercial and even industrial properties. While their approaches and functions may be significantly different from each other, they do have several goals in common. These include:

- Providing a healthier and more comfortable environment for those who live and work within them.

- Using energy and water-efficient technologies to reduce consumption.

- Reducing the waste generated during construction and demolition of the building.

- Incorporating renewable energy technologies wherever possible.

- Improving the indoor air quality.

- Using nature where possible to provide building needs and create a more "connected" lifestyle environment.

- Reducing the impact of the building on the surrounding community and the environment.

Energy Issues in Buildings

Buildings consume a tremendous amount of energy. In 2002, for example, the powering of buildings used about 36% of all the energy generated in the U.S. Within the electrical use in buildings, lighting commercial buildings accounted for about 31% of the total energy consumed, heating the interior space used another 22% and cooling accounted for 18%.

This energy use produces a significant portion of the greenhouse gases emitted into the atmosphere. About 47% of the sulfur dioxide, 22% of the nitrogen oxide and 35% of all carbon dioxide emissions in the U.S. can be traced to energy used in buildings.

Solid Waste in Buildings

During construction of a typical new home in the U.S., about 8,000 pounds (3600 kilograms) of waste material is generated, enough to fill an average room in that home from floor to ceiling.

When remodeling, 35-45% of the demolition material simply ends up in landfills. Renovation of existing buildings produces 70-100 lbs of waste material per square foot (340 – 490 kg per square meter). This waste from demolition accounts for about 92% of the estimated 145 million tons of waste generated each year by the construction industry (the remaining 8% is waste produced during new construction).

Why Buildings are Going Green

In recent years there has been a remarkable growth in sustainable construction. The number of new green buildings or existing buildings renovated to more sustainable standards has grown at an annual rate of around 50%. As indicated in Table 6-1, educational and governmental institutions have led this change. While the commercial and institutional segment of the building industry has led the way in adopting green building concepts, industrial and residential structures are converting at a rapid rate as well.

Table 6-1: Projected Growth Rates (2007) for Green Buildings

MARKET SECTOR	ANNUAL GROWTH RATE
Educational	65%
Governmental	62%
Institutional (Churches, Prisons, Museums, etc)	54%
Offices	48%
Health Care Facilities	46%
Residential Homes	32%
Hospitality (Hotels, Motels, etc)	22%
Retail	20%

There are a number of reasons for this recent interest in sustainable construction and renovation. These include:

- Increased energy prices. The price of a barrel of oil has increased significantly in recent years, as shown in Figure 6-1. Wide oil price fluctuations make financial planning difficult. A low-energy green building adds stability to the cost of operating the home or business.

- Additional incentives. The Energy Policy Act of 2005 and the Economic Recovery Act of 2009, along with expanded state and utility-based incentives, have combined to make renewable energy alternatives more affordable in recent years.

- Increased demand. As more green buildings are available on the market, demand for them increases. The availability of green buildings increases public awareness of this as an option, which in turn increases demand.

- Selling feature. Slow periods in the housing market provide incentives for builders and developers to "differentiate" themselves from their competition. The offering of green building alternatives has proven a popular and successful marketing tool.

- Evaluation programs. The emergence of green building rating systems (such as LEED, Energy Star, and others) has provided an objective way to evaluate and compare green buildings, as well as track the growth of this industry segment.

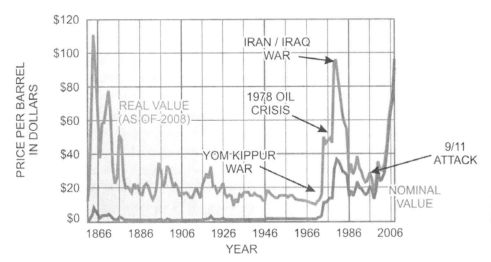

Figure 6-1:
Market Price for Crude Oil

SCIENCE NOTE: HISTORY OF GREEN BUILDING

As they say, *"Everything old is new again."*

In a lot of ways, almost all buildings were at one time "green buildings." Of course, before there was oil, no electricity, no extra material to waste—you had to be green to survive.

For example, the ancient pueblo people who lived in the Four Corners area of the Western U.S. (where Colorado, New Mexico, Arizona and Utah meet) up until around 1300 AD built homes that used local materials (mud and wood), used passive heating and cooling concepts, captured rainwater—and were most of all—sustainable in their way of life.

Ancient Persians cooled their homes with under-floor natural ventilation. Romans incorporated geothermal into many of their structures to provide warm air and hot water. Even the early pioneers in Pennsylvania dug comfortable homes into south-facing hillsides, staying warm in the winter and cool in the summer. Of course, officials made them tear these homes down and replace them with wooden buildings as soon as possible (that were more suitably "British"). These newer homes were so cold in the winter that colonists had to literally sit in the fireplace to write letters, just to keep the ink from freezing.

But to find the history of the "modern" green building movement, we need to look to the 1970s. Many early environmentalists began exploring ways to live in a more "connected" way—looking to nature for answers and adopting many of the older indigenous building techniques to lower their impact on the environment and to conserve resources.

It wasn't until the 1990s that green building began to become more "mainstream." In 1989 the **American Institute of Architects (AIA)** established its Committee on the Environment (COTE). Three years later, the United Nations Conference on Sustainable Development met in Rio de Janeiro, Brazil.

In 1993 the Union of Architects (**UIA**) and the AIA issued a joint statement outlining a code of principles and practices aimed at boosting sustainable development. That same year, President Bill Clinton announced the "Greening of the White House," a very high profile project designed to renovate the White House and the Old Executive Office Building (a 600,000 sq ft building nearby), making them more energy and water efficient.

About this time, building trade associations and governments around the world started arguing and writing down just what they felt a green building looked like. A modern industry was born. It only took us a few hundred years.

The Goals of Green Building

Through a number of high-tech and low-tech approaches, green buildings are designed to meet several goals. These include:

- Reduced energy use.
- Reduced water use.
- Reduced material use.
- Increased human health.
- Intelligent use of space.
- Working with nature.
- Integration within the community.

Reduced Energy Use

The goal of high-performance buildings is to reduce the amount of energy the building uses to about one-tenth that consumed by an average "traditional" building. This is accomplished through the use of passive heating and cooling techniques, location, daylighting, energy conservation methods, structural mass, landscaping and thoughtful design.

Alternative energy sources such as wind, solar, geothermal, and/or biomass are also incorporated into the design of the structure. By designing for efficiency, eliminating waste, constructing with recycled and reused materials, and using alternative methods of energy generation—a truly green building can reduce its carbon footprint to almost zero.

Reduced Water Use

As with energy, a highly-efficient building uses only about ten-percent of the water used in an average building. Low-flush or composting toilets, reduced water-use fixtures, wastewater recycling, and water capturing devices (like rain barrels, wetlands or cisterns) can reduce the amount of water used and/or wasted in a commercial, industrial or residential building.

Reduced Material Use

The goal for all green buildings is to construct them totally out of renewable materials that are either made from recycled material, reused, repurposed or recyclable. Newly constructed green buildings are made from carefully selected materials that minimize the impact on the environment or materials that would otherwise be thrown away. The building is designed in way that there is little waste generated during construction.

Additionally, a green building is designed so that when it is remodeled or demolished at some point in the future, the materials used to build it can be easily used again, either in the same building or for some other purpose.

Increased Human Health

Ultimately almost all buildings are places designed for people. How the building is constructed can have a big impact on the health of those who live or work in and around it. Air quality, noise levels, lighting quality and temperature/humidity control are important to maintaining a pleasant and healthy environment. Also, green buildings do not use materials that can give off toxic gases and/or odors that make them dangerous or uncomfortable.

Intelligent Use of Space

The size, shape, orientation and basic design of a building will impact how well it works and how much energy it uses. As part of the green building process, designers seek to do the most with as little material as possible. Smaller, more efficiently designed rooms are easier to cool. Homes that face the sun are easier to heat.

Working With Nature

Many traditional designers have viewed nature as something to battle against. They focus on how to keep the water out; how to keep the heat in. They see the building as something separate from nature—not a part of nature. As a result, many building systems are designed to work against or imitate natural processes—using fossil fuels to perform tasks that nature performs automatically.

Many green systems exist that take advantage of the natural heating and cooling properties of the earth. In green buildings, water can be deflected or collected, used, reused and purified—rather than eliminated and then pumped in from a commercial source.

Green homes seek to incorporate landscaping into the design of the building, using the natural shading and cooling properties of plants to the building's advantage. During the construction process, the project again seeks to work with nature rather than against it. Existing plants and animals are disturbed as little as possible. Land is left undisturbed if at all possible.

Settling Easily into the Community

Green builders understand that every home and business is part of a larger community. The appearance, design, siting and construction processes should enhance, rather than detract from the surrounding area.

Considerations such as access to mass transportation, walkability (locating the building so residents can walk to as many places as possible), environmental preservation and restoration, plus farmland preservation are just a few concerns among many that sustainable developers must consider when selecting a site to develop green structures.

Advantages of Sustainable Development

Green building techniques offer significant advantages over traditional construction practices. These include:

- Lower cost. While the initial investment in constructing the building (capital costs) may be higher, an evaluation of the **Life-Cycle Cost** (**LCC**) will almost always indicate that a green building is less expensive than traditional construction over the life of the building. An LCC is a process by which a **Cost/Benefit Analysis** is made of the building for each year of its probable life. The money saved (discounted to account for the fact that money today is generally worth more—due to inflation—than money saved in the future) by the green aspects of the building is then calculated and compared against the higher initial construction cost. Typical LCC evaluations have found that an increased up-front investment of 2% for example, have led to a savings of over 20% (a ten-to-one return on investment).

- Better health. As many as 30% of new and remodeled buildings generate excessive complaints about indoor air quality. The U.S. Environmental Protection Agency (EPA) estimates that building-related health problems cost businesses more than $150 billion per year.

- Resources saved. Green buildings use fewer resources than traditional buildings—in materials, energy and water. They are a cost-effective and ethical response to increased pollution and diminishing resources concerns.

- Better productivity. Studies have found that people working in green buildings are 3-5% more productive, due to their comfort and quality of life advantages.

- Enhanced public image. Businesses have found that incorporating green construction in their facility planning demonstrates a tangible commitment to the environment as well as a commitment to the health and comfort of their employees.

- Longer building life. Many commercial buildings are constructed with a very limited lifespan in mind. Developers assume that the structure will be torn down and replaced in 10-15 years. Green building incorporates a higher quality and longer anticipated life of the building and contents, reducing waste and resulting in better quality buildings.

- Better financing. Many lending institutions offer better terms for projects that incorporate green building processes.

- Higher resale value. Green buildings consistently sell for more money than do similar traditional buildings. The advantages of a green building (such as lower energy bills) translate into higher selling prices.

Life-Cycle Cost (LCC)

Cost/Benefit Analysis

Barriers to Sustainable Development

So, if green construction is so great, why isn't every building green? While the advantages of this form of construction are substantial, barriers to widespread adoption do exist. These include:

- Perceived higher cost. While the life-cycle cost of the building is lower, the initial cost of construction is typically as much as 5% higher than traditional construction. Public perception, therefore, is that green buildings are more expensive.

- Lack of information. The benefits of green building are not widely reported or understood. A recent survey of commercial building managers found that 64% of them reported they did not know of any benefits associated with green buildings.

- Complexity. Building a regular building is difficult enough, but adding the complexity of green design, finding green materials and locating construction firms familiar with the process is simply too much work for many people.

- Fear of the unknown. People are afraid of what they do not understand. Investing in a home or commercial building is an expensive undertaking, and people will not risk that investment unless they are completely convinced the investment will pay off.

- Habits. Builders, designers, educators and developers form habits over time. They become very good at what they do. Green building design and construction require many of these habits be changed. These methods also call into question many of the time-honored assumptions that have served them well over the years.

- Legal and governmental restrictions. Often local laws and ordinances prohibit what are, in fact, sound and environmentally beneficial building practices. Some governmental bodies still restrict the use of composting or low-flush toilets, for example. Homeowner associations may prohibit the use of photovoltaic panels where they can be viewed by neighbors. Rules and laws are slow to change.

- Accounting methods. In many businesses, institutions and industries, the capital costs (the initial cost of building a store, school or office) are separate (and usually managed by different people or departments) from the operating budget for running and maintaining that building. It is often the case that the decision-maker for construction simply does not factor in or "care" about future operating costs—as these costs are not their responsibility.

Resource-Conscious Design Concepts

Everything begins as an idea. In buildings, those ideas find their way into a design. It is the design that then becomes the blueprint, guiding the building process from start to finish. But even before the idea emerges—there is a philosophy that helps to shape the idea.

Seven Principles of Sustainable Construction

In 1994, the Conseil International du Batiment (CIB), an international construction "think tank" published their **Seven Principles of Sustainable Construction**. These include:

1. Reduce resource consumption.

2. Reuse resources.

3. Use recyclable resources.

4. Protect nature.

5. Eliminate toxics.

6. Apply life-cycle costing.

7. Focus on quality.

Resource-Conscious Design

These are the underlying principles, or philosophy that helps guide a school of thought in architecture known as **Resource-Conscious Design**. The aim of this movement is to minimize the amount of natural resources consumed by buildings and to take advantage of natural processes (such as passive solar heating) whenever possible.

Resource-conscious design attempts to close loops in the materials process. A **Closed-Loop** approach (as it applies to materials) views every material used as an on-going resource. This process, also sometimes called **Cradle-to-Cradle**, tries to create new buildings from recycled or reused materials as much as possible. Then it takes it one step further and considers how the new building can be dissembled when its useful life has come to an end, the materials used, then recycled once again.

Additional Sustainable Construction Concepts

While resource-conscious design forms the basic foundation, or core, of the sustainable construction philosophy, there are a number of other complementary ideas and ideals that often influence a specific design or building.

Industrial Ecology

In the late 1980s, a movement within industrial design emerged where architects and engineers looked to nature to see if industrial processes could be improved. They were concerned with the vast amounts of waste generated during traditional manufacturing techniques (where only about 6% of the extracted materials end up in the final product). This became known as **Industrial Ecology**.

Industrial systems had long been viewed as linear. Raw materials came into the process, finished products left. How the materials were obtained (other than cost and availability) were rarely considered. What happened to the product after it was purchased was also of little consequence.

Industrial ecology looks at the industrial process as a whole—from material extraction to the manufacturing of the product, to what happens to that product when its useful life is over—to see how the processes can be improved. The process is circular, rather than linear and the entire circle of production must be explored and improved.

Construction Ecology

A subcategory of the industrial ecology movement is the concept of **Construction Ecology**. It employs many of the same principles, but targets the ideas specifically to the construction industry.

Biomimicry

Another popular term in green building circles is **Biomimicry**. This is the conscious imitation of nature in the design of a building, system or product. Advocates of this philosophy argue that through 4 billion years of "trial and error," nature has created some very ingenious and sustainable systems.

Many mammals in very cold or very hot climates build underground homes to take advantage of the thermal mass of the earth to moderate temperatures. Construction of underground homes is another form of biomimicry, looking to nature for ideas and inspiration in construction design.

An example of biomimicry can be seen in Figure 6-2, where designers in Glasgow, Scotland have proposed installing solar "lily pads" on the Clyde River to generate power for the city's electrical grid and to stimulate riverfront development. Imitating the form and function of a common aquatic plant, designers hope to create an aesthetically pleasing and low-impact energy source.

**Figure 6-2:
Biomimicry**

Design for the Environment

Sometimes called **Green Design**, the **Design for the Environment (DfE)** movement advocates spending more time "up front" during the design phase of a project, creating products that can easily be disassembled then recycled, reused or remanufactured for other uses. This design process seeks to reduce the amount of waste generated during construction. DfE also tries to eliminate waste during demolition by anticipating that the building will one day be torn down or remodeled. They design the building in such a way as to make "deconstruction" as green as possible.

Ecological Economics

Ecological economics argues that nature has value, and that this value should be calculated and stated (in dollars) when evaluating any product or project. Those who subscribe to this school of thought argue that contemporary economic theories fail to recognize that resources are limited and that the environmental impact of waste and toxins has a very real economic impact (the "**True Cost**" of goods and services).

Ecological economics believes that a healthy natural ecosystem, and the free goods and services it provides (such as clean air) are essential to the economic success of a society.

For example, in contemporary (or neoclassical) economics, the cost of a product (such as a car) is limited to the **Direct Costs** (the money spent by the car manufacturer purchasing the components, assembling them, transporting and ultimately selling the product to the consumer) and the **Indirect Costs** (such as insurance, taxes, office help, interest on loans, etc.).

Ecological economics would add additional costs to that automobile, such as the cost of health care that is a direct result of the pollution the car expels, the cost of cleaning up the environment where the materials to make the car were extracted, the cost of lost farmland due to the highway system required to serve the car, the cost of disposing of the car, the environmental cost of oil spills resulting from the transport of fuels to service that car, and so on.

This form of accounting has led to groups such as the International Center for Technology Assessment determining that external costs add an additional $14 or more to the true cost of every gallon of gasoline.

While the auto or gasoline manufacturers might argue that many of those costs are outside their control and not their responsibility, ecological economics would counter that the costs are real and that someone must pay them. As raw materials grow more scarce, the allocation of these real costs will be a debate that will without a doubt take on a more central role in the manufacture of any goods or services over the coming decades.

The Biophilia Hypothesis

The **Biophilia Hypothesis** suggests that humans need and crave a connection with nature and living things. Studies show that simple daily interactions with nature, such as natural light, windows with a view to the outside, plants within the living area and fresh air reduce stress, increases worker productivity, and leads to better health.

Sustainable Construction Terminology

Every profession creates its own terms that are used to define concepts unique to that industry. The green building industry is no different.

Ecological Footprint

The amount of land required to support a certain lifestyle or activity is often referred to its **Ecological Footprint**. For example, the ecological footprint of the city of London extends well beyond the city limits. It requires a land area 125 times larger than the city itself to support the level of activity that takes place within the city (production of food, fuel, materials and products).

Ecological footprint calculations are a convenient way to compare land use and lifestyles to determine if they are sustainable given the finite resources available. The North American lifestyle, for example, consumes a great deal of the planet's resources. It has been calculated that if everyone on Earth adopted this lifestyle, it would require five planets with the resources of Earth to support it.

Carrying Capacity

Any specific location can support only a certain number of people given the limited resources available. A desert environment may support only one or two people per acre (given its limited water and vegetation resources), while a city center in a mild climate with abundant water (Paris, for example) can support a considerably larger population. The upper limit of how many people a given area can support (in a sustainable way) is known as its **Carrying Capacity**.

Carrying capacity is only concerned with the relationship between the number of people in a given area and that area's ability to support them. It does not address quality of life issues (a given area may support quite a lot of people, but the crowded conditions may make it unpleasant to live there). What is clear, however, is that no society can live beyond the land's ability to support the population for very long.

Ecological Rucksack

To extract any material from the earth usually involves some disruption to the environment. The more earth that has to be moved (to get to the wanted resource) the more the environmental disruption. The resulting product is then said to carry with it a certain amount of ecological "baggage" or its **Ecological Rucksack** (backpack). This is usually expressed as a number signifying the amount of material pulled from the earth to generate a specific amount of the product.

The environmental damage for specific products can be dramatic. To make a 10-gram golden wedding ring, over 300 tons of raw material must be extracted from the earth to get the gold used in that single band. A diamond engagement ring is even more damaging to the planet. As seen in Table 6-2, 53 million times the weight of the diamond must be extracted to find that diamond.

Table 6-2: The Ecological Rucksack of Common Materials

MATERIAL	ECOLOGICAL RUCKSACK
Aluminum	85
Recycled Aluminum	4
Steel	21
Recycled Steel	5
Platinum	350,000
Gold	540,000
Diamond	53,000,000

The ecological damage of extraction of materials is actually understated by its ecological rucksack, since it does not include surface material moved to get at the raw material used in the resource's production. Extraction techniques, such as **Mountain Top Removal** (in the coal industry) are much more ecologically damaging than deep mining techniques designed to extract the same resource.

Embodied Energy

It takes energy to produce any product. When the energy required to extract, produce, transport and install a product is calculated, the result is that product's **Embodied Energy**. The embodied energy of common building materials is listed in Table 6-3. The lower the number, the less energy required.

MATERIAL	EMBODIED ENERGY (Megajoules per kilogram)
Aggregate (gravel & crushed rock)	0.1
Concrete	1.3
Lumber	2.5
Brick	2.5
Cellulose Insulation	3.3
Gypsum Wallboard	6.1
Particleboard	8.0
Aluminum (recycled)	8.1
Steel (recycled)	8.9
Asphalt Shingles	9.0
Plywood	10.4
Fiberglass Insulation	30.3
Steel	32.0
PVC	70.0
Copper	70.6
Paint	93.3
Linoleum	116.0
Polystyrene Insulation	117.0
Carpet (synthetic)	148.0
Aluminum	227.0

Table 6-3: Embodied Energy of Common Construction Materials

Embodied energy is an important concern when selecting materials for green building, but the lifespan of that product must also be considered. For example, a product with an embodied energy twice that of another material may still be a much better energy choice if it is expected to last ten times as long.

Certifying Green Buildings

As the building industry slowly defined what makes a green building, it soon became apparent that there needed to be a neutral third party, verifying that certain buildings were in fact green. Often the features that make a building sustainable are not obvious; buyers might easily be deceived. Also, with so many factors involved in the definition of sustainable development, it would be very helpful to have an objective set of standards to serve as a guide for designers and builders.

Building Research Establishment Environmental Assessment Method (BREEAM)

Building Research Establishment Environmental Assessment Method (BREEAM)

In 1988, the Building Research Establishment (a national building research organization in the United Kingdom) established a set of guidelines to rate the ecological aspects of office buildings. The rating system became known as the **Building Research Establishment Environmental Assessment Method (BREEAM)**.

Under BREEAM, credits were awarded to buildings for energy use, management policies, indoor air quality, transportation issues, health issues, land use, conservation, use of materials and water efficiency. Depending on the score, a building was then rated on a scale of PASS, GOOD, VERY GOOD, or EXCELLENT.

The program was adopted throughout the UK, Canada, and many parts of Europe and Asia. Other nations followed suit, creating similar green building assessment programs tailored to their national construction industry. CASBEE (the Comprehensive Assessment System for Building Environmental Efficiency) was developed in Japan. The **Green Star** assessment system was developed for the Australian building industry. But BREEAM was easily the most widely adopted green building assessment program in the world until 1998, when the **US Green Building Council (USGBC)** created their own assessment program.

Green Star

U.S. Green Building Council (USGBC)

Leadership in Energy and Environmental Design (LEED)

Leadership in Energy and Environmental Design (LEED)

Formed in 1993, the USGBC is a non-profit trade association that emerged from the construction industry's growing interest in sustainable building. In 1998 the USGBC unveiled the **Leadership in Energy and Environmental Design (LEED)** program, which quickly became the assessment tool of choice for the U.S. building industry.

The LEED program assigns specific point values to the various sustainable aspects of a building (similar to how the BREEAM program was designed). Buildings are then awarded the designation of CERTIFIED, SILVER, GOLD or PLATINUM depending on their score. The entire application and evaluation process is managed by the USGBC.

Over the years the program has undergone a number of revisions and expansions. In 2009, LEED Version 3 (v3) was released. The revised program builds upon the existing rating system, but adds increased focus on building energy issues as well as incorporating new technologies into the evaluation process.

The LEED rating system is actually a collection of separate rating programs, each designed to address a specialized market within the building industry. These programs include:

- LEED-NC: New Construction in commercial buildings. Specific certification programs based on this rating system are also available, targeted to schools and health care facilities.

- LEED-EB: Existing Buildings (addresses renovation for commercial buildings).

- LEED-CS: Core and Shell projects. In many speculative commercial buildings, the developers design and construct only the shell and core (e.g., mechanical, electrical, plumbing, and fire protection systems) of the building, and then the commercial tenant is responsible for designing the interior space.

- LEED-CI: Commercial Interior. Designed as a complimentary program to the Core and Shell rating, this program allows commercial tenants to have the interior improvements rated.

- LEED-H: Homes (for residential construction).

- LEED-ND: Neighborhood Development.

LEED for New Construction

The most developed and most widely adopted of the LEED assessment programs is the rating system targeted to new construction in commercial buildings. The program has grown rapidly, from only 25 certified projects in 2000, to more than 2,300 by 2008.

Buildings applying for this certification are rated on criteria ranging from site selection, to water efficiency, to their use of alternative energy sources, to indoor air quality (a more detailed rating checklist can be seen in Table 6-4).

Table 6-4: LEED 2009 Checklist for New Construction

BUILDING FEATURE EVALUATED	POINTS AVAILABLE
Sustainable Sites	**26 Possible Points**
Construction Activity Pollution Prevention	Required
Site Selection	1
Development Density and Community Connectivity	5
Brownfield Redevelopment	1
Alternative Transportation—Public Transportation Access	6
Alternative Transportation—Bicycle Storage and Changing Rooms	1
Alternative Transportation—Low-Emitting and Fuel-Efficient Vehicles	3
Alternative Transportation—Parking Capacity	2
Site Development—Protect or Restore Habitat	1
Site Development—Maximize Open Space	1
Storm Water Design—Quantity Control	2
Heat Island Effect—Non-roof	1
Heat Island Effect—Roof	1
Light Pollution Reduction	1
Water Efficiency	**10 Possible Points**
Water Use Reduction	Required
Water Efficient Landscaping	2-4
Innovative Wastewater Technologies	2
Water Use Reduction	2-4
Energy and Atmosphere	**35 Possible Points**
Fundamental Commissioning of Building Energy Systems	Required
Minimum Energy Performance	Required
Fundamental Refrigerant Management	Required
Optimize Energy Performance	1-19
On-site Renewable Energy	1-7
Enhanced Commissioning	2
Enhanced Refrigerant Management	2
Measurement and Verification	3
Green Power	2

Table 6-4: LEED 2009 Checklist for New Construction (Continued)

BUILDING FEATURE EVALUATED	POINTS AVAILABLE
Materials and Resources	**14 Possible Points**
Storage and Collection of Recyclables	Required
Building Reuse—Maintain Existing Walls, Floors and Roof	1-3
Building Reuse—Maintain Existing Interior Nonstructural Elements	1
Construction Waste Management	1-2
Materials Reuse	1-2
Recycled Content	1-2
Indoor Environmental Quality	**15 Possible Points**
Minimum Indoor Air Quality Performance	Required
Environmental Tobacco Smoke (ETS) Control	Required
Outdoor Air Delivery Monitoring	1
Increased Ventilation	1
Construction Indoor Air Quality Management Plan—During Construction	1
Construction Indoor Air Quality Management Plan—Before Occupancy	1
Low-Emitting Materials—Adhesives and Sealants	1
Low-Emitting Materials—Paints and Coatings	1
Low-Emitting Materials—Flooring Systems	1
Low-Emitting Materials—Composite Wood and Agri-fiber Products	1
Indoor Chemical and Pollutant Source Control	1
Controllability of Systems—Lighting	1
Controllability of Systems—Thermal Comfort	1
Thermal Comfort—Design	1
Thermal Comfort—Verification	1
Daylight and Views—Daylight	1
Daylight and Views—Views	1
Innovation in Design	**6 Possible Points**
Innovation in Design	1-5
LEED Accredited Professional	1
Regional Priority	**4 Possible Points**
Regional Priority	1-4

Newly constructed projects are evaluated against these criteria. One-hundred base points are possible, with an additional six points assigned to encourage design innovation and four points allocated if the project addresses specific regional needs (for example, increased emphasis on water conservation in high drought-prone areas). LEED awards are based on the total number of points (as indicated in Table 6-5) earned during the evaluation process.

Table 6-5: Points Required for LEED-NC Rating Awards

Platinum	80 points or above
Gold	60-79 points
Silver	50-59 points
Certified	40-49 points
No Rating	Below 40 points

LEED Professional Accreditation

The USGBC also accredits individuals, testing them on their knowledge and skills needed to walk building owners through the LEED certification process. **LEED Accredited Professionals (LEED APs)** have been tested on green building practices and principles and the LEED Rating System. More than 75,000 people have earned this credential since the Professional Accreditation program was launched in 2001.

Additional Certification Programs

While the LEED certification program is the most widely recognized program focused on sustainable building within the U.S., there are others as well. These include:

- The **Sustainable Project Rating Tool (SpiRiT)** developed by the U.S. Army focused on the unique conditions faced in constructing military bases.

- The **ICC-700-2008 National Green Building Standard**, jointly developed by the National Association of Home Builders (NAHB) and the International Code Council (**ICC**) is a certification program designed for the residential building market.

- **Green Globes** is a rating system that emerged out of the work of BREEAM, and was introduced to the U.S. market by the Green Building Initiative (a not-for-profit industry organization) in 2004.

- **Energy Star Certification** for buildings. Since 1999, the U.S. Environmental Protection Agency (EPA) has sponsored a rating system where buildings can be evaluated as to their energy and indoor air quality performance.

Green Design

Every building begins with an idea that must be captured and incorporated into a design that others can follow in the construction of the project. The process that seeks to preserve the natural relationships between natural systems and people is known as **Green Design** (or ecological design, environmental design, or sustainable design).

Very early in the process, a designer creating a green building must ask some fundamental questions—questions that are rarely asked during the design of more "traditional" buildings. These may include:

- Is the building even necessary, or are there existing structures that can be adapted to meet the needs of the project?

- What aspects of nature and the surrounding environment can be designed into the building?

- How can natural systems be directly incorporated into the design to improve the look, comfort and efficiency of the building?

- How can the building be designed so that people and nature interact to the best benefit of both?

Many green designers have turned to systems in nature for inspiration or ideas. The honeycomb design from bees, for example, led to the development of lightweight but very strong materials (used in aircraft and construction).

Green Design

Green Design Considerations

There are a number of issues or considerations that are central to the green building and design process. In many respects, they are the guiding principles of the green building industry. These include:

- The building shell should be designed to be as energy efficient as possible.

- All resources should be used only at the rate at which they can naturally be produced, and discarded only as quickly as the environment can naturally reabsorb them (sustainability).

- All resources should be viewed as part of a balanced system; a natural and sustainable level of consumption exists that should not be exceeded. Often referred to as the **Seventh Generation** concept (adopted from Native American philosophy)—designers must always ask, "How will this impact my children and grandchildren, seven generations into the future?"

- Locally available resources (local stone, wood, wind, sun, shading, drainage) should be incorporated into the design.

- Resource-efficient materials should be used to minimize the local and global impact of the project.

Seventh Generation

- Waste during construction (and throughout the building's life cycle) should be kept to a minimum.

- The materials used, and the design of the building, should strive to create a healthy environment for humans as well as for the natural systems on the site.

- The location of the building should take into account its relationship with the community, keeping commuting distances to a minimum and integrating with mass transit whenever possible.

- Water should be managed as a limited and valuable resource.

- The functions and design of the building should be viewed as a whole, and not as a group of separate sub-systems.

- The structure should be built to last, and its impact on the community should be considered over its entire anticipated life cycle.

The Land

Green building and design begins "from the ground up." Construction projects can use land well, or use it poorly. The way land is used is critical to the sustainability of the overall project. Sustainability concepts can be incorporated into land use in the following ways:

- Avoid using land that has not previously held a structure. Former building sites have already been "compromised" from an environmental point of view, so additional construction activities will have a minimal impact. Construction on **Brownfields** (properties that have been contaminated with pollutants), **Greyfields** (former building sites in urban environments), and **Blackfields** (abandoned coal fields or industrial sites) serve to improve the environment through the building project rather than creating a potential problem (which might be the case if the building was constructed on a **Greenfield**, a site where no building has ever been placed).

- Protect and preserve wetlands and other sensitive environmental features on the site.

- Use native plants and trees.

- Reuse existing buildings rather than construct new structures.

- Preserve the key natural features of the site (rock formations, views, etc.) and incorporate them into the design.

- Minimize the impact of construction on the site, by keeping the disturbed "footprint" of the building and surrounding area as small as possible, and avoiding unnecessary earthmoving and soil compaction.

- Keep impervious surfaces (areas such as parking lots and rooftops that do not absorb water) to a minimum, and retain water on site for as long as possible through the use of plants, rain gardens (areas that hold and absorb surface water), and living roofs.

Landscaping

The use of plants, water and even the contour of the land itself can not only affect the look and feel of a building (its traditional role in building design) but it also has a tremendous impact on the energy efficiency of the structure.

For example, planting evergreen trees on the north side of a building (in the northern hemisphere) can serve as a windbreak against cool breezes throughout the year without affecting the passive solar design aspects of the structure. Deciduous trees (trees that lose their leaves in the winter) can then be planted on the south side of the building, providing shade in the summer (cooling) but not blocking the passive solar gain (heating) during the winter months.

The principles of landscaping within sustainable construction incorporate **Xeriscape** (xeri, from Greek meaning "little water"). These principles:

- Ensure the existing healthy ecosystem is not damaged or disturbed by the construction of the building.

- Use native or existing plants whenever possible.

- If building on a previously damaged site (such as a brownfield), heal the injured ecosystem. For example, sunflowers (growing them) will actually draw pollutants from the soil and store them in the stems of the plant but not in the seeds. The stems can then be disposed of as hazardous waste, leaving the soil at the site less polluted. Repeated plantings will eventually clean a significantly polluted site in an environmentally friendly and cost-effective manner.

- Favor living material rather than artificial structures. Soil retention, for example, can be handled through the intelligent use of plants rather than constructing large retention walls.

- Respect water. Try to harvest and store the natural waters of the site as much as possible. Keep artificial irrigation to a minimum. Limit paving or other surfaces that do not allow water to soak into the soil.

- Employ organic processes, using compost, organic fertilizers and natural pest control wherever and whenever possible.

- If irrigation is required, low-volume efficient systems (such as drip irrigation) should be used.

- Use deep layer mulch to retain moisture, control weeds and reduce soil erosion.

- Design to bring the outside in. The use of outdoor "rooms" enhances the beauty and comfort of the building. Plants inside the building are not only attractive, but can help improve indoor air quality.

- Landscaping should be used to enhance the lighting of the site. Natural shading should be used when possible, and artificial lighting should not interfere with the normal biology of the plants.

- Use landscaping to reduce or eliminate noise. Thick vegetation between the building and passing traffic, for example, will greatly reduce noise levels within the building.

- Use native plants that require little or no maintenance. The use of water (other than rain), fertilizers and pesticides should be avoided wherever possible.

SCIENCE NOTE: LAWNS

NASA recently announced (after studying images from space), that lawns are the single largest crop grown in America. Nearly 32 million acres of land are covered with turf grass (the stuff people spend every Saturday mowing). That's enough lawn to cover the entire state of Kentucky!

So what does this crop produce? Well, nothing really. Sure, a well-kept lawn can look pretty. But at what cost?

Lawns cost a bunch, in money, time and in the harm they do to the environment. Let's run down the list.

- It was estimated in 2002 that every household in America spent $1,200 (on average) taking care of their lawn. That's about the same amount spent on electricity for the year.

- On average, 50-70% of all the water used in the home is used to water the lawn.

- People put three times as much pesticide on their lawn as farmers put on their crops. About 67 million pounds (30 million kilograms) of pesticides are dumped on lawns in the U.S. each year. Of the 30 most commonly used "lawn care" products, 16 were found to be toxic to birds, 11 deadly to bees and 24 killed fish. About 7 million birds die each year in the U.S. from exposure to lawn care pesticides.

- People use up 800 million gallons (3,000 million liters) of gasoline in the U.S. each year just mowing the lawn. Of that, it is estimated that 17 million gallons (64 million liters) are just spilled on the ground while filling the mowers (more than all the oil spilled by the Exxon *Valdez* in Alaska in 1989.)

- Lawn mowers generate a lot of pollution. Studies have found that using a small lawnmower for an hour will generate as much pollution as driving 100 miles in a large car. Lawn equipment generates about 5% of the nation's air pollution.

- People put a lot of fertilizer (mostly nitrogen) on their lawns. One study found that more fertilizers were put on American lawns than were used to fertilize all the crops grown in India. As much as 10% of the nitrogen found in ground water can be traced to lawn fertilizers—and excess nitrogen put on the lawn breaks down into nitrous oxide, a very damaging greenhouse gas.

- And what do we do with all this grass? We throw it away. Lawn clippings account for about 160 million pounds (72 million kilograms) of solid waste each year. Yard waste is the second largest component of material found in the nation's landfills.

So, plant some native plants. Plant some trees. Plant flowers or a garden or a prairie or call it a meadow and take care of it naturally. The birds and bees will thank you, you'll save money, time and maybe even your little corner of the planet.

Living Roofs

One location not often considered when designing the landscaping for a project is the roof. Planting low-maintenance shallow-root vegetation on the roof of a structure can offer a number of benefits to the occupants. These include:

- Increased insulation. The thermal mass of the earth and the insulating value of the plant material can add additional energy savings by retaining heated or cooled air within the building. Living roofs have been found to reduce building energy costs by 10%.

- Added Protection. The waterproof membrane protecting the roof is covered with an additional layer of earth and plant material, protecting it from damage from wind, hail or other environmental factors.

- Appearance. Green roofs can add an attractive and unusual element to a home or office building.

- Reduced roof surface temperature. Just as the skin's surface cools when sweat evaporates (a process known as **Transpiration**), the surface of the roof cools as moisture within the plant material evaporates. Living roofs have been found to reduce the summertime surface temperature of the roof by as much as 70°F (39°C).

- Storm water runoff. By retaining much of the water on the roof, the flow of storm water runoff is delayed or reduced, reducing the likelihood of sewer and drainage system overflows.

- Urban Gardens. Roofs can provide a large growing area for food crops within an urban environment, where available land for gardens may be too expensive or simply unavailable.

Heat Islands

Living roofs are one way to combat a problem known as the **Urban Heat Island Effect**. Temperatures within a city are 2 to10°F (1 to 4°C) warmer than those of the surrounding countryside, as depicted in Figure 6-3.

Heat islands are caused by the removal of vegetation, which is then replaced (through construction) with asphalt, concrete and metal surfaces. Higher temperatures not only require additional energy for cooling, but also increase the reaction rate between nitrogen oxides and volatile organic compounds (VOCs), resulting in higher levels of ground-level ozone pollution.

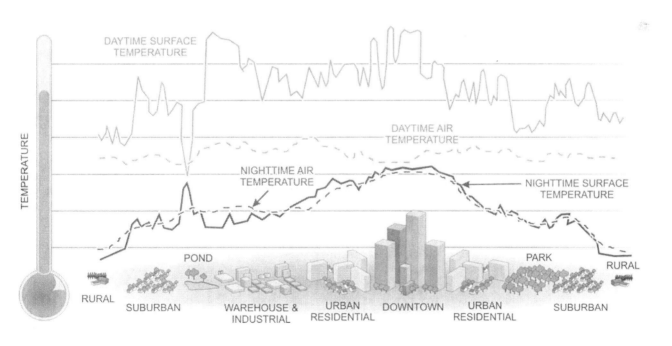

Figure 6-3: Urban Heat Island Effect

Heat islanding can be addressed by:

- Installing reflective (high albedo) surfaces on roofs. In some areas, white roofs have been found to save 10-20% on the cost of cooling the building. Estimates indicate that if all the roofs in the world were painted white, over the life of those roofs building energy savings would offset as much CO_2 pollution as generated by all the cars and trucks driven for 11 years.

- Using light-colored construction materials whenever possible.

- Planting shade trees. Not only will trees provide shade, but a mature tree will transpire ("sweat") as much as 40 gallons (150 liters) of water each day, reducing the surrounding air temperate by about 3°F (1.5°C).

Location

Real estate agents love to say that the three keys to success are "location, location, and location." The same is true with green building. The location of a building can greatly affect its sustainability.

Building location in green design can be used to:

- Minimize dependence on the automobile. Locating buildings within walking distance to shops or near mass transit lowers the use of daily vehicle activity.

- Minimize the impact on the surrounding environment. By leaving the site as undisturbed as possible and incorporating existing features and plants into the design, the building will not only preserve the local habitat, but will be easier to maintain.

- Encourage "**In-Fill**" **Development**. Buildings located close together (or on greyfields) reduce the amount of resources required (in land used as well as reducing supply lines to support the building once constructed).

Energy Consumption

A key component of a good green design is to reduce the amount of artificial energy required to heat, cool and sustain the building, as well as to utilize passive or renewable energy sources whenever possible.

Green building design encourages the use of solar thermal, solar photovoltaic, wind, microhydro, biomass and other renewable energy sources whenever possible. These systems may be located on the building site (for instance, a wind turbine or PV panels may be installed on or near the building) or purchased from a utility company that obtains energy from green sources (such as a hydro power plant).

Additionally, energy conservation practices and systems should be put in place to minimize the amount of power used within the building. Improvements to the building's shell (insulation and minimal air infiltration), energy efficient systems and appliances, automatic lighting and temperature controls, low water-use fixtures, as well as other active energy efficient systems, should be incorporated into the design.

There are also a number of passive systems (those that do not require energy from an outside source) that can be incorporated into the design to assist in reducing the need for energy within the building. Some of these may include:

- Awnings that provide shade in the summer but allow sunlight into the building during winter months.

- Airlocks at doors that provide a contained space to minimize the amount of heated or cooled air lost as people enter or leave the building.

- Thermal mass that incorporates a large mass (such as earth piled up against the north wall of the structure) that effectively stores heat as well as slows heat loss from the building. Thermal mass releases heat during cool periods and absorbs it during warmer periods of time. Additionally, as warmer outside air (for example) attempts to find its way toward the cooler, indoor air, the mass of the structure will slow the flow. If the mass is large enough, it may slow it significantly, creating a dynamic form of insulation. How well the building performs this task is known as its **Mass-Enhanced R-Value**.

- Effective use of daylighting incorporates natural light into the building design to create a more pleasant and healthier (in most cases) environment. Plus it is inexpensive or free.

- Orienting the building to take advantage of the passive solar heat provided by the sun is an effective way to lower heating bills.

- Passive ventilation systems that allow outside air into the building and stale air from within the building to leave, improve the air quality and comfort of the facility. These systems are designed to perform this task automatically, without the need for outside power sources. They also assist in reducing the need for energy within the building.

SCIENCE NOTE: ZERO ENERGY HOMES

There have been a lot of changes in thinking in recent years, and buildings are getting much more energy efficient. But it's just not enough. The U.S. government has recognized that these savings will not be enough to address the growing climate change problems and dwindling fossil fuel supplies.

The U.S. Department of Energy recently set some pretty ambitious goals of increasing whole-house energy efficiencies by 50% by the year 2015 (using existing green building technologies). Then, through new technologies (they don't bother to tell us what THOSE are) and better building practices, homes can reduce the amount of power they need by another 40% by the year 2020.

The remaining energy needed by the home will be provided through renewable sources—effectively reducing energy consumption to zero, resulting in a **Zero Energy Home**. And they plan to do all this without costing anything to anybody.

Size and Shape of the Building

The size, and even the shape of the building can affect how resource-efficient it is.

Homes are getting bigger in the U.S. And bigger homes require more materials to build, and more energy to heat, cool and light. Since 1973, the average new single-family home has increased in size 46% - from 1,660 sq ft (154.2 sq m) to 2,434 sq ft (226.1 sq m). In many more affluent parts of the country, home sizes have grown much larger. The average single-family home in Aspen, Colorado, for example, is 15,000 sq ft (1,393.5 sq m).

While it is clear that larger homes consume more resources, it is less clear how the shape of a home can affect the amount of resources it may require to construct and service. One way to measure resource efficiency is in the exterior wall surface compared to the interior living space. Since most energy loss is through exterior walls and roof space, minimizing this ratio will save energy.

The most efficient shape for this purpose is a sphere. Perhaps the most famous building type to take advantage of this shape was architect Buckminster Fuller's famous **Geodesic Domes**, shown in Figure 6-4. First proposed in the 1950s, today there are thousands such structures constructed around the globe. This nature-inspired design has the advantage of a very high ratio of interior space to exterior surface area, can be made of extremely lightweight material and theoretically can support its own weight regardless of the size of the structure (there have been designs that enclose entire cities below a geodesic dome).

Geodesic Domes

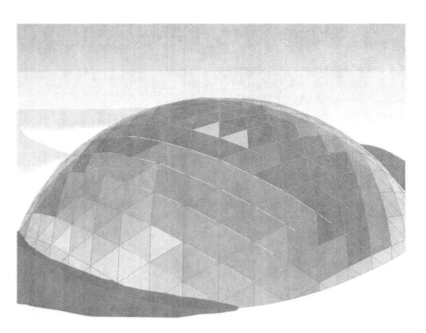

Figure 6-4:
Geodesic Dome

But in most instances, buildings have flat surfaces and sharp corners, rather than a circular design. Even in these cases, however, the shape of the building will affect the structure's resource efficiency.

Figure 6-5 illustrates this point. In this example, a square home with exterior walls measuring 264 ft (80 m) will enclose an interior living space of 4,356 sq ft (400 sq m). A rectangular-shaped building (House B) with the same exterior wall length only encloses an interior floor space of 2,756 sq ft (255.17 sq m). More irregular shapes (such as demonstrated in Home C) have even lower exterior wall to floor surface ratios.

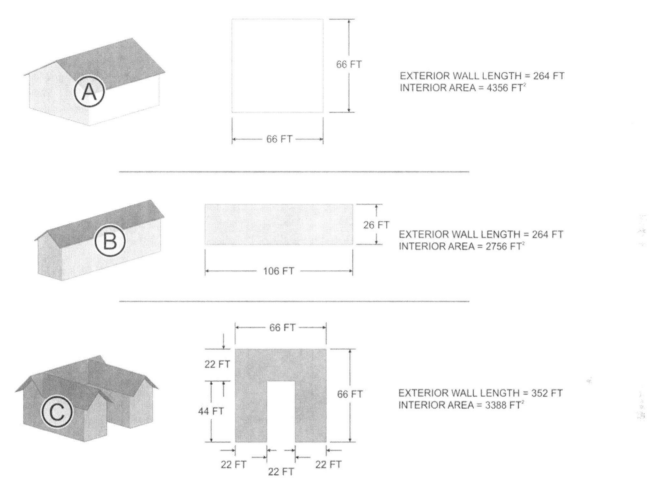

66 FT

66 FT

EXTERIOR WALL LENGTH = 264 FT
INTERIOR AREA = 4356 FT^2

26 FT

106 FT

EXTERIOR WALL LENGTH = 264 FT
INTERIOR AREA = 2756 FT^2

66 FT

22 FT

44 FT

66 FT

22 FT   22 FT

22 FT

EXTERIOR WALL LENGTH = 352 FT
INTERIOR AREA = 3388 FT^2

A multi-story building, rather than a larger single-story building, is also a more resource-conscious design (in most cases). Not only does the structure consume less land (for the amount of interior living space), but roofing materials are also minimized. Also, multi-story buildings are often more efficient to heat, taking advantage of passive systems that channel rising heated air.

**Figure 6-5:
House Shape to
Floor Space**

Water Issues

Green design focuses heavily on reducing water use within the building, as well as managing the rain and storm water runoff that affect the site. A number of methods of managing this goal have been integrated into green design to address these issues. These include:

- Low water-use fixtures. Low-flush or no-flush toilets, water restricting shower heads, automatic sensing faucets, and other efficient fixtures can greatly reduce the amount of water used in a building. Composting toilets (waterless toilets that are designed to break down waste so that it can be used to enhance the soil) are increasingly being used to address **Blackwater** (water containing human waste) disposal issues.

- Water recycling. **Graywater** (water from showers, sinks, washing machines, etc.) can typically be reused to water plants or lawns with only minimal treatment. This gray water can be filtered within constructed wetlands (such as illustrated in Figure 6-6), designed to imitate nature (filtered naturally with plants removing impurities) to purify wastewater for later use.

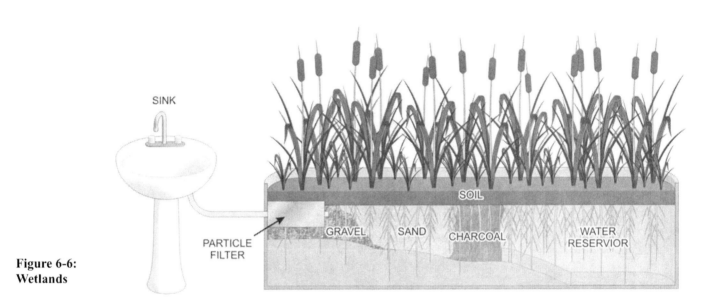

Figure 6-6: Wetlands

- Reclaimed water. While gray water is harvested from the building and reused on site, many municipalities offer **Reclaimed Water** (water not considered treated enough to drink) that may also be used for industrial or landscaping purposes. Municipal waste water reuse currently amounts to 4.8 billion gallons (18 million cubic meters) each year, equal to about 1 percent of the total freshwater pumped.

- Rainwater harvesting. Rain can be harvested and used in a variety of ways. Typically rain is collected from rooftops, then stored in rain barrels or cisterns. The rain collected can then be used for landscaping or filtered and used within the home or building.

Like so many things in math, the metric system can make it all so simple. This is certainly true when calculating how much rain can be collected from a roof.

If you lived almost anywhere except America, you could figure that for every 1 millimeter (mm) of rain that falls on every square meter of roof, you get 1 liter of water that can be collected in your cistern or rain barrel. Simple enough.

The calculations for good old American water are just a bit more complex. First we will need the following equivalents:

- One square meter, for example, is 10.76 square feet. So far, so good.
- One millimeter is 0.0394 inches (And one inch is 25.4 mm.)
- A liter is equal to 0.264 gallons
- One gallon = 231 cubic inches
- One square foot = 144 square inches

So plugging these into our metric equation, we get:

0.0394 inches x 10.76 square feet = 0.0394 inches x 1549.44 square inches = 61.048 cubic inches / 231 cubic inches = 0.264 gallons

Not very enlightening since we usually think of things in terms of a full inch (when speaking of rainfall, for example) and in terms of a square foot when speaking of roofs. So let's do some conversions.

Since one inch equals 25.4 mm, we can convert the full equation to reflect an inch of rain by multiplying both sides by 25.4.

1 inch x 10.76 sq ft = 0.264 gallons x 25.4 = 6.7 gallons

To reduce the area down to a square foot, we simply divide each side of the equation by 10.76:

1 inch of rain x 1 sq ft = 6.7 gallons / 10.76 = 0.623 gallons

So whenever you want to figure out how many gallons of water a roof (an American roof, that is) will collect for every inch of rainfall, simply multiply the square footage by 0.623.

For example, a home that has 2,000 sq ft of roof space will put almost 1,250 gallons of water into the cistern for every inch of rain. That's a bunch of free water—no matter what currency you use.

Selecting Green Building Materials

It takes raw materials and manufactured products to construct a building. One goal of green construction is to select materials that have a minimal impact on the environment (in their extraction, transportation, manufacture and disposal). For instance, a very energy efficient product (an efficient window system, for example) may be made from some very "ungreen" materials (such as vinyl). So are less efficient windows made of wood (a renewable material) better? Clearly there are many factors to weigh in the selection process.

Life Cycle Evaluation

The products and materials used in construction must be evaluated based on their entire life cycle—from the harvesting of the raw materials to the disposal or reuse of the finished product after its useful life is over.

In the harvesting of the raw materials, issues to consider include:

- Are the materials used in the product renewable, or limited (such as fossil fuels or old-growth forests)?

- How much environmental damage is done during the harvesting process?

- How much energy is consumed and how much waste is generated during extraction?

- What was the "human cost" of obtaining that product (an extreme example might be in the harvesting of "blood diamonds" in Africa)?

- Can local sources of the product be used, reducing shipping?

- Is the product made with a significant amount of recycled material?

During installation, some other issues arise:

- How much waste or packaging is discarded?

- Are damaging adhesives or chemicals required during installation?

Then, during the operational cycle of the product, still more questions must be asked:

- Is the product energy, water or resource efficient?

- Is it durable, lasting a long time with little or no maintenance required?

- Can it be repaired, or is it designed to be thrown away (**Planned Obsolescence**)?

- Is the product toxic? Will it affect the health of people or the environment?

And all products eventually must be disposed of:

- Is the product biodegradable?

- Can it be easily recycled?

- Can it be reused?

- Does it contain any contaminants such as heavy metals that will harm the environment during disposal?

Biobased Products

One selection criteria is not enough to determine which product to use. Many factors must be considered. An increasingly popular selection option in construction is a movement towards **Biobased Products**. Biobased products are commercial or industrial products (other than food or feed) that are made almost entirely of natural plant or animal materials.

A good example of a biobased construction process is straw bale construction. Building with bales of straw (as illustrated in Figure 6-7) satisfies several of the green building material selection goals.

- Straw is usually locally harvested. More than 200 million tons of straw are harvested in the U.S. each year, so it is widely available and produced in all farming regions of the nation.

- Straw is a waste product from the production of grain crops such as wheat, oats, barley, rye or rice. There is little additional environmental impact in the harvesting of this waste product.

- Straw bales have a very high R-value (about R-28), providing a very energy-efficient, comfortable environment.

- Straw bale construction is durable. If properly maintained, straw bale housing can last for hundreds of years.

- Straw is biodegradable. At the end of its useful life (when the building is demolished, for example), the material can be composted.

- Straw bales are generally non-toxic.

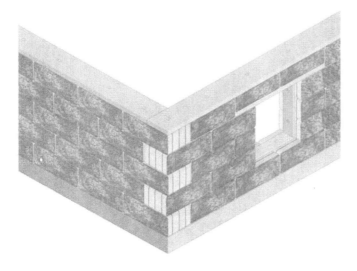

Figure 6-7:
Straw Bale Wall

Composting

All organic material can be composted. Green building practices attempt to incorporate composting into the construction and the ongoing use of the building. Food waste, cardboard, paper products, and landscape trimmings can all be composted on site to provide high-quality soil amendments.

In addition to reducing waste (yard trimmings and food make up 23 % of the garbage in U.S. landfills), composting can also:

- Suppress plant diseases and pests.

- Reduce the need for chemical fertilizers.

- Help clean soils that contain hazardous waste

- Remove solids, oil, grease and heavy metals from storm water runoff

- Capture and destroy up to 99.6% of all airborne volatile organic chemicals (VOCs)

Closed-Loop Materials Strategy

Green building looks at the process of creating structures as a circle, or closed loop, rather than a straight line (linear) system where materials flow in and products (buildings) flow out. The goal of a closed-loop system is to be as waste-free as possible throughout the circular process. Buildings designed with a closed-loop strategy would ensure that:

- Buildings must be **Deconstructable** (can easily be taken apart rather than demolished and thrown away).

- The materials used in the building must be easily disassembled, with the parts reused whenever possible.

- The remaining materials are recyclable.

- The products and materials used in the building do not cause human or environmental harm during their production or in their use.

- Any waste materials generated during the lifecycle of the building are harmless to people and the environment.

Green Certification Programs

Determining whether a product is "green" can be a complicated process. As a result, a number of product-certification programs have emerged that can verify that specific products meet their definition of green. While these programs are helpful in comparing products, the evaluation criteria used will vary from program to program and the reputation of the organization issuing the certification should be considered in determining if the program has value to the material selection process.

Some green certifications include:

- Carpet: The Carpet and Rug Institute (CRI) has created the Green Label and Green Label Plus programs designed to test and certify carpets that emit low levels of volatile organic compounds (VOCs).

- Wood: The Forest Stewardship Council certifies wood products made from wood that has been harvested in a sustainable way.

- Chemical Emissions: Greenguard, Scientific Certification Systems and Green Seal certify that products such as adhesives, paints, insulation and wall coverings, have met their environmental claims and certify the level of chemical emissions given off by the various products.

- Life Cycle: Cradle to Cradle (C2C) certifies products have been designed in an "environmentally intelligent" way, examining the entire life cycle in evaluating the product.

Indoor Health Issues

The U.S. Environmental Protection Agency (EPA) estimates that over 15% of all Americans are allergic to their own home. Lowering the level of indoor contamination and improving the health and comfort of those living and working within the building is a major component to green design. Contaminants within buildings generally fall within two broad categories: chemical and biological.

Biological Contaminants such as molds, dust, pollen, animal dander and bacteria (often referred to as **Bioaerosols**) can cause allergic reactions on the skin or within the respiratory system. Reactions to these biological contaminants can be severe or even fatal in people who are sensitive to their effects.

Bioaerosols have been traced to a number of building-based ailments such as Legionnaire's disease (named after a 1976 outbreak at an American Legion convention in Philadelphia where 221 people were infected by an airborne bacteria found growing in the hotel's cooling system).

Other indoor health concerns that have gained widespread attention in recent decades include the use of lead paint that can cause brain and nervous system damage, especially in children, asbestos (can lead to serious lung damage), and radon gas trapped within buildings (a leading cause of lung cancer, claiming up to 20,000 lives each year in the U.S.).

Many building materials contain chemicals that can also lead to health issues. **Volatile Organic Compounds (VOCs)** are chemicals that easily evaporate at room temperature. This chemical "off gassing" can result in chronic or acute conditions, from eye irritation, headaches and nausea to, in extreme cases, liver or nerve damage and even cancer.

Every year, 700 new chemicals are introduced to the U.S. market, but less than 1 percent have been tested on their impact to human health. Few, if any, have been tested as to how they interact with other chemicals already present in the building environment (the interaction of these chemicals can result in a condition known as **Multiple Chemical Sensitivity**).

Common Products that Off-Gas

Many common building products produce a great deal of VOCs within the home or office. While it would not be possible to list them all, some of the most common problem products include:

- Vinyl Chloride: A component in PVC (poly-vinyl chloride) pipes and fixtures, vinyl chloride is believed to be connected to many serious health problems, from cancer to damage to the nervous, circulatory and immune systems.

- Formaldehyde: One of the most common adhesives used in construction (widely used in particleboard), urea formaldehyde is known to cause eye, respiratory and skin irritation. It has also been linked to some forms of cancer. Formaldehyde will off gas from products within the building for many years after the materials have been installed.

- Carpets: New carpets contain toluene, benzene, formaldehyde, ethyl benzene, styrene, acetone and a host of other chemicals that are known to cause cancer and produce fetal abnormalities. Chemicals contained in new carpets have also been known to cause hallucinations, nerve damage and respiratory illness in humans. Older carpets are also a major source of bioaerosols within the building.

Minimizing Indoor Air Quality Issues

A number of considerations can be incorporated into a building during its design and construction to improve the indoor air quality of the structure and reduce possible health problems. These include:

- Moving and filtering the air. Building filtration systems constantly refresh the air within the building while filtering contaminants out.

- Using safer products. Materials and products used within the building should be selected in part based on their non-toxic characteristics.

- Blocking radon gas. Areas where radon gas is a concern, systems should be installed during construction to collect radon under the building and vent it away from the living space.

- Isolating the garage. The barrier between the garage and the indoor living space must be tight, ensuring no air exchange between the two spaces. No only can car exhaust find its way into the home or office (leading to carbon monoxide poisoning) but garages are often used to store toxins such as pesticides, cleaners, polishes, waxes and other chemicals that may pollute the indoor air space if given a chance to infiltrate the living space.

Indoor Comfort Issues

Green design also expects that the quality of life of those working and living within the building will be enhanced by the design of the structure. This aspect of green design addresses more than just the health and welfare of the occupant, but the physical comfort as well.

In commercial applications, the vast majority of the cost of operating a building is in the wages and benefits paid to employees, as shown in Figure 6-8. A small investment in providing a comfortable environment can pay huge dividends in worker productivity, health, and reduced absenteeism.

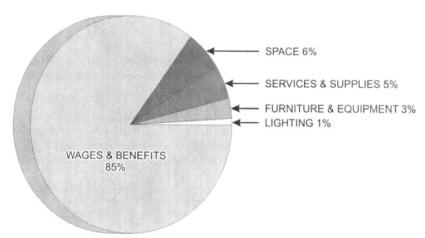

Figure 6-8: Annual Operating Costs of Typical Office Space

Lighting

Natural lighting, when compared to artificial, is more pleasant. Natural sunlight contains an equal distribution of visible light frequencies that combine to form a "white light." While artificial lighting often strives to imitate this aspect of natural light, it generally falls short in one way or another. Some lighting (like older florescent lights) produce a light that is so unnatural (or is subject to flickering) that it can lead to eye strain. A recent study by the American Society of Interior Designers found that poor lighting and the resulting eyestrain is the most common office worker complaint.

Additional studies have found that low-level task lighting (lighting only where it is needed) and views to the outdoors (windows and skylights) improve worker productivity and reduce absenteeism.

Sound

Noise pollution is increasingly becoming recognized as an environmental problem, both inside buildings and out. Green design seeks to improve the comfort of buildings and the surrounding landscaped area by reducing the intrusions of sound, whether generated inside the building or from the outside.

Standard exterior walls will normally block 45-50 decibels (dB) of sound. This is about the level of sound generated by a normal conversation between two people standing about three feet apart (one meter). Busy street traffic is louder, generating noise levels at about 70 dB.

Sound Transmission Class (STC)

How effectively a building material blocks sound is known as its **Sound Transmission Class (STC)**. The STC assigned is roughly equal to the amount of sound in decibels the material or system will block. Table 6-6 provides an indication of the STC of several wall construction methods. STC ratings of 45 or higher are recommended where noise can be an issue.

Table 6-6: Estimated STC Wall Ratings

WALL ASSEMBLY	STC RATING
2x4 studs, two layers of 5/8-in. gypsum, batt insulation	34-39
3 5/8-in metal studs, two layers of 5/8-in. gypsum, no insulation	38-40
3 5/8-in metal studs, two layers of 5/8-in. gypsum, batt insulation	43-44
2x4 studs, double layer of 5/8-in. gypsum on each side of wall, batt insulation	43-45
Double 2x4 wall separated by an air space, 5/8-in. gypsum, batt insulation	56-59
Double 2x4 wall separated by an air space, four layers of 5/8-in. gypsum (two each side), batt insulation	58-63

If air can enter the building, so can sound. So a tightly-built structure will perform better at blocking sound (just as it blocks air infiltration). Windows, even very well-insulated windows, will generally block less sound than a poorly constructed wall.

Distance, barriers and sound absorbing (acoustical) materials are effective ways of reducing noise levels. If possible, locate the living space further away from the noise source (or the noise source further away from the living space if it is generated as part of the building structure or systems). A backup generator, for example, could easily be located as far from the living or working space as is practical.

Noise barriers such as earth berms, walls or vegetation are effective ways of reducing noise levels. To be effective, the barrier must block the line of sight between the source of the noise and the living area.

Another effective way to combat unwanted noise is to select and maintain quiet running appliances and building systems (heating and cooling, for example). Fan vibrations and buzzing ballasts on florescent lights not only increase irritating noise pollution, but affect the efficient operation of the unit.

Temperature Control

What is considered comfortable tends to vary from person to person. But it is generally accepted that winter temperatures between 68°F (20°C)and 75°F (24°C) and summertime temperatures between 72°F (22°C) and 80°F (26.6°C)—with a relative humidity of between 30-60%—are considered comfortable.

Automatic systems that keep the indoor environment within these ranges when occupied and reduce heating/cooling levels when unoccupied not only save energy, but make the indoor environment more pleasant. Systems should also be properly balanced, to avoid all-too-common situations where one part of the building is very cold while another part is uncomfortably warm.

Odor Control

Odors within the home or workplace can be cured with a good green building design, enhancing the health and comfort of those working or residing within the building. Once again, however, disagreeable odors, like temperature comfort are highly personal in nature. What may be pleasant to one person (such as the smell of popcorn in a microwave) may make another person nauseous.

Common odor complaints (particularly in an office environment) include: tobacco smoke, human body odor, perfumes, cleaning products, or off-gassing from newly installed products such as carpets.

While it may be impossible for the building designer to address every worker's complaint, there are some steps that can be taken during the design and construction phase that will minimize these possible problems. Some of these include:

- Maintain a good internal ventilation system, refreshing the air frequently. It is recommended that homes receive .35 air changes per hour (air completely refreshed every 3 hours), but not less than 15 cubic feet per minute (cfm) per person.

- Keep designated smoking areas outside the building and away from doors or other high traffic areas.

- Good moisture protection. Many odors originate with molds that grow in damp areas within the building. This may create a bad smell, but more importantly, may lead to health concerns.

- Locate kitchens and bathrooms away from work areas and vent them properly to the outside.

- Select materials that do not off-gas (low internal VOC levels).

Construction Processes

The philosophy of green construction extends, not only to the finished product, but the way in which the building is created.

In commercial construction (and to a lesser extent in residential construction) three major processes have emerged guiding how buildings are designed and constructed. These include:

- **Design-Bid-Build**: In this process an owner selects a designer who produces construction documents (including **blueprints**) that define the location, appearance, materials and methods to be used. The construction is then put out to bid, resulting in the selection of a contractor who oversees the construction of the building.

- **Construction Management-at-Risk**: In this process (sometimes called the negotiated work system), the owner hires a construction manager (who usually provides guarantees of some sort, such as that the project will not exceed a maximum price and/or will be completed by a certain date) and a design team. The construction manager and the design team work together to create the construction documents. This process attempts to avoid many of the traditional conflicts between the designers and the construction teams.

- **Design-Build**: The owner selects a single person or firm that is responsible both for the design and the construction of the building.

In a large green building project, a variation of the construction management-at-risk process is often employed, but rather than simply including the designer and the builder in discussions from the beginning of the project—all stakeholders are involved from as early a point in the process as possible. Who is involved will vary from project to project, but may include nearby residents, members of the community, politicians, funders (bankers or, in the case of a non-profit, large donors)—anyone who may be affected by the project.

A **Charrette** (a design meeting) is held with input from all the stakeholders. The goal of the process is to make the decision-making, design and construction as transparent as possible to all involved through every step—from concept to construction. The four guiding principles include:

1. Involving everyone from the start. This will help to avoid potential problems or solve them early in the process, saving time and money.

2. Working concurrently and cross-functionally. The building is viewed as a whole—not the sum of smaller systems or tasks. Plumbers, electricians, masons, architects, landscapers and others should discuss with each other how their individual efforts might affect other aspects of the building.

3. Meeting regularly. As the project progresses, all the stakeholders should meet often so that changing situations are understood by all and incorporated into the project.

4. Discussing the details. Even the smallest detail can dramatically affect other systems or the overall project.

Design-Bid-Build

Blueprints

Construction Management-at-Risk

Design-Build

Charrette

The Economics of Green Building

It is generally accepted that constructing a sustainable building costs a bit more (about 2%) than other "modern" building techniques. But studies have indicated that over the life of the building (life-cycle costing) the added investment saves 10 times that amount.

Eco-Efficiency

Apart from the obvious environmental advantages of green construction, many economists feel that the building industry should take into account the **Eco-Efficiency** of the project. This school of thought argues that there are very real economic costs to environmental concerns such as resource depletion, environmental damage during resource extraction, disposal of waste, pollution created during the manufacture and transportation of the product, etc.

Environmental Impact Fees

These costs, they argue, should be applied to the project that uses the product or material. This becomes the true cost, rather than simply the realized cost of the project. **Environmental Impact Fees** (localized fees charged at the permitting phase of a project designed to offset some of the anticipated costs the project will create for the environment) are one example of how this theory may impact the cost of a project. Many local communities reduce these impact fees or offer other financial incentives to encourage green building practices.

Measurable Savings

While the intangible benefits of sustainable development may be enough to motivate many people to use them, most construction decisions are also complicated economic decisions. So tangible, measurable savings are a large factor in determining if a specific project will be green. Some of these savings include:

- Reduced resource costs. Green buildings use less water and energy, generally 30-50% less energy. This represents a significant savings over the life of the building.

- Reduced maintenance costs. Studies show that the proper commissioning (testing systems before occupancy) of energy-efficient systems can save owners an additional 10-15% in future energy costs.

- Increased building value. The energy-saving nature of the building results in a higher resale value in the future.

- Tax benefits. Many states now offer tax credits and other incentives to encourage green building.

- Better financing. Many lending institutions provide more favorable terms for projects that incorporate green elements.

In addition to these very tangible benefits, there are other benefits that also produce very real savings but are perhaps less obvious. These include:

- Better health. Companies and individuals spend over 15% of their annual income on health care. Studies indicate that green buildings reduce health complaints by those living and working within them by 41.5%.

- Increased productivity and retention. In commercial enterprises, the cost of a building when compared to the cost of employees is quite low. Studies have found that working within a green building environment improves productivity. Even a 5% improvement in worker productivity will typically pay over half the total cost of rent or the building's construction.

Intelligent Communities

Just as a building is viewed as a complete system (rather than the sum of its parts) in green design, the building itself must be viewed as part of a community. How the building fits into the community, both visually and functionally, are important design considerations.

But green design can be extended to the community as well. Many city planners, residents, designers and even politicians are beginning to realize that the post-World War II American model of suburban sprawl is unhealthy, damaging to the environment, and unsustainable.

In recent years there has been a movement back to developments where residential and commercial buildings are located closer together. This "new urbanism," form of mixed-use development provides opportunities to walk or bike to shops, schools or work. A recent survey of developers found that 93% felt that these "**Intelligent Community**" projects would grow in importance over the next 5 years.

Intelligent neighborhood design is evaluated on:

- Smart location. For example, is there ample water available to support the community? Has already-developed land been used for the development, or is it constructed on virgin farmland? Is it built in a floodplain? Is there access to local food supplies?

- Links to mass transit. Are there energy efficient ways for people to get around within the community, such as bus, train, tram or bicycle paths.

- Compact, complete, walkable and connected neighborhoods. Are existing or planned schools, shops, offices and public spaces located nearby?

- Green construction and technology. Does the community incorporate a large number of green buildings? Does the community as a whole incorporate green building design principles, such as reduced water use, heat island reduction, solar orientation, on-site energy generation, recycled wastewater, decreased light pollution, etc.?

The following questions test your knowledge of the material presented in this chapter.

1. List four reasons why there has been a significant increase in buildings that have been designed and constructed using green building methods during the past decade.

2. Discuss the various advantages of constructing a green building commercial property as compared to traditional construction and design processes.

3. Give several examples of buildings or products that have incorporated the concept of biomimicry into their design.

4. Define what is meant by an "ecological rucksack."

5. Describe the LEED evaluation process for new buildings and what building features factor into the certification process.

6. List five factors that should be considered when designing a green building.

7. Discuss the many problems associated with lawns in the U.S.

8. List three advantages to incorporating a living roof on a building.

9. List five passive systems that can be designed into a building to lower energy consumption within the structure.

10. Discuss how the shape of the building can affect energy use and the amount of materials required to construct the structure.

11. Describe several ways to minimize the use, collection or reuse of water in a building. Why is this important?

12. Discuss the issues that should be considered when conducting a life cycle evaluation of materials and products used in a green building.

13. Explain why the presence of bioaerosols and volatile organic compounds can affect the health of those living and working in a building. How can green design minimize these indoor health problems?

14. Discuss the measurable and intangible economic benefits associated with green buildings.

15. Describe the features that distinguish an Intelligent Community and how these features could result in energy savings for the residents.

1. Which of the following is NOT a goal of green construction and design?
   a. Provide a healthier and more comfortable housing alternative.
   b. Reduce the amount of waste generated during the construction of the building.
   c. Design the building in such a way that it can easily be demolished and its materials reused.
   d. Provide economical, low-income housing in city centers.

2. Which of the following is NOT a common reason why many commercial enterprises decide against constructing a green building?
   a. The widely held perception that green buildings are more expensive.
   b. Banks and financial institutions are more reluctant to loan money to green building projects.
   c. The process is much too complicated.
   d. The person or department responsible for paying for the building's construction is different than the person or department responsible for maintaining the building once it is built.

3. Closed-loop design in green construction:
   a. Assumes every material used in construction must be evaluated over its entire life cycle, from extraction through use to disposal to reuse.
   b. Evaluates the economic impact of a product or material over its entire life-cycle, not just the initial cost.
   c. Eliminates the traditional disconnect between the design and construction of the building itself and the people who must live or work within the building.
   d. Invites all stakeholders who may be affected by the construction of a building into the process early in order to address any concerns they may have regarding the structure.

4. In 1998 the U.S. Green Building Council (USGBC) unveiled a green building assessment program known as:
   a. Leadership in Energy and Environmental Design (LEED)
   b. Low Energy and Environmental Development (LEED)
   c. Lowering Environmental Emissions through Design (LEED)
   d. Lower Emission and Energy Design (LEED)

5. In green building, which of the following locations for a potential building site is the LEAST environmentally responsible?
   a. brownfields
   b. greenfields
   c. greyfields
   d. blackfields

6. Which of the following is NOT an effective method of combating the urban heat island effect?
   a. Lower the use of volatile organic compounds (VOCs) in buildings.
   b. Paint the roof white.
   c. Plant trees around the building.
   d. Incorporate a living roof into the building design.

7. Which of the following is NOT a product commonly associated with the off-gassing of volatile organic compounds within a newly constructed building?
   a. concrete
   b. carpets
   c. particleboard
   d. PVC pipes

8. The design meeting held early during a green building construction project is commonly referred to as a:
   a. charrette
   b. charade
   c. stakeholders inquiry
   d. closed loop evaluation

9. According to the American Society of Interior Designers, which of the following indoor comfort issues is the most common complaint amongst office workers?
   a. poor lighting
   b. too much noise pollution
   c. poor temperature control
   d. foul odors

10. Chemicals contained within building materials that evaporate at room temperature and are often linked to serious health issues are called:
    a. multiple chemical sensitivity compounds (MCSCs)
    b. biobased products
    c. volatile organic compounds (VOCs)
    d. charrettes

CHAPTER
7
SAFETY

LEARNING OBJECTIVES

Upon completion of this chapter you will be able to perform the following tasks:

1. List tasks that may or may not be performed by trained first aid workers.

2. List the level of electricity (shock) considered lethal to humans.

3. Describe the OSHA body restraint rules, and list hazards associated with the use of ladders and of working at heights.

Safety

INTRODUCTION

Safety is an important aspect of every green technology system installation. This chapter discusses the safety concerns that you as a professional green energy technician should be aware of, and the safety precautions that you should practice on a daily basis. Green energy technicians typically work in settings that provide potentially dangerous conditions. It is crucial that every technician maintains safety as a top priority on every job site.

The first key to performing safe install operations is to use appropriate personal protective gear and to make sure you use tools and equipment properly. These safety aspects are covered in the initial sections of this chapter. In the United States, worker safety regulation is primarily the responsibility of the *Occupational Safety and Health Administration (OSHA)*. This organization provides guidelines for the safety and health of America's workers by setting and enforcing various job site standards. It also provides applicable training, outreach, and education designed to promote these standards, establish meaningful partnerships, and encourage continued improvement in the aspects of safety in the workplace and for maintaining health of the workers.

Accidents can happen anywhere, but there are typically many more opportunities for accidents and injuries at industrial and residential work sites. You should know what to do in case of an accident or injury. In fact, the very act of providing first aid assistance also carries with it potential liabilities, so you must be aware of the limitations that exist for giving first aid at your location. The central sections of this chapter deal with different types of injuries and the first aid efforts that can be employed until professional medical help can be secured.

Several organizations have been empowered to establish guidelines or codes to insure that electrical and electronic installations are performed in a safe manner for both the installer and the customer. Installers are required to observe these codes and implement them in their work. Failure to do so can create a liability situation for both the installers and their employers. These safety codes exist at several levels of jurisdiction—including local, state, national, and international. In many circumstances, the installer must be aware of which jurisdiction takes precedence for a given job. The final sections of this chapter describes the various code organizations, and the codes that apply to residential installers.

IMPORTANT NOTE! While the information in this chapter provides an overview of key workplace safety issues, it is NOT a substitute for professional safety training. In addition, the first aid information presented here should not be considered as a replacement for certified first aid training.

PROTECTIVE GEAR

Protective Gear is available to cover workers from head to toe, including protection for the eyes, head, hands, feet, lungs, and ears. In addition, there are special devices to help prevent injuries caused by heavy lifting or repetitive work.

Eye Protection

Eye Protection

Eye Protection normally takes the form of safety glasses with side shields, as depicted in Figure 7-1. No one can predict when an accident will occur, so the only way to prevent potential hazards to your eyes is to wear eye protection at all times. Many hazardous situations are overlooked as a risk to your eyes, such as falling or flying objects and excessive temperatures.

The most common eye injuries occur when a cable installer is working on network components located above eye level. In this type of situation, falling debris is a constant threat and every precaution should be taken. Another common way eyes can be injured is by objects becoming airborne through the use of power or hand tools. **Safety Glasses** or other standardized protection should be worn whenever there is a potential hazard to your eyes.

Figure 7-1: Safety Glasses with Side Shields

Safety Glasses

American National Standards Institute (ANSI)

Ordinary prescription glasses do not qualify as safety glasses, although safety glasses often look just like regular glasses. The main difference between safety glasses and regular glasses is their resistance to impact. The **American National Standards Institute (ANSI)**, which sets standards for safety glasses, requires them to withstand the impact of a quarter-inch steel ball traveling 150 feet per second. Prescription glasses cannot provide this kind of protection. Only frames that are stamped with the imprint "Z87" meet ANSI's stringent standards for strength and resistance.

It is important to remember that standard safety glasses protect you from impacts from the front only. For this reason, your safety glasses should have side shields to provide you at least partial protection from injuries to the sides of your eyes. If you prefer, goggles can be used instead of safety glasses, or a face shield can be worn over your safety glasses to provide additional protection.

Before removing your eye protection, always wash your hands with soap and water. This will prevent debris on your hands from getting inside the eye protection area. When placing your eye wear onto any type of surface, make sure the protective lenses face upward. You need to do this for two different reasons. First, it will prevent debris from falling into the glasses and becoming a safety concern. Second, this will prevent the protective lens from becoming scratched and possibly obscuring your vision. Scratches not only interfere with your ability to see what you're doing, which is a hazard in itself, but they may also weaken the structure of the lens and its resistance to impacts.

Safety glasses are designed to protect you from accidental injury, but they will not withstand repeated impact or abuse. Inspect them regularly for scratches, cracks, or other wear and replace them if they are scratched, bent, or uncomfortable. Cleanliness of your safety glasses is also extremely important. Immediately clean your glasses if they become smudged or dirty. Once again, the obstruction of your vision poses the risk of injury. When you take care of your safety glasses, they will take care of you and continue to protect your eyes. If you neglect to use eye protection, permanent vision loss or even blindness may result.

Protection from **UV Radiation** is often an overlooked eye safety concern. Many installations will require you to work outside, and your eyes should be protected from UV radiation. Eye tissue does not develop a tolerance to UV radiation, and damage to eye tissue by repeated exposure to UV radiation is incremental and irreversible. No one is immune to this type of optical damage, and some medications can even increase eye sensitivity to UV radiation. Some tinted glasses offer only partial protection, while others offer no protection at all! A material known as **CR39 Resin** is used in conjunction with a UV inhibitor to provide full UV radiation protection. Polycarbonate-based and crown glass-based lenses also provide the necessary UV radiation protection for working in these types of environments.

Head Protection

Safety Hats, also known as **Hard Hats**, must be worn when working in areas that pose the danger of falling or flying objects. Hard hats provide protection from light bumps and small falling objects striking the top of the head. They are effective against small tools, small pieces of wood, bolts, rivets, sparks from overhead work, and similar types of hazards. Safety hats only reduce the amount of force from impact blows; they do not provide complete protection from severe impact blows. In addition, most hard hat designs, as shown in Figure 7-2, only provide a limited amount of protection from rear and side blows.

Residential installers should ensure that their hard hats provide electrical protection before working around power lines or heavy-duty electrical equipment. Hard hats that contain no metallic parts, or are painted with nonconductive paints, provide the cable installer with a limited amount of electrical protection.

Most hard hats are equipped with adjustable **Suspensions** to allow for a proper fit. The suspension system in the hard hat normally consists of a network of bands designed to:

- Fit the hard hat to different sized heads

- Absorb the impact from an object impacting the shell of the hard hat

Figure 7-2: Hard Hats

Your hard hat must fit properly to ensure adequate head protection. A properly sized hard hat will not slip over your face and block your vision. Chin straps are available, but these might not be recommended in some working environments that may cause the hard hat to slide behind the user's head, thus making the chin strap a choking hazard.

Maintenance of Hard Hats and Suspensions

Hard hats can be cleaned with simple soap and water, or by using a damp towel. The modern plastic suspensions, shown in Figure 7-3, come with a sweatband in the front or back of the hat. These sweat bands can be gently washed by hand, but they probably won't last as long as the hard hat itself. Several universal brow pads are available at an economical price.

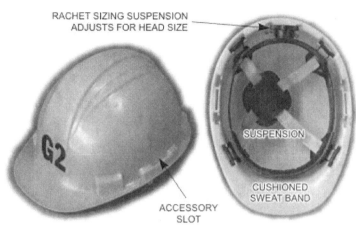

RACHET SIZING SUSPENSION
ADJUSTS FOR HEAD SIZE

SUSPENSION

CUSHIONED
SWEAT BAND

ACCESSORY
SLOT

Figure 7-3: Hard Hat Suspensions

Replace any hard hat when:

- Cracks appear in the shell
- Its shiny surface appears dull or chalky
- The shell becomes brittle

Replace the suspension when:

- It becomes brittle
- One or more of the mounts break off
- It no longer holds securely to the head
- Cradling straps break or become worn

Inspect your hard hat before and after each use. Although there is no set expiration date for a hard hat, manufacturers recommend a maximum service life of 5 years for suspensions.

Hand Protection

Work Gloves protect your hands from injuries such as abrasions, cuts, or punctures, as well as irritation caused by certain chemicals or solvents. There are three major material categories of work gloves: synthetics, cottons (or strings), and leather. Each type provides a different form of protection to the wearer.

Synthetic Gloves, depicted in Figure 7-4, are used for protection against solvents, and offer resistance to chemicals, while providing some protection against abrasions, cuts, and punctures.

Cotton Gloves, shown in Figure 7-5, offer comfort and breath ability in general-purpose applications and in heavy lifting. In addition, cotton gloves provide protection from abrasion and excessive heat.

Work Gloves

Synthetic Gloves

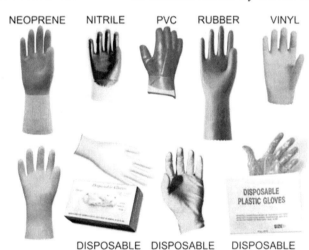

NEOPRENE   NITRILE   PVC   RUBBER   VINYL

LATEX   DISPOSABLE LATEX   DISPOSABLE VINYL   DISPOSABLE POLYETHYLENE

DISPOSABLE PLASTIC GLOVES

Figure 7-4: Synthetic Gloves

Cotton Gloves

INSPECTORS   CANVAS   JERSEY   TERRY CLOTH   CHORE   DOUBLE PALM   HOT MILL

Figure 7-5: Cotton Gloves

String Gloves, shown in Figure 7-6, are considered part of the cotton family. They are designed for general-purpose work applications and for cut and abrasion resistance using high-performance yarns. Various weights, where needed, provide longer durability or additional dexterity.

Leather Gloves are used for protection from rough objects, sparks, and heat. They also work well for the cushioning of blows in heavy-duty work environments. All kinds of leather gloves, such as those shown in Figure 7-7, provide comfort, durability, dexterity, mild heat resistance, and abrasion protection. These advantages make leather a traditional favorite for industrial workers.

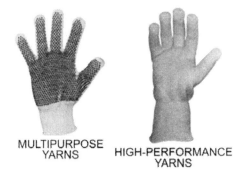

MULTIPURPOSE YARNS   HIGH-PERFORMANCE YARNS

Figure 7-6: String Gloves

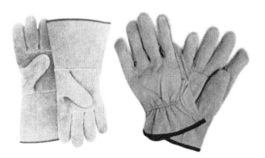

Figure 7-7: Leather Gloves

To help prevent potential injuries, be sure to choose the right pair of gloves for the job you are performing, and discard any ripped or worn gloves.

Foot Protection

Protective **Footwear**, such as depicted in Figure 7-8, should be worn when there are potential hazards to your feet. Considerations should be made for falling objects, stepping on sharp objects, and/or the possibility of you or a coworker injuring your foot while working with certain tools or equipment. Obviously, open-toed shoes or tennis shoes do not qualify as proper foot protection for the workplace.

Also keep in mind that neoprene or rubber boots should be worn in wet or muddy conditions. Steel-toed boots should be worn when there is a potential hazard of objects falling onto your feet; but keep in mind that steel-toed boots also conduct electricity and might constitute an electrical hazard under certain circumstances.

Figure 7-8: Protective Footwear

Breathing Protection

The effects from inhaling harmful particles may not fully develop until hours, weeks, or even years after the exposure. Cable installers must wear a **Respirator Device**, examples of which are shown in Figure 7-9, whenever harmful pollutants are present on the job site.

Figure 7-9: Respirators

Respirators

In July of 1995, the *National Institute of Occupational Safety & Health* (*NIOSH*) updated the federal regulation for the certification of air-purifying particulate **Respirators**. The changes are contained within a new certification standard spelled out in 42 CFR Part 84. These new standards supersede 30 CFR Part 11, which was issued by the *Mine Safety and Health Administration* (*MSHA*) in 1972. Since October 5, 1998, you cannot use 30 CFR Part 11 respirators unless you can prove through sampling and documentation that the particle size of the contaminant is greater than 2.0 microns. 42 CFR Part 84 respirators will protect the user from particles smaller than 0.03 microns.

Respirators certified under the new regulation are tested under much more demanding conditions. Because the new respirators are more practical and efficient, they are projected to save industry a significant amount of money. And best of all, the updated standards promise to give workers even greater protection in the workplace.

Hearing Protection

As sound enters the outer ear, it is channeled down the ear canal until it reaches the eardrum. The eardrum, a thin membrane stretched over a tube, is moved by the sound waves. When the sound vibrations reach the coiled, liquid-filled tube called the cochlea, thousands of hair cells in the cochlea (known as cilia) translate these vibrations into electrical impulses that are transmitted to the brain for interpretation. Repeated exposure to loud sounds can permanently damage the cilia, which, once damaged, never grow back.

Hearing Loss

Continued, unprotected exposure to noises louder than 85 decibels (dB) for 8 hours or more can be dangerous, and may result in hearing loss. Permanent damage by sounds reaching over 100 dB can occur in 2 hours or less. If you are exposed to loud and continuous sound for more than 15 minutes per day at 100 to 110 dB, you need to wear hearing protection. Even brief exposure to gun blasts or jet engine noise, as shown in Figure 7-10, can cause pain and permanent injury if your ears are not protected.

Hearing loss is a cumulative event, and once hearing is lost, it can never be regained. The best way to protect your hearing is to start a habit of wearing hearing protection. Several types of earplugs and earmuffs are available, as shown in Figure 7-11. Select hearing protection that is comfortable for you. In addition, make sure that you wear the hearing protection, and wear it correctly. Each type of hearing protector is slightly different.

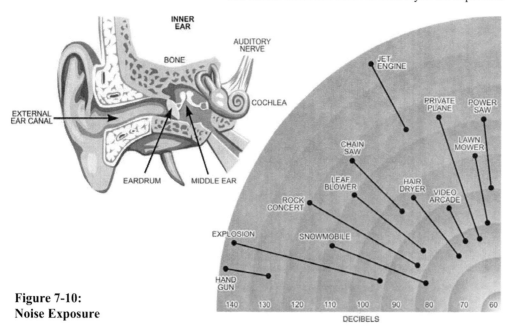

Figure 7-10: Noise Exposure

For example, **Earplugs** are small, flexible insertion devices that fit into the outer ear canal. To be effective, earplugs must totally block the ear canal with an airtight seal. They are available in a variety of shapes and sizes to fit individual ear canals. For those individuals who have trouble keeping insertion devices in their ears, earplugs can be fitted to headbands, as depicted in Figure 7-11. They can also be custom made. It's important to remember that an improperly fitted, dirty, or worn-out earplug may not properly seal, and can often irritate the ear canal.

The following descriptions are general fitting instructions for earplugs. Remember to ensure that your hands are clean before fitting any earplugs.

When fitting a disposable earplug:

1. Hold the earplug between your thumb and forefinger.

2. Roll and compress the entire earplug to a small, crease-free cylinder.

Figure 7-11: Hearing Protection

3. While still rolling the earplug, use your other hand to reach over your head and pull up and back on your outer ear. This straightens the ear canal, making way for a snug fit.

4. Insert the earplug and hold for 20 to 30 seconds. This allows the earplug to expand and fill your ear canal.

When fitting a reusable earplug:

1. Holding the stem end of the earplug, insert it well inside your ear canal until you feel it sealing and the fit is comfortable.

2. Reach over your head and pull up and back on your outer ear. This straightens the ear canal, making way for a snug fit.

3. Insert the earplug into your ear canal.

To test the fit, cup your hands over your ears, and then release. If you can hear a difference, you may not be wearing your hearing protector correctly. Remove the earplugs, and then try to fit them again. When removing the earplugs, slowly twist them to break the seal with your ear canal. If you remove them too quickly, you could damage your eardrum.

By following these simple earplug guidelines, you can save your hearing from hazardous exposure and potential hearing loss.

Earmuffs are alternate hearing protection devices that fit over the entire outer ear. They are designed to cup the outer ear and form an air seal around it, so that the entire circumference of the ear canal is blocked. They are normally held in place by an adjustable band that runs across the top of the head. They may also be permanently attached to a hard hat.

The tension of the headband must be sufficient to hold the earmuffs firmly around the ear. Typical earmuffs will not seal around eyeglasses or long hair. Properly fitted earplugs, or earmuffs, will reduce noise levels by 15 to 33 dB. High-quality earplugs and earmuffs are nearly equal in sound reduction capabilities. However, earplugs tend to be much better for reducing low-frequency noise, while earmuffs are better at reducing high-frequency noise. The use of earplugs and earmuffs together should be considered when noise levels exceed 105 dB. The type of protection that you wear in the working environment may depend on its availability, other protective gear worn, and the company requirements.

Ergonomic Safety Devices

Ergonomics, also known as **Human Engineering**, is an applied science concerned with the design and arrangement of things so that people interact with them more efficiently and safely. Items such as back support belts, wrist supports, kneepads, and lifting belts are considered *Ergonomic Safety Devices* (*ESDs*), some of which are depicted in Figure 7-12. ESDs aid in the prevention of *Musculoskeletal Disorders* (*MSDs*), which are caused by heavy or repetitive work.

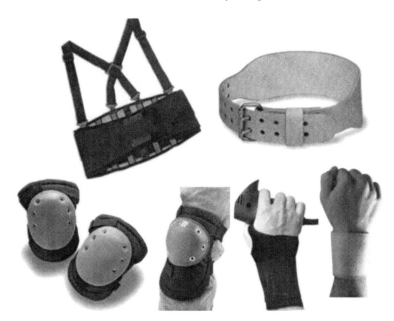

The use of ESDs is dependent on the specific job being performed, and the availability of the required devices from your employer. The main school of thought on the use of ESDs is that they are not top-priority safety devices. However, worker's compensation claims are greatly reduced within companies that provide their employees with ESDs. Many businesses are starting to realize this fact and are supplying such devices.

Work-related MSDs currently account for one-third of all occupational injuries and illnesses reported to the *Bureau of Labor Statistics* (*BLS*) by employers every year. These disorders constitute the largest job-related injury and illness problem in the United States today. In 1997, employers reported a total of 626,000 MSD-related workdays that were lost to these disorders, accounting for $1 of every $3 spent for workers' compensation in that year.

**Figure 7-12:
Ergonomic Safety
Devices**

Employers pay more than $15 to $20 billion in workers' compensation costs for these disorders every year, and other expenses associated with MSDs may increase the total cost from $45 to $54 billion annually. Workers with severe MSDs can face permanent disabilities that prevent them from returning to their jobs, or handling simple, everyday tasks like combing their hair, picking up a baby, or pushing a shopping cart.

Thousands of companies have taken action to address and prevent these problems. OSHA estimates that 50 percent of all employees, but only 28 percent of all workplaces in general industry, are already protected by an ergonomics program because their employers have voluntarily elected to implement one. These estimates indicate that most large companies employing the majority of the workforce already have these programs in place, while smaller employment firms have not yet implemented them.

THE WORKING ENVIRONMENT

Being prepared is the most crucial element in a safe working environment. Simple steps that are often overlooked may prevent serious injuries to you, or the people working around you. The tools and materials you work with have an important role in job safety. The proper handling of ladders, scaffolding, hand tools, power tools, and low-voltage wiring is crucial to avoiding accidents.

When dealing with safety considerations, it's important to realize that knowledge is power. Knowing and understanding your working environment (and the potential hazards that may arise) is an important part of any safety program. For example:

- Always read any safety warnings that deal with your equipment.

- Attend any safety training courses such as basic first aid and **Cardiopulmonary Resuscitation (CPR)**, which are both offered by the American Red Cross.

- Implement a notification plan to inform everyone around your work area of potential hazards. Make sure you consider coworkers, building employees, or other construction workers.

Designating the Work Area

Always take into consideration all of the people that may enter or come close to your work area. Consideration should also be given if you are working in someone else's work area. For example, suppose that another crew from your company is installing cable directly above you. Does this create an area where falling objects should be considered? Of course it does.

Designation may include the use of orange cones, warning signs, marked yellow tape, or a combination of these to mark a working area. Various work area warning signs are depicted in Figure 7-13. These signs should be posted in such a way as to always leave ample working room to complete the job. If you shortchange yourself on space, you may wind up creating the very type of dangerous environment you are trying to prevent. Make everyone aware of your designated work area.

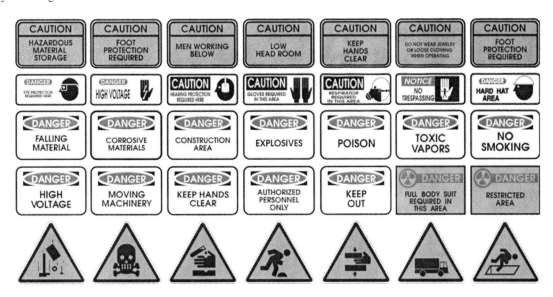

Figure 7-13: Warning Signs

Emergency Planning and Training

A good internal **Safety Policy** should be in place on every job site. For example, the locations of the first aid kit, eye wash station, and chemical showers, should all be clearly designated, as well as the display of instructions on how to use each of them. A well thought out safety policy provides the rules to which members of the organization can turn for guidance in the day-to-day execution of their work in an ever-changing environment.

When well prepared, a safety policy establishes the basic points of operational philosophy upon which all employees can agree. These points serve as the foundation for answering various what-to-do questions, in the event of an emergency. Find and study the safety procedures for your organization.

Basic first aid and CPR certifications should be taken and renewed before their expiration. **Safety Training** is also important to organizations that are rapidly incorporating new technologies and consequently increasing the likelihood of injury due to unfamiliarity with new equipment. This training can also increase the level of commitment of employees to the organization, and increase their perception that the organization is a good and safe place to work. Increased commitment can result in less turnover and absenteeism, thus increasing an organization's productivity.

Ladder Safety

When using a **Ladder** at a job site, read and follow the manufacturer's instructions affixed to the ladder if you are unsure about how to use it properly. Installers should inspect and use ladders as prescribed in the OSHA regulations. Remember that ladders, like any other tools, need to be maintained and used in accordance with the manufacturer's instructions. Figure 7-14 depicts various types of ladders in their deployed configurations.

Figure 7-14: Ladders

The following tips and precautions will help you enjoy longer, safer use of your ladder and keep you and the people around you safe while you are using it.

Ladder Inspection

Before using a ladder, it should be inspected for several very important conditions. For example, ladders SHOULD:

- Always be free from oil, grease, or similar materials
- Have rounded corners to prevent the snagging of clothing
- Be properly rated for weight capacity
- Have nonconductive side rails when used around energized circuits

Ladders should NOT:

- Be painted with any type of opaque substance that may obstruct an inspection for cracks or defects
- Have any missing steps or supports

Using Step Ladders Safely

Basic safety tips for using a stepladder should always be kept in mind when applicable. These include:

- Always moving the ladder in its closed position
- Using ladders only on level surfaces
- Opening the ladder fully with the retaining arms extended and locked in place
- Always facing the ladder when climbing the steps
- Only one person using or mounting a ladder at any time
- NOT standing above the safe working height of the ladder
- NOT using a ladder if the side rails are broken, cracked, or damaged in any way
- NOT using a ladder as a support for staging, or for supporting cable reels
- Never leaving tools or stock resting on stairs or rungs

Using Extension Ladders Safely

Applicable safety rules for using an extension ladder include:

- Clearing all entrance and exit areas to and from the ladder of tools, materials, and other obstructions that may contribute to someone falling
- NOT using an extension ladder on any surface that does not equally support the side rails
- Using only extension ladders equipped with non-slip footing, to prevent kick outs
- Tying off the extension rope to the bottom section, whenever the ladder is extended
- Extending the top of the ladder 36 inches above the working surface
- Overlapping the rail section a minimum of three rungs when extended
- Using extension ladders at an angle where the horizontal distance from the top support to the foot of the ladder is approximately one-quarter of the ladder's working length
- Bracing, or securing a ladder on telephone or cable line/strand, or a power pole prior to beginning a work procedure
- When placing an extension against the wall the bottom of the latter should be placed one foot out from the wall for every four feet of rise

Ladder Safety Training

The OSHA regulations also require an employer to provide training to employees in various areas with respect to ladder safety. These include:

- Identifying potential fall hazards
- Knowing the locations of power lines when they share areas where home electronics integrators are required to operate
- Knowing the proper procedures for use and maintenance of fall protection
- Performing the proper inspection, use, and placement of ladders
- Checking and knowing the load-carrying capacity of various ladders
- Keeping ladders away from fellow workers during high winds or other dangerous conditions

Scaffolding Safety

Scaffolding, depicted in Figure 7-15, may be set up and taken down many times during a construction project. Because scaffolding is considered temporary equipment and is moved from place to place at the job site, it is no surprise that sufficient care is not always taken in erecting it. As a result, inadequate scaffolding is responsible for many construction-site accidents.

Scaffolding

Figure 7-15:
Scaffolding

Scaffolding Accident Prevention

To prevent accidents associated with scaffolding, a number of safety precautions should be taken during its construction and use. These include:

- Avoiding the use of makeshift platforms, planning each job carefully to ensure that scaffolding is used only when required, and ensuring that the scaffolding conforms to all applicable construction and safety regulations
- Only using scaffolds designed, built, and inspected by trained and experienced workers
- Placing base plates, sills, or footers on solid ground, and making sure that the scaffold is leveled or plumbed
- NOT using damaged end frames or braces, attaching braces at all points provided, and NOT shortchanging the bracing requirements
- Tying the scaffold to the structure being worked on, if possible
- Using only scaffold-grade wood or metal catwalks for platforms, and inspecting each scaffold platform thoroughly for breaks, knots, cracks, or warping before each job
- Using planks with permanently attached cleats, to keep them from sliding off the scaffolding
- Using guardrails and toe boards on platforms higher than 6 feet
- Inspecting the scaffold after it is first erected, and every day during its use on the site
- Roping off the area underneath the scaffold
- Using a ladder when mounting the scaffold, and not climbing the braces
- Keeping tools and materials away from scaffold edges, so they cannot be knocked off onto people working below
- Avoiding an off-balance position when pulling, pushing, or prying, especially when working at heights
- Not using rolling scaffold units higher than four times their narrowest base measurement
- Keeping the casters of rolling scaffolding locked, when not being moved
- Never riding on rolling scaffolds

Fall Prevention

If you don't follow these safety precautions while working on scaffolding or a ladder, severe injuries can result. Each year, many workers are injured by falls at the job site. Various steps can and should be taken to ensure protection from falls. These include:

- Determining the proper equipment, such as deciding if the task would be safer to perform from a lift, staging, or a ladder
- Ensuring that the working area and walkways are free of debris
- Ensuring that anchorage points are properly rated, and that a personal fall-protection system is being used

- Inspecting any fall-protection devices, such as safety belts or harnesses, before using them
- Immediately removing any damaged component from service
- Verifying that all guardrail systems are properly installed, including toe boards and midrails
- Replacing as soon as possible, any guardrail that must be removed temporarily to facilitate your job
- Having all personnel certified in the use of aerial lifts, if they must be used on the job site
- Making sure that all through-floor openings are covered and marked with an appropriate warning
- Ensuring that all employees are trained to recognize potential fall hazards
- Checking to see that all employees know how to select and use fall-protection devices

Several fall-protection devices are depicted in Figure 7-16.

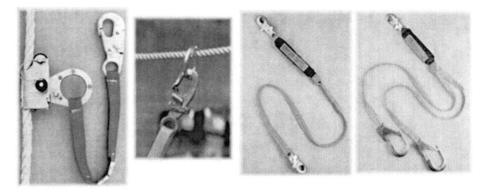

Figure 7-16:
Fall-Protection
Devices

OSHA Body Restraint Rules

Lanyard

Body Harness

Anchorage

A restraint system prevents a worker from being exposed to any fall. If the employee is protected by a restraint system, either a body belt or a harness may be used. When a restraint system is used for fall protection from an aerial lift, or a boom-type elevating work platform, the employer must ensure that the *lanyard* and *anchorage* are arranged so that the employee is not potentially exposed to falling any distance. A **Lanyard** is a flexible rope or line that is suitable for supporting one person when one end is fastened to a body harness and the other end secured to a substantial object, or a lifeline. A **Body Harness** is comprised of straps that help distribute fall arrest forces over at least the thighs, pelvis, waist, chest, and shoulders and that can be attached to other components of a fall arrest system, such as a lanyard, lifeline, or deceleration device. **Anchorage** can be any secure point of attachment for lifelines, lanyards, or deceleration devices.

For example, OSHA Standard 1910.66 sets a uniform threshold height of six feet for providing consistent free fall protection, including body restraints and lanyards. The only permitted exceptions are for employees making an inspection, investigation, or assessment prior to the start of actual construction work, or after all of the construction work has been completed. Protection can generally be provided through the use of guardrails, safety nets, or fall arrest systems.

Body Belt

Body Belt

The only time a **Body Belt** may be used for fall protection is when an employee is using a "positioning device." In OSHA's 1926.500 of the construction standards for fall protection, a "positioning device system" is defined as a body belt or body harness system rigged to allow an employee to be supported on an elevated vertical surface, such as a wall (or a pole), and work with both hands free while leaning. Therefore, in construction or installation work, a positioning device may be used only to protect a worker on a vertical work surface. These devices may permit a fall of up to 2 feet (0.6 m). They may be used in concrete formwork, installation of reinforcing steel, and certain telecommunications work. Since construction or installation workers positioned in bucket trucks, scissor lifts, and boom-type elevating work platforms are on a horizontal surface, a positioning device may not be used for those workers.

Fall Arrest Systems

Fall Arrest System

A device that permits an arrested fall is considered a **Fall Arrest System**. In construction or installation work, a body harness must be used in these systems. A fall arrest system can only be used where the aerial lift or scaffold is designed to withstand the vertical and lateral loads caused by an arrested fall. Fall arrest systems used in construction must comply with OSHA's 1926.502(d). That provision prohibits the use of a body belt in a fall arrest system, and instead requires the use of a body harness.

OSHA regulations detail exactly what fall protection is required for work performed at certain heights. For example, OSHA standards often dictate the use of:

- Fall arrest systems consisting of a full body harness, shock absorbent lanyard(s), or self-retracting lifelines. Specific types of work may mandate the use of 100% fall protection, requiring two shock absorbent lanyards.
- Guardrail systems
- Work platforms with standard guardrails
- Interior and exterior safety nets

Most states have instituted their own monthly inspection and documentation regulations covering body harnesses, shock absorbent lanyards, and self-retracting lifelines, regardless of their configurations. These documents must be maintained by all construction and installation professionals, and kept readily available to appropriate local, state, and federal agencies.

Examples of such regulations include various color-coded tapes for harnesses and lanyards, indicating that the required monthly inspections have been performed. These tapes must be placed around the D-rings located in the middle of the back of the harness, and the shock absorber ends of the lanyards. Other regulatory requirements may dictate that additional types of inspections be performed. According to OSHA standard 1926.502(d)(21), personal fall arrest systems shall be inspected prior to each use for wear, damage, and other deterioration, and defective components shall be removed from service.

OSHA Personal Fall Arrest Definitions

The OSHA Standard 1910.66 Appendix C also provides definitions for the various fall arrest terms used in the text of its requirements. In addition to the descriptions for anchorage, body harness, and lanyard, already mentioned, these definitions include:

- *Body Belt*: This is a strap with means both for securing it about the waist, and for attaching it to a lanyard, lifeline, or deceleration device. Recent standard revisions no longer permit its use under most circumstances, due to the possibility of the belt itself causing severe injury to its wearer during a fall.

- *Buckle*: This is any device used for holding the body belt, or the body harness, closed around the employee's body.

- *Competent Person*: This is the person who is capable of identifying hazardous or dangerous conditions in the personal fall arrest system, or any component thereof, as well as in their application and use with related equipment.

- *Connector*: This is any device used to couple (or connect) parts of the system together. It may be an independent component of the system (such as a carabineer), or an integral component of part of the system (such as a buckle or D-ring sewn into a body belt, or body harness, or a snap-hook spliced or sewn to a regular or self-retracting lanyard).

- *Deceleration Device*: This can be any mechanism, such as a rope grab, ripstitch lanyard, specially woven lanyard, tearing or deforming lanyard, or an automatic self-retracting lifeline/lanyard, which serves to dissipate a substantial amount of energy during a fall arrest, or otherwise limits the energy imposed on an employee during fall arrest.

- *Deceleration Distance*: This is the additional vertical distance, through which a falling employee travels, excluding lifeline elongation and free fall distance, before stopping, from the point at which the deceleration device begins to operate. This is measured as the distance between the location of an employee's body belt, or body harness attachment point, at the moment of activation (at the onset of fall arrest forces) of the deceleration device during a fall, and the location of that attachment point after the employee comes to a full stop.

- *Equivalent*: This includes alternative designs, materials, or methods which the employer can demonstrate will provide an equal or greater degree of safety for employees than the methods, materials or designs specified in the standard.

- *Free Fall*: This is the act of falling before the personal fall arrest system begins to apply force to arrest the fall.

- *Free Fall Distance*: This is the vertical displacement of the fall arrest attachment point on the employee's body belt, or body harness, between onset of the fall, and just before the system begins to apply force to arrest the fall. This distance excludes both deceleration distance, and lifeline/lanyard elongation, but includes any deceleration device slide distance, or self-retracting lifeline/lanyard extension, before they operate and fall arrest forces occur.

- *Lifeline*: This is a component consisting of a flexible line for connection to an anchorage at one end to hang vertically (vertical lifeline), or for connection to anchorages at both ends to stretch horizontally (horizontal lifeline), and which serves as a means for connecting other components of a personal fall arrest system to the anchorage.

- *Personal Fall Arrest System*: This is a system used to arrest a falling employee from a working level. It consists of an anchorage, connectors, a body belt or body harness, and may include a lanyard, deceleration device, lifeline, or suitable combinations of these.

- *Qualified Person*: This is someone with a recognized degree, or professional certificate, and extensive knowledge and experience in the subject field, capable of providing design, analysis, evaluation, and specifications in the subject work, project, or product.

- *Rope Grab*: This is a deceleration device which travels on a lifeline and automatically frictionally engages the lifeline, and locks, so as to arrest the fall of an employee. A rope grab usually employs the principle of inertial locking, cam/lever locking, or both.

- *Self-Retracting Lifeline/Lanyard*: This is a deceleration device containing a drum-wound line, which may be slowly extracted from, or retracted onto, the drum under slight tension during normal employee movement. After the onset of a fall, it automatically locks the drum and arrests the fall.

- *Snap-Hook*: This is a connector comprised of a hook-shaped member with a normally closed keeper, or similar arrangement, which may be opened to permit the hook to receive an object. When released, it automatically closes to retain the object. Snap-hooks are generally one of two types:
    - The locking type with a self-closing, self-locking keeper, which remains closed and locked until unlocked and pressed open for connection or disconnection, or
    - The non-locking type with a self-closing keeper, which remains closed until pressed open for connection or disconnection.

- *Tie-Off*: This is the act of an employee, wearing personal fall protection equipment, connecting directly or indirectly to an anchorage. It also means the condition of an employee being connected to an anchorage.

Hand Tool and Power Tool Safety

It's estimated that about 7% of industrial accidents involve the unsafe use of **Hand Tools**. These accidents result from using the wrong tool for the job, using the right tool incorrectly, or failing to follow the approved safety guidelines. Basic guidelines for the proper use of hand tools can be included in a checklist. Among items in this checklist, include:

- Knowing the precise purpose for each tool in your toolbox, and using them only for the specific task they were designed to do
- Never using any hand tool or power tool unless you are trained to do so
- Inspecting tools before each use, and replacing or repairing any tools that appear worn or damaged
- Cleaning tools after every use, and keeping any cutting edges sharp
- Testing a cutting edge on scrap materials, and NEVER with your fingers
- Selecting the right size of tool for the job

The use of cheaters is strictly prohibited. For example using a circular saw to cut a small piece of wood is a prohibited solution. A cheater is a tool that will do the job, but is the wrong tool for the job being performed.

- Securing yourself and your tools whenever working on ladders or scaffolding, to prevent a falling tool from seriously injuring a coworker or a bystander
- Carrying tools correctly by never placing their sharp or pointed surfaces in your pockets
- Pointing cutting edges away from you and towards the ground, whenever carrying tools by hand

- Preventing rust by lightly oiling metal tools, before storing them in a clean, dry place

- Wearing **Personal Protective Equipment** (**PPE**), such as safety goggles, face shields, and gloves whenever they are required

When working with any tool, make sure to follow the manufacturer's recommended directions. Be sure to wear clothing that doesn't hang loosely, or dangle. **Safety Guards** for all tools should be in place and operable. Proper tool maintenance will also help to prevent potential disaster, such as sharpening a saw blade before it becomes dull, for example. If a tool is damaged or not operating properly, replace it immediately.

Lifting and Handling Safety

Many work-related injuries happen due to improper *material handling* and *lifting techniques*. For example, Figure 7-17 illustrates the correct and incorrect lifting techniques. As demonstrated, you should lift with your legs, and not your back!

INCORRECT LIFTING

CORRECT LIFTING

**Figure 7-17:
Lifting Techniques**

Proper lifting and moving guidelines can help you to avoid such injuries. They include:

- Evaluating the size of the load before lifting, and getting help if it is too large for one person

- Bringing the object to be lifted close to you, and centering the weight over your feet

- Lifting the object smoothly, avoiding quick, jerky motions

- Shifting your feet instead of twisting your body, when carrying a heavy load

- Whenever lifting a load above waist height, resting it on a table or bench, and shifting your grip before lifting again

- If necessary, using two people when carrying a heavy load

- Planning, in advance, the route along which the load will be moved

- Always having a clear view of where you are going, and not allowing the object being moved to obstruct your vision

- Scouting the planned route by making sure the surface you will be traveling on is clean and in good condition

- Avoiding steep ramps along the planned route

- Carrying conduit and other long objects on your shoulder

- Pushing or pulling at waist height, while avoiding bending and twisting

- Pushing objects instead of pulling them, whenever possible

Low-Voltage Wiring Safety

Workers new to the field frequently assume that live **Low-Voltage Cabling** does not present a shock hazard. A 50- to 60-volt **Direct Current (DC)** is normally present on an idle tip-and-ring pair. Sometimes a ringing voltage of 90 volts **Alternating Current (AC)** is present and, under certain circumstances, can deliver an electrical shock. Many accidents have occurred due to improper or careless handling of such cabling, and failure to observe proper safety procedures. Determining the type of cable being utilized is one way to differentiate between low voltage and high voltage lighting control wiring.

Always assume that hazardous voltages exist in any wiring system. A safety check, using a known and reliable voltage measuring or detection device, should be made immediately before working with any wiring. Figure 7-18 depicts the use of various voltage measuring or detection devices.

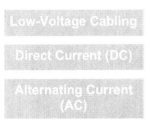

Figure 7-18: Voltage Measuring or Detection Devices

Wiring Separation

Table 7-1 lists the suggested minimum separations between residential and light commercial telecommunications wiring and other wiring.

Table 7-1: Residential and Light Commercial Telecommunications Wiring Purpose and Minimum Separation

PURPOSE	TYPES OF WIRES INVOLVED	MINIMUM SEPARATION
Electrical Supply	Bare light of any voltage	5 feet
Electrical Supply	Open wiring not over 330 volts; wires in conduit, or in armored or nonmetallic sheath cable and power ground wires	2 inches
Radio & TV	Antenna lead and ground wires without grounded shield	4 inches
Signal & Control Wire	Open wire not over 300 volts	none
Cable TV	Community television system's coaxial cables with grounded shield	none
Telephone & Drop Wire	Aerial or buried	2 inches
Signs	Neon signs and associated wiring from transformer	6 inches
Fluorescent Lighting	Fluorescent lighting wire	5 inches
Lighting System	Lighting rods and wires	6 feet

Minimum separations between residential and light commercial telecommunications wiring and other wiring are specified in the **EIA/TIA-570** standard. When in doubt, use the rule of sixes: six feet of separation between telephone wiring and open high-voltage wiring, lightning grounding wire, or grounding rods; six inches of separation from all other high-voltage wire unless in conduit.

Wiring Safety Guidelines

Always consider the correct wiring safety guidelines to obtain the safest results. They include:

- Always using insulated tools and avoiding all contact with bare terminals and grounded surfaces
- Disconnecting the dial-tone service from the premises wiring while working on it, to drop the DC level and prevent the delivery of AC ringing current
- Taking the telephone handset off-hook, if you cannot disconnect the service
- Not cutting or drilling through or into concealed wiring or pipes
- Making a small, visual inspection opening before you start cutting
- When running telephone wiring on or near metallic siding, checking for stray voltages
- Bonding to ground by attaching a ground wire from an earth or frame ground to any metallic siding, directing possible voltages away from the installer before beginning work
- Keeping telephone wiring away from bare power wires, lightning rods, antennas, transformers, steam or hot-water pipes, and heating ducts
- NOT placing telephone wire in a conduit, box, duct, or other enclosure containing power or lighting circuits of any type
- Always providing adequate separation between any telephone and electrical wiring
- NOT working on telephone wiring while wearing a pacemaker, where telephone-circuit voltages can disrupt its operation
- Never installing or connecting telephone wiring during electrical storms

Most electrical injuries involving telephone wiring result from sudden surges of high voltage on normally low-voltage wiring. Always remember that a fatal lightning surge can be carried over telephone wire for many miles. The TIA/EIA 570 standard specifies the minimum separations between residential and light commercial telecommunications wiring. The rule of sixes specifies six feet of separation between telephone wiring and all high-voltage wiring, unless running in conduit.

The Final Electrical Inspection

Local building codes require a final inspection of all electrical work in new and remodeled homes. This usually applies to all low voltage installations as well. The state electrician's license may be required to specify that the electrician is qualified for low voltage work, or a low voltage specialty license may be required as an addendum.

Prior to the final inspection of new or remodeled wiring, all devices and fixtures must be installed. In addition, the service equipment must be completely installed and labeled properly. All wiring must be free from short circuits, ground faults, and open circuits.

FIRST AID

First Aid is the initial care of an injured person as soon as possible after an accident. Your immediate response could mean the difference between the full or partial recovery of the victim, or possibly between life and death.

First Aid

First aid saves lives! Just ask any person who works in the emergency medical field. *IMMEDIATE RESPONSE* is one of the most important steps to saving a victim's life. If quick effective first aid is provided, the victim has a much better chance of a complete recovery.

It should be remembered that any actions undertaken are to be deliberate, and that panic by the first aid provider and bystanders will not be beneficial to the victim. Always remain calm and think your actions through. A calm and controlled first aid provider will give everyone confidence that the event is being handled efficiently and effectively.

Basic first aid and CPR training should be taken by all residential electronics systems installers, and should be renewed annually. It is unlikely that the victim, when treated by a trained first aid provider, will come to any additional harm, provided that the care and treatment is rendered in accordance with the provider's level of training. If there is the threat of death for the victim, first aid provided by an untrained person is better than the alternative. If first aid is administered quickly, but with due care, then the victim may not suffer any additional harm.

Calling "911"

To get expert medical assistance, call "*911*" as soon as possible. If you are attending to a casualty, get a bystander to telephone for help. If you are on your own, you may have to leave the victim momentarily to make the call. Use common sense, take your time, and act rationally. Before calling "911," remember to collect all of the necessary and valuable information. This includes:

- The type of injury or illness suffered by the victim
- The time that the accident or injury took place
- The address or location of the accident
- The pertinent information from the victim's medical alert bracelet, or necklace, if any
- Any other important information that would help prepare the emergency response team before they arrive

Once medical assistance has been notified, you'll have more time to thoroughly examine the casualty by conducting a head-to-toe secondary examination. Your main goals are to attend to the victim's wounds and to keep the victim calm. Inform medical technicians of any and all relevant information once they arrive.

Medical Alert Identification

Medical Alert
Pendants

Vial of Life

Some individuals suffer from certain medical conditions that cause them to have or show various signs and symptoms. As a form of assistance and notification, these people may wear a form of medical identification, usually a special bracelet or necklace. These are commonly referred to as **Medical Alert Pendants**, but other types are available, such as the **Vial of Life**.

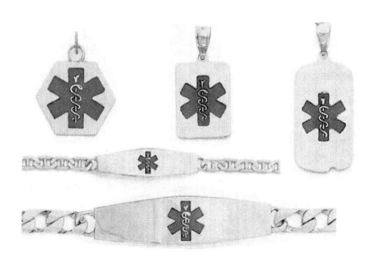

Figure 7-19: Medical Alert Pendants

Medical alert pendants, such as those shown in Figure 7-19, are imprinted with the person's identity, the relevant medical condition, and other important details such as which drugs are required, or the phone numbers of specialized medical contacts. The listed medical conditions may include specific heart diseases, diabetes, epilepsy, asthma, or serious allergies.

The Vial of Life, shown in Figure 7-20, is simply an oversized prescription bottle containing the victim's important medical information. Vial of Life kits, often found at pharmacies, contain two large labeled prescription bottles and two health questionnaires. After completing the questionnaires, one is placed into each bottle. One bottle is to be left at the person's home, while the other is to be placed in his or her vehicle. If you are attending to a victim, have a bystander search for the vial. If you are alone, don't look for the vial until emergency crews arrive, as crucial emergency response time may be wasted while you search.

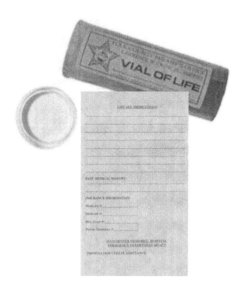

Figure 7-20: Vial of Life

DR. ABC

DR. ABC

Whenever you are aiding in the care and treatment of a victim, you should think of the acronym **DR. ABC**. "DR. ABC" stands for:

- *Danger* - *Response* - *Airway* - *Breathing* - *Circulation*

These key elements, discussed in Table 7-2, should be considered whenever you encounter an emergency situation.

Table 7-2: DR. ABC

DANGER	Don't put yourself in danger. Don't allow bystanders to be exposed to danger. Whenever possible, remove the danger from the victim, or the victim from the danger.
RESPONSE	Gently "shake and shout" at the victim. (Warning: Do NOT shake young children or infants!) Is the victim alert? Is the victim drowsy or confused? Is the victim unconscious, but reacting? Is the victim unconscious with no reaction? If the victim is unconscious, turn him/her to a stable side position. However, if the injury to the victim is unknown or due to a fall, do NOT move the victim!
AIRWAY	Is the airway open and clear? Are they breathing noisily? Are there potential obstructions such as blood? If so, open and clear the obstructions from the airway.
BREATHING	Look to see if the chest rises. Listen for the sound of breathing. Feel for movement by putting your hand on the lower part of the chest. If breathing is absent after 5 seconds, pinch the victim's nostrils closed, take a deep breath, completely cover the victim's mouth, and give two slow, effective breaths. Check for a pulse and signs of breathing. If a pulse is present: For adults - continue rescue breathing at a rate of one strong breath every 5 seconds. Check for pulse and breathing every twelve breaths. For infants or small children - continue rescue breathing at a rate of one strong breath every 3 seconds or 20 breaths per minute.
CIRCULATION	Is there a carotid pulse? Is it strong? Is it regular? If pulse is NOT present, begin cardiopulmonary resuscitation (CPR). (Steps to perform CPR are on pages 44-48.) If the victim is conscious, then treat the injuries or illness according to the signs and symptoms. Remain with the victim and have someone call for assistance. If you are alone, reassure the victim that you will return after you call for an ambulance. If the victim is unconscious but breathing spontaneously, leave him or her in the stable side position, then treat any injuries.

First Aid Hygiene

Infectious Diseases are those that cause infections to the human body, and in some cases are transmitted by contact or cross-infection. Infection may be due to bacteria, viruses, parasites, or fungi. When providing first aid to a victim, the risk of contracting an infectious disease is always present. The usual methods of contamination include:

- Direct contact, such as touching an infected person

- Indirect contact, such as through air conditioning ducts, or from soiled linens

- Through a host, such as by contact with insects, worms, rodents, or other animals

Examples of infectious diseases are:

- *Bacterial Infections:* These include throat infections, whooping cough, diphtheria, rheumatic fever, tuberculosis strains, cholera, staphylococcus infections, and some forms of meningitis.
- *Viral Infections:* These include measles, mumps, rubella, hepatitis, influenza, chicken pox, HIV, the common cold, and bronchitis.

- *Parasitic Infections:* These include malaria, tapeworms, hookworms, itch mites, as well as pubic and body lice.
- *Fungal Infections:* These include ringworm, athlete's foot, and thrush.

Limiting the Spread of Infection

While there is little that a first aid provider can do to prevent exposure to the victim who is already stricken with an infectious disease, there is a great deal that can be done to limit the risk of spreading the infection to others. The first aid provider should be familiar with the signs and symptoms of common diseases in order to avoid further contamination.

It is important that first aid procedures be conducted with due regard for the danger of cross-infection. Simple rules of personal hygiene and the wearing of gloves, if available, are sufficient to guard both the first aid provider and the casualty from contamination.

If at all possible, wash your hands with soap and water prior to treatment, or rinse them with an antiseptic cleanser. Make sure that your hands are washed thoroughly between the fingers and under fingernails. If gloves are available, wear them. After putting on gloves and/or cleansing your hands, as shown in Figure 7-21, be careful not to touch any unclean objects.

During treatment, use only clean bandages and dressings. Also, try to avoid contact with the victim's bodily fluids. If there is more than one victim, do not treat the second victim without first washing your hands again, and changing gloves. After treatment, clean up both the casualty and yourself. When cleaning up the immediate vicinity, dispose of dressings, bandages, gloves, and soiled clothing, preferably by burning them. After cleaning up, wash your hands with soap and water, even if you were previously wearing gloves.

**Figure 7-21:
Wearing Gloves**

Basic Human Anatomy

The human body is composed of a number of systems, each with a specific role in the function of the body as a whole. The function of these individual systems is known as the body's physiology. **Physiology** is the branch of biology that deals with functions and activities of life, or of living matter such as organs, tissues, or cells.

It is important that as the first aid provider, you are aware of the major systems of human anatomy and their basic functions. This basic knowledge will assist you in your first aid diagnosis, and will provide a foundation on which to base your care and treatment for the victim.

The Nervous System

The nervous system, as shown in Figure 7-22, consists of two main parts: the *brain* and the *spinal cord*. This system is often referred to as the **Central Nervous System**, and it is the control center for all functions of the body. The motor and sensory nerves, which involve movement, are known as the peripheral nervous system, and function as directed by the brain. Some peripheral or autonomic nerves function without conscious thought. For example, blinking and breathing are two bodily functions that are attributable to autonomic nerves.

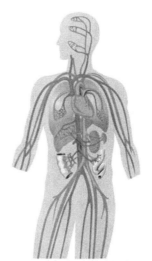

Central Nervous System

Figure 7-22: The Nervous System

The Cardiovascular System

The **Cardiovascular System**, as shown in Figure 7-23, involves the heart, its related blood vessels, and the blood. The heart is the pump that circulates blood throughout the body. The body's blood vessels include arteries (which take the blood from the heart) and veins (which return the blood back to the heart). There are also smaller blood vessels such as arterioles, venules, and capillaries, most of which are located at the body's extremities, and are usually positioned close to the skin. The blood's primary action is to transport oxygen from the respiratory system to all of the body's cells.

As the heart pumps blood, each beat can be felt at various body locations known as pulse points, as shown in Figure 7-23. Therefore, each pulse beat is equal to one heartbeat and the pulse can be used to determine a person's heart rate. The heart rate of the average adult, at rest, should range between 60 to 100 beats per minute depending on age, medical conditions, and general fitness level. The most accessible pulse points are located either at the wrist, or the carotid arteries in the neck. Knowledge of these pulse point locations is essential for the first aid provider.

Cardiovascular System

CARDIOVASCULAR SYSTEM

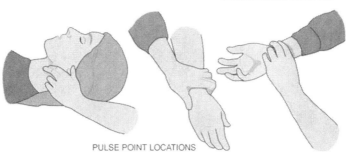

PULSE POINT LOCATIONS

Figure 7-23: The Cardiovascular System and its Pulse Locations

The Respiratory System

The **Respiratory System**, depicted in Figure 7-24, is composed of the airway and the lungs. Its function is to provide oxygen to the blood. Oxygen is extracted from the air that is inhaled via the airway, and is passed into the bloodstream through membranes of the lungs. For the first aid provider, the maintenance of a victim's airway is of obvious importance.

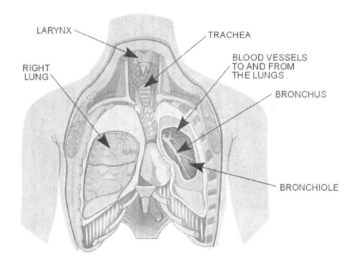

Figure 7-24: The Respiratory System

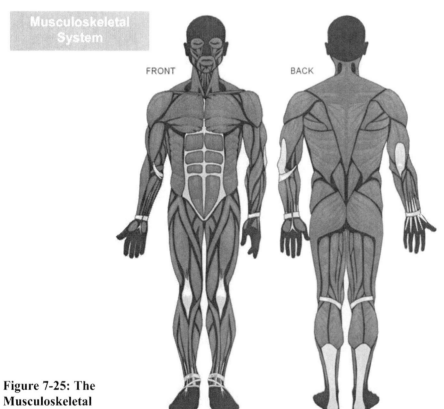

Figure 7-25: The Musculoskeletal System

The Musculoskeletal System

The **Musculoskeletal System** involves the body's bones and muscles, as shown in Figure 7-25. Most muscles that cause movement work by contracting and relaxing in conjunction with a bone. The action of raising your leg, for instance, involves the contraction of several muscles creating an opposing force in the leg, causing it to move upwards. Some muscles, such as the diaphragm that makes the lungs expand and contract, do not need bones to work with, but rather attach to large masses of tissue.

The remaining bodily systems are the lymphatic, digestive, endocrine, reproductive, and integumentary systems. However, we will not discuss these systems here.

Basic First Aid

It is important to not miss anything when treating a casualty. Make sure that you absorb all the information available. It is vital that you approach the incident with confidence. With this type of attitude, the victim is more likely to be calm and respond to your assistance.

What do you see when you approach the accident scene? Has a person fallen from a ladder? Is there more than one victim? Quickly assess the situation at hand, including the victims, any bystanders, motor vehicles, collapsed ladders, fallen scaffolding, and so on. Remember the DR. ABC routine.

Primary Examinations

Check to ensure that the victim is conscious. If the victim is unconscious, check the victim's airway and breathing capacity. Clear the airway if required. If the casualty is not breathing, place he or she on his or her back and give two effective breaths.

- Is there a pulse?
- Is there any severe bleeding?

Try to obtain details of the accident from a conscious casualty, or from any bystanders. If you determine that the victim's airway is not blocked and yet, he or she is not breathing, nor is there a detectable pulse, immediate medical assistance is required. Either you or a bystander must call "911" immediately, as shown in Figure 7-26.

Figure 7-26: Call "911"

Secondary Examinations

You now have more time to thoroughly examine the casualty by conducting a head-to-toe secondary examination, as shown in Figure 7-27.

Follow these steps in order:

1. Begin at the top of the head, and check for bleeding, fractures, swelling, and pain.

2. Move to the victim's face, and check his or her airway for unobstructed breathing. Examine the eyes, ears, nose, and mouth for facial fractures, bruising, and jaw line pain.

3. Move down to the neck area, shoulders, and chest, while checking for bleeding, fractures, bruising, swelling, and pain. Look for any medical alert necklace.

4. Examine the arms and check for bleeding, fractures, soft tissue injuries, pain, and the victim's grasping power. (This power is the victim's ability to squeeze tightly with their hands.) Search for any medical alert bracelet.

5. Next, observe the abdomen and pelvis, while checking for rigidity, pain or tenderness, "guarding," and incontinence.

6. Finally, examine the legs and check for bleeding, fractures, soft tissue injuries, and pain.

7. Remember to be sensitive to the victim's age, as extra caution should be taken with young children and infants.

Figure 7-27: Secondary Examination

Expired Air Resuscitation

Expired Air Resuscitation (EAR) is the method by which a rescuer breathes for a victim who is in respiratory arrest, yet still has a pulse. This is most commonly known as "mouth-to-mouth resuscitation." There are actually three key methods for delivering EAR. These are:

- *Mouth-to-mouth*: This is the resuscitation method in which the rescuer seals the victim's mouth with his or her mouth, and breathes into the victim's mouth, as illustrated in Figure 7-28.

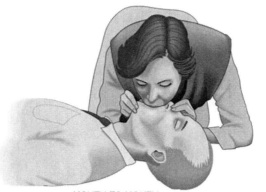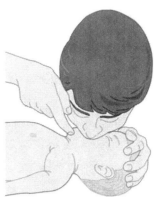

MOUTH-TO-MOUTH   MOUTH-TO-NOSE-AND-MOUTH

Figure 7-28: Expired Air Resuscitation

- *Mouth-to-nose*: This is the resuscitation method used when the victim has sustained facial injuries that prevents breathing directly into the victim's mouth. The rescuer closes the casualty's mouth with his or her hand, seals the nose with his or her mouth, breathes gently, and then releases the casualty's jaw to allow exhalation.

- *Mouth-to-nose-and-mouth*: This is the method used when resuscitating a child, as the rescuer's mouth can cover and seal the child's nose and mouth, and is also illustrated in Figure 7-28.

Breaths need to be effective. You may determine effective breaths by watching the rise and fall of the victim's chest as you give each breath. You may make up to five attempts to achieve the initial two effective breaths.

Performing EAR

Figure 7-29 illustrates the steps for performing EAR.

These steps include:

1. Checking the victim's airway and opening it, if necessary. If the victim isn't breathing, place the victim on his or her back. Ensure that the airway is open by tilting the victim's head back.

2. Using the appropriate method for the victim. Give two effective breaths, making up to five attempts to achieve them. Watch the rise and fall of the chest. If an obstruction is suspected, attempt to open the airway again.

3. Checking the victim's pulse. If a pulse is present and the victim is not breathing, commence EAR for adults and older children by giving one effective breath every 4 seconds (15 breaths per minute). For younger children and infants, give one effective breath every 3 seconds (20 breaths per minute). Check the victim's pulse and airway once each minute, and always be ready for the victim to vomit.

4. Using full breaths for adults or older children (9 years and above). Make sure that you lessen the force of the breaths when breathing into a young child, or an infant. If delivered too forcefully, the air will be directed into the stomach, possibly causing the child to vomit. The method to be employed for infants is known as puffing. Puffing is when the rescuer fills his or her mouth with air, and puffs it into the infant's mouth. This will allow enough air pressure to satisfy the lung's requirements, but not enough to impact on the stomach.

5. Continue EAR until the casualty begins breathing on his or her own, you are relieved by professional medical aid, or the victim goes into full cardiac arrest (at which point you must start cardiopulmonary resuscitation).

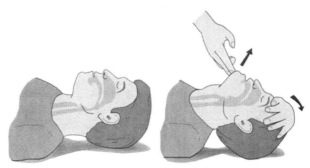

TILT THE HEAD TO OPEN THE AIRWAY

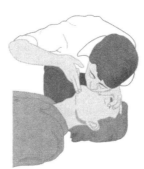

CLEAR THE AIRWAY IF NECESSARY

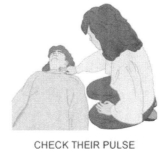

CHECK THEIR PULSE

USE THE APPROPRIATE METHOD FOR THE VICTIM

Figure 7-29: Steps for Performing EAR

Cardiopulmonary Resuscitation

Cardiopulmonary Resuscitation (CPR) is *expired air resuscitation (EAR)* used in conjunction with *external cardiac compressions (ECC)*. It is the single most effective form of active resuscitation available, and is used by trained first aid providers and medical personnel. Participation in a CPR course is strongly recommended. The technique is used to assist in the resuscitation of cardiac arrest victims.

Cardiac Arrest is the unexpected collapse of a victim whose heart has ceased to function. Cardiac arrest occurs suddenly, and is closely linked with sudden chest pain. A victim of cardiac arrest has only minutes from collapse until death.

While expired air resuscitation is the method by which oxygen is provided to the victim, external cardiac compressions mimic the heart's function of pumping the blood through the body. Effective CPR can sustain the victim until professional medical treatment is available. CPR must be started immediately if it is determined that the victim is unconscious, has no pulse, and has no respiration (although there may be brief, irregular, or gasping breaths).

CPR Hand Positioning

When starting CPR, it is crucial that your hands are positioned correctly on the victim's chest. There are two methods used to locate the correct position of the hands. One is called the xiphoid location, and the other is named the caliper method.

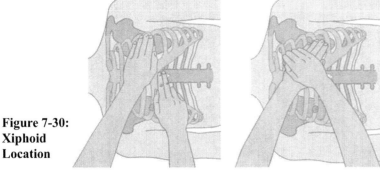

Figure 7-30: Xiphoid Location

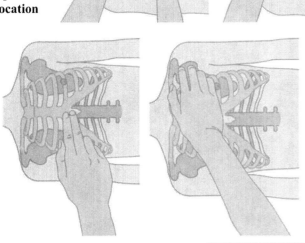

Figure 7-31: Caliper Method

- *Xiphoid Location*: Locate the small bone, or bump, at the base of the sternum. Using two fingers of one hand, measure up the sternum toward the victim's heart. Place the palm of your other hand at this point. Your palm should now be over the center of the sternum, above your two fingers. Once you have located the victim's heart, begin the external cardiac compressions, as illustrated in Figure 7-30.

- *Caliper Method*: The middle finger of one hand is placed on the notch located above the sternum directly below the victim's throat. The middle finger of the other hand is placed on the small bone located at the base of the sternum. Both hands are moved together until the thumbs meet in the middle of the sternum. The lower hand is then positioned palm down at the location of the thumb of your upper hand. This also determines the location of the victim's heart for you to begin external cardiac compressions, as depicted in Figure 7-31.

For adults and children 9 years of age or older, place one hand on the located position, then place your second hand over the first and entwine your fingers for stability. Your second hand may also grip the wrist of your first hand. Compress the chest approximately 1/3 the depth of the chest, with pressure exerted through the heel of the bottom hand.

CPR Hand Position for Children

Hand position for a young child is in the same location on the lower half of the sternum. Compressions are performed approximately 1/3 the depth of the chest using the heel of one hand only. Your pressure must be lessened so as not to cause damage to the child's rib cage.

An infant's heart is located by placing two fingers centrally on the sternum, one finger width below the inter-nipple line. Compressions are then performed by pressing with two fingers approximately 1/3 the depth of the chest. The pressure is modified to reflect the fragility of the child's chest. The pulse is detected by placing two fingers directly over the infant's upper arm, just above the elbow.

Performing CPR

CPR may be performed by one person, no matter what the age of the victim, or by two people if the victim is an adult or older child. CPR administered by two people requires synchronization and technique. It is normally more effective for two people performing CPR to use the individual form of CPR, and rotate every five minutes or so.

Figure 7-32 illustrates the administration of one-person CPR between an adult and an older child. For this type of CPR, you must:

1. Check and clear the airway. Look, listen, and feel for breathing. If no breathing is detected, place the victim on his or her back, on a firm flat surface.

2. Give two effective breaths. Assess the rise and fall of the chest.

3. Check for a pulse (5-10 seconds).

4. Kneel beside the victim's chest, and locate the correct hand position.

5. Place hands centrally over the heart, with your fingers entwined. Lean over the victim with your arms straight, and your elbows locked.

6. Perform 15 compressions, using even pressure and compressing up to 1/3 the depth of the chest.

7. Give two effective breaths, and then relocate the correct hand position.

8. Continue this cycle, and check for the victim's pulse approximately once every minute.

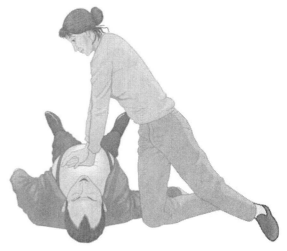

Figure 7-32: One-Person CPR - Adult and Older Child

Performing CPR on Children

Figure 7-33 depicts the administration of one-person CPR between a younger child and an infant. For this type of CPR, you must:

1. Check and clear the victim's airway. Look, listen, and feel for breathing. If breathing cannot be detected, place the victim on his or her back, on a firm flat surface.

2. Open the airway, and give two initial effective breaths.

3. Check for the victim's pulse for 5 to 10 seconds.

4. Perform five compressions.

5. One breath should be given after every five compressions.

6. Continue this cycle and check the victim's pulse at least once every minute.

Figure 7-33: One-Person CPR - Younger Child or Infant

Two-Person CPR

Figure 7-34 depicts a two-person (adult and older child) CPR upon the victim. For this type of CPR, you must:

1. Check and clear the airway. Look, listen, and feel for breathing. If no breathing can be detected, place the victim on his or her back, using a firm flat surface.

2. One rescuer positions close to the casualty's head, and delivers breaths. The other rescuer positions on the opposite side of the body beside the chest, and performs compressions.

3. Open the victim's airway, and give two initial effective breaths.

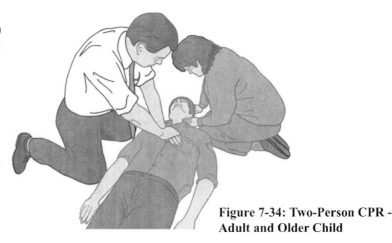

Figure 7-34: Two-Person CPR - Adult and Older Child

4. Check for the carotid pulse for a period of 5 to10 seconds.

5. Perform five compressions.

6. Be sure to deliver one breath on completion of the fifth compression.

7. Continue this cycle, and check the victim's pulse at least once every minute.

CPR Notes

Rescuers must be alert at all times to watch for the airway becoming blocked by vomit. If the victim does vomit, roll him/her onto their side and clear the airway. When the airway is clear, roll the victim onto their back and resume CPR.

No matter what the age of the victim, once you begin CPR, it is to be continued until the victim is revived, the rescuer is relieved by expert medical aid, or until the rescuer is too exhausted to continue.

Trauma

Trauma is an injury or wound that is caused by an external agent, such as the situation depicted in Figure 7-35. Unfortunately, trauma accidents also happen at the workplace and need to be addressed in this chapter.

There are several types of trauma wounds that may be encountered These include:

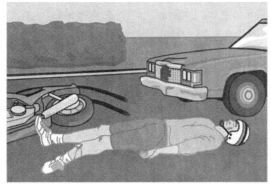

Figure 7-35:
Trauma Accident

- *Incisions*: These are the type of wounds made by the slicing of the skin with a sharp instrument.

- *Lacerations*: These are deep wounds with associated loss of tissue. These types of wounds occur when the skin is ripped.

- *Abrasions*: These are wounds where the skin layers have been scraped off.

- *Punctures and Perforations*: These types of wounds may be caused by anything from a corkscrew to a bullet.

- *Amputations or Avulsions*: These are wounds involving the loss of a digit, or limb, by trauma.

Wound Care

Before beginning any type of *wound care*, be sure to wear health care gloves to avoid contact with the victim's blood. To help prevent infection, perform the following steps:

1. Cleanse the wound and the surrounding area gently, with a mild soap and water, then rinse. Blot dry the area with a sterile pad or clean dressing.

2. Treat the wound.

3. Cover the wound to absorb fluids, and to protect it from further contamination.

4. Secure the cover with first aid tape to keep out dirt and germs.

Bleeding

Minor cuts or abrasions may be treated quite easily with no follow-up medical attention. The following steps will help control the bleeding:

1. Have the victim lie down. Elevate the injured limb higher than the victim's heart, unless you suspect a broken bone.

2. Control the bleeding by applying direct pressure on the wound with a sterile pad, or clean cloth.

3. If the bleeding is controlled by direct pressure, bandage firmly to protect the wound. Figure 7-36 depicts several bandage types that are available. Be sure not to apply the bandage too tightly.

4. If bleeding is not controlled by use of direct pressure, apply a tourniquet only as a last resort. A tourniquet may be applied if there is a threat of death due to severe loss of blood.

5. Call for medical help.

Figure 7-36: Bandages

Puncture Wounds

Puncture Wounds are more serious than minor cuts and abrasions. The following steps will aid you in the treatment of puncture wounds:

1. Check the wound, but do NOT remove any penetrating objects.

2. Control the bleeding by applying direct pressure on the wound with a sterile pad, or clean cloth.

3. If the bleeding is controlled by direct pressure, bandage firmly to protect the wound. Be sure not to apply the bandage too tightly.

4. Elevate the injured limb, if injuries permit.

5. Call for medical help.

Amputation (Avulsion)

Obviously, **Amputation** is a very serious injury. Partial amputations must be stabilized by immobilization. This can be accomplished through the use of splinting and/or pressure dressing. Keep the victim calm, and preferably lying down with legs elevated. Control bleeding and move the casualty to the hospital, as soon as possible, together with the severed part. Call emergency services as quickly as possible.

In the case of a complete amputation, control bleeding by applying firm direct pressure with gauze, towels, clothes, or newspaper. If you are familiar with arterial pressure points, you can apply pressure on the pressure point directly above the amputation. Take great care not to damage the stump.

Wrap the severed part in a moist, sterile dressing such as gauze, or any clean cloth or paper towel. If possible, it is preferable that the dressing be soaked in a saline solution (such as contact lens solution made of sodium chloride). Place the wrapped detached part in a waterproof, zip-lock bag and put the bag in a container containing a water-ice mixture to keep it cool.

Do not put the severed part in direct contact with the ice or water. Take care to prevent the exposed tissue from becoming wet. Make sure to send the part with the emergency medical team for possible surgical attachment. Mark the package clearly with the victim's name, and the time the amputation occurred. Transport the victim to the nearest emergency services facility as soon as possible.

The following are steps to amputation treatment:

1. Stop the bleeding immediately.

2. Treat for shock as described in the following section, if necessary.

3. If the wound is not deep, or bleeding too badly, cleanse the wound and surrounding area gently with a mild soap and warm water.

4. Cover the wound to absorb fluids and to protect it from further contamination.

5. Get professional medical help immediately.

Shock

Shock is a disturbance of the blood that can upset all body functions. Symptoms may include unusual weakness or faintness; cold, pale, clammy skin; rapid, weak pulse; shallow, irregular breathing; chills; nausea; unconsciousness. The following steps will help you treat a victim that is in shock:

1. Treat the known cause of shock as quickly as possible.

2. Maintain an open airway.

3. Keep the victim warm, and lying flat.

4. Do not give the victim anything by mouth.

Burns and Scalds

Never clean **Burns** or break blisters, or remove any clothing that may stick to the burn. Also, never apply any type of grease, ointment, or medication onto a severe burn. The three degrees of burns are:

- *First Degree*: This type of burn displays the discoloration of skin surface (redness), mild swelling, and pain. Under most circumstances, additional medical treatment is not necessary.

- *Second Degree*: This is a deep burn that displays red or spotted appearance, blisters, considerable pain, swelling, and the surface of the skin appears wet. These burns may be potentially serious, requiring additional medical treatment, depending on their extent and location.

- *Third Degree*: These burns result in severe tissue destruction with a charred appearance, but do not provide the pain levels one would expect for their severity. Seek professional medical help immediately!

Immediate treatment consists of the application of cool, wet cloths or the immersion in water, if possible. Do not use ice! Blot the burn gently, and apply a dry sterile patch, if necessary.

Electrical Shock

The human body is an electrical conductor. When a victim receives an **Electric Shock**, the electricity is conducted directly through the body. A victim may receive significant burns, or the electric shock may interfere with his or her heart's electrical system.

Electric Shock

Electrical Burns to the victim may be greater than they appear on the surface. When attending to a victim exposed to electricity, danger is the priority. While the level of danger varies from person to person, serious danger considered potentially lethal to humans only appears when the voltage is higher than 40 volts. The criteria for the lethal effects of electric shock were established in May of 1956 by Charles F. Dalziel, in his "The Effects of Electric Shock on Man," Industrial Radio Engineers Transactions on Medical Electronics.

Electrical Burns

This work includes the observations that:

- Currents in excess of a human being's voluntary "let-go" maximum of 16 mA at 60 Hz can produce collapse, unconsciousness, asphyxia, and even death if passing through the chest.

- Respiratory inhibition is produced by currents at, or greater than, 30 mA at 60 Hz flowing through the nerve centers that control breathing. These effects can last for some time after interruption of the current.

- Any current greater than, or equal to, 1.0 ampere at 60 Hz flowing in the region of the heart can directly cause cardiac arrest.

- Fatal damage to the central nervous system can result from relatively high currents ranging between 0.25 to 1.0 amperes.

- Deep body and/or organ burns, substantial increases in body temperatures, and immediate death can result from currents greater than 5 amps.

- Even serious electrical burns or other complications can cause delayed reactions and eventual death.

Obviously, the most dangerous current flow occurs via the chest cavity, through the heart. **Ventricular Fibrillation** is the result of such a shock, when it occurs during the time relative to the normal heart rhythm. In such cases, the current may cause repeated, rapid, and uncoordinated contractions of the heart ventricles. A current flow of 75 mA, or more, for 5 seconds through the chest cavity, can initiate a fatal alteration of the heart's normal rhythmic pumping action.

Ventricular Fibrillation

When considering the probability of ventricular fibrillation, two calculations are most often considered.

1. To determine the 5-second current flow (in mA) necessary to cause a 0.5% probability of ventricular fibrillation, the subject's body weight (in pounds) should be multiplied by 0.49.

2. To determine the 5-second current flow (in mA) necessary to cause a 99.5% probability of ventricular fibrillation, the subject's body weight (in pounds) should be multiplied by 1.47.

Be alert for danger to yourself and to other rescuers, and approach any electrical accident scene with extreme caution. Electricity can be classified as originating from two distinct source types: residential voltage and high voltage.

Residential Voltage

When electrical shock originates from residential voltage sources, it is critical that the victim be disconnected and/or removed from the electrical source. This can be accomplished, either by:

1. Turning off the power supply, disconnecting any plugs from the outlet, and isolating the electricity supply at the main power board if possible; or

2. Removing the casualty from the electrical source by separation with non-conducting materials, for example, a wooden stick or board, a rope, or a blanket.

3. Pushing or dragging the victim off of live electrical conductors prior to administering artificial respiration.

WARNING: Be careful not to touch the victim's skin before the electrical source is disconnected. Also, be alert for the presence of water or conducting materials that may be in contact with you, or the victim.

High Voltage

When high-voltage electricity is involved in an accident, do not touch the victim until the scene has been declared safe by the relevant electrical authorities, or by a workplace supervisor. Do not approach the scene if you feel any unusual sensations, such as tingling through your footwear. Ensure that bystanders do not approach the scene, and remain at least 20 feet away from the nearest suspected site containing energized material.

Symptoms of serious electrical shock include:

- Difficult or non-existent breathing
- Absent, weak, or irregular pulse
- Evidence of burns
- Evidence of fractures
- Entrance and exit wound burns
- Collapse and unconsciousness

In the event of an electrocution, there are only a limited number of things that first aid providers can do. These include:

1. Performing the DR. ABC routine
2. Calling "911" for an ambulance
3. Informing electrical authorities if high voltage is involved
4. Commencing with EAR if the victim is in respiratory arrest
5. Commencing with CPR if the victim is in cardiac arrest
6. Cooling and covering burns with non-adhesive dressings
7. Reassuring the victim that everything will be okay

Fractures (Broken Bone)

A **Broken Bone** may be indicated if the victim hears or feels the bone break, the affected area is extremely tender to the touch, excruciating pain occurs in one spot, swelling is noted around the suspected fracture, the limb is in an unusual or unnatural position, movement is painful, motion is abnormal, there is a loss of function, there is a grating sensation, and/or any discoloration of the affected area appears.

There are two main types of bone fractures. These are:

- *Closed fracture*: This is where the fracture of a bone does not pierce the skin.
- *Compound fracture*: This is where the piercing of the skin accompanies the fracture.

Treatment: Keep the victim warm, still, and treat for shock if necessary. Other necessary treatment includes:

- *Closed fracture*: Splint the limb before the victim is moved, immobilizing the joint above and below the suspected fracture point.
- *Compound fracture*: Do not touch or clean the wound. Secure a sterile pad, or clean cloth, firmly in place over the wound, and then tie with bandages or cloth strips. No matter which type of fracture is suspected, get medical assistance immediately.

WARNING: Do not move the victim until a splint has been applied, as shown in Figure 7-37. If there is a chance of spinal injury, do not move the victim until medical assistance has arrived.

**Figure 7-37:
Splint Applied**

Heat Exhaustion

Heat Exhaustion symptoms may include fatigue, irritability, headache, faintness, weak and rapid pulse, shallow breathing, cold and clammy skin, and/or profuse perspiration. The following steps will help you aid a victim suffering from heat exhaustion:

1. Instruct the victim to lie down in a cool, shaded area or an air-conditioned room, and elevate the victim's feet.

2. Massage the victim's legs towards the heart. The heart is not the primary mover of blood through the legs; muscle action is. With inactivity or shock, blood can tend to pool in the legs.

3. If the victim is conscious, give them cool water every 15 minutes until they recover. If the victim is unconscious, apply a cool wet compress to the head.

Head Injuries

Head Injuries

Head Injuries can easily mislead the first aid provider by not exhibiting the expected signs and symptoms immediately after the incident. In many instances, the victim will initially appear unaffected, only to collapse with life-threatening symptoms hours later. This problem is caused by bleeding in the brain, eventually reaching the point where excessive pressure is applied against the victim's brain tissue.

A doctor should always examine any casualty who has been rendered unconscious, or received a hard blow to the head, with NO exceptions! Head injuries are generally classified as either open (a head injury with an associated head wound) or closed (with no obvious external sign of injury). A **Concussion** is a closed type head injury. In most cases victims have developed the injury several hours after the incident.

Concussion

Facial Injuries are also head injuries. The first aid provider should not be unduly distracted by obvious facial injuries so that they forget to assess the victim for potential brain injury. Facial injuries can also interfere with the victim's airway (as was mentioned in the section on CPR).

Facial Injuries

Identifying Head Injuries

In many instances, serious head injury is readily identified by:

- *A straw-colored fluid oozing from the nose or ears.* This is *cerebrospinal fluid* (*CSF*), which surrounds the brain. When a fracture occurs, usually at the base of the skull, the fluid leaks out under pressure into the ear and nose canals.

- *The appearance of black eyes.* This may indicate an impact elsewhere on the skull, and not just the face. The kinetic energy from a blow, which is transmitted through the head and brain, is expelled through the eyes and behind the ears, causing bruising at these points.

- *Blurred or double vision.* This symptom is common with concussions, indicating that the brain has been dealt a blow that temporarily affects its ability to correctly process the senses.

Eye Injuries

The eye is an organ that can sustain quite serious damage, and yet, with proper treatment, make a full recovery. In some instances, though, an eye can suffer what might initially be considered a minor injury, and be permanently damaged. Care should always be taken to avoid eye injuries by wearing the appropriate protective gear. All eye injuries can generally be placed into two categories. These are: minor and major.

Minor Eye Injuries

Minor eye injuries are injuries where the eye has been struck by a foreign object, or has a small object adhering to its surface, causing irritation. These injuries are characterized by bloodshot eyes and an urge by the victim to rub the injured areas. The treatment of a minor eye injury is a follows:

- Flush the eye with water, and wash the foreign object out of the eye, as depicted in Figure 7-38.
- If this fails, touch the corner of a clean cloth to the object and lift it off the surface of the eye.
- Seek professional medical aid if vision is affected.
- Do not push the object around the eye's surface.
- Do not permit the victim to rub his or her eyes.
- Only use eye drops if they are prescribed by a doctor.

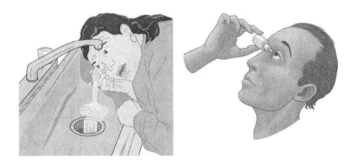

Figure 7-38: Flush the Injured Eye

Major Eye Injuries

Major eye injuries are injuries that involve the penetration of the eye, or involve severe blunt trauma to the eye. Symptoms may include blood in the eye, penetrating objects protruding from the eye, the disturbance of vision, the protrusion of eye contents, and severe pain and spasms. Victim care in case of a major eye injury is critical, and should be left to the medical professionals. Seek help immediately!

Welder's Flash

Welder's Flash is the result of staring, or inadvertently looking, at the intense light caused during welding fabrication, while not wearing appropriate eye protection. The damage caused to the eye's cornea by exposure to this intense light can be painful and, in some cases, permanent. If welder's flash is suspected, apply cool compresses and cover the eyes with pads. Seek medical attention if the pain and/or spots persist.

Welder's Flash

REVIEW QUESTIONS

The following questions test your knowledge of the material presented in this chapter:

1. In the United States, which organization is responsible for the formulation and enforcement of worker safety regulations?

2. According to the American National Standards Institute (ANSI), what is the protection against impact required for safety glasses?

3. When a hard hat no longer holds securely to the head, what action should be taken?

4. What precaution should be taken when wearing steel-toed boots?

5. Under what working conditions can permanent hearing damage occur?

6. What does the acronym CPR stand for?

7. What is the uniform threshold height set by OSHA Standard 1910.66 for providing consistent free fall protection?

8. What operational principle is used by a rope grab deceleration device?

9. Prior to conducting work on any wiring, what should be done?

10. What forms of identification are commonly worn by people who suffer from certain medical conditions for which signs and symptoms are readily observable?

11. Which of the body's blood vessels are responsible for returning blood to the heart?

12. Define the term cardiac arrest.

13. Lethal danger from electrical shock appears at what voltage level?

14. What observation identifies a compound fracture?

15. What is a closed type of head injury that usually develops several hours following an incident?

1. Select the correct approach for to the administration of first aid to an injured fellow worker.
   a. First, place the injured worker in a sitting position.
   b. Push or drag the victim off of live electrical conductors prior to administering artificial respiration.
   c. Connect the defibrillator paddles quickly.
   d. Do not administer first aid procedures unless you are professionally trained in first aid.

2. List the possible level of electricity (shock) considered lethal to humans.
   a. 25 microamps
   b. 250 microamps
   c. 25 milliamps
   d. 2.5 amps

3. Which of the following OSHA body restraint rules is the law?
   a. No body restraints are required unless you are working on federal projects.
   b. Performing work above 3 feet in height requires an observer.
   c. OSHA approved helmets are required for work performed above 3 feet in height.
   d. Body restraints and lanyards are required for contractor employees' workers in positions to fall possibly 6 feet or more.

4. Which ladder safety policy is not correct?
   a. Extension ladders should be placed against a building angled at least 30 degrees from vertical.
   b. A ladder utilizing or braced on telephone or cable line strand, or a power pole, should be secured to the pole or strand prior to beginning a work procedure.
   c. Fellow workers can be injured if wind or another event causes a worker carrying a ladder to drop it.
   d. Power lines are located above the levels where home electronics integrators are required to operate.

5. Identify which of the following fall prevention measures is incorrect.
   a. Inspect all fall-protection devices, such as safety belts or harnesses, after using them.
   b. Ensure that all employees are trained to recognize potential fall hazards.
   c. Keep all working areas and walkways free of debris.
   d. Remove any damaged component from service immediately.

6. All of the following guidelines for hand and power tool safety are valid, except:
   a. cleaning tools after every use, and keeping any cutting edges sharp.
   b. always testing a cutting edge with your fingers, rather than on scrap materials.
   c. selecting the right size of tool for the job.
   d. preventing rust by lightly oiling metal tools, before storing them in a clean, dry place.

7. To prevent injuries during the lifting of work-related materials, never:
   a. use two people when carrying a heavy load.
   b. plan in advance, the route along which the load will be moved.
   c. evaluate the size of the load before lifting.
   d. twist your body, when carrying a heavy load.

8. Which of the following is not a key element of the DR. ABC approach in the care and treatment of a medical emergency victim?
   a. Danger
   b. Retreat
   c. Breathing
   d. Circulation

9. Infectious diseases cannot be contracted through:
   a. various hosts, such as insects, worms, rodents, or other animals.
   b. direct contact.
   c. phone contact.
   d. indirect contact.

10. Which of the following is not a recognized method for delivering EAR?
    a. Mouth-to-ear
    b. Mouth-to-mouth
    c. Mouth-to-nose
    d. Mouth-to-nose-and-mouth

CHAPTER 8

BUILDING CODES AND COMPLIANCE

Upon completion of this chapter you will be able to perform the following tasks:

1. Understand the difference between standards, codes, regulations and laws – and the role of each as it applies to green technology.

2. List those standards, codes and governmental agencies that have a major impact on work performed within the green technology industry.

3. Understand the National Electrical Code and the sections contained within it that apply to green technology projects.

4. Discuss the role of building codes such as the International Building Code, the International Energy Conservation Code and NFPA 5000 within the building industry.

5. Understand the role of Underwriters Laboratories (UL) in the evaluation and certification of products.

6. Describe the role of the Environmental Protection Agency (EPA) in relation to green technology, the services and programs they offer as well as the regulations they enforce.

7. Be familiar with the Master Format and its role within the construction industry.

8. Be prepared to list and discuss the various local and state regulations that may affect air pollution, water pollution, and hazardous waste management.

9. Discuss the process by which industry standards are made and their impact.

10. Explain the purpose and reasons for technician adherence to the National Electric Code (NEC) and National Fire Protection Association (NFPA) codes.

11. Explain the purpose and usage of the International Residential Code.

Building Codes and Compliance

INTRODUCTION

There are many people at many levels within industry and government that create rules that must be or should be complied with when creating green systems. The rules take a number of forms. They include:

- **Standards**: Usually written by industry experts, standards seek to explain the way systems should be designed and/or installed so that they will work the way they were intended to work. They may also try to enforce a consistency on the industry (such as all plugs fitting into the appropriate wall socket). Usually standards do not have the force of law, but are recommended **Industry Best Practices**. Often these standards are referenced in contracts as a convenient way to make sure that the project is designed and installed properly (for example, the contract might state that the insulation in the building must comply with ASTM C739 - 08 Standard Specification for Cellulosic Fiber Loose-Fill Thermal Insulation. In this way the customer (who probably does not know a great deal about insulation) can feel assured the system will be designed and installed properly.

- **Codes**: Codes (also typically written by industry experts) normally focus on health and safety issues (how to install a system so no one is hurt or killed) to a greater extent than performance issues (how well the system works). Codes often are adopted by governmental bodies and once they are adopted, they do have the force of law.

- **Regulations**: Usually created by administrative agencies or within the executive branch of a government (mayors, governors, etc), regulations are designed to control certain behaviors or practices that government finds either objectionable, or wishes to encourage. For example, a city may require that a permit be obtained in order to install a composting toilet within a building. It is best to assume that these regulations also have the force of law (although they are often challenged in court).

- **Laws or Statutes**: Passed by a legislative body (city council, county commissioners, Congress, etc), these are laws. Failure to follow these rules can result in fines and/or jail time.

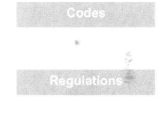

GREEN TECHNOLOGY REQUIREMENTS IN THE UNITED STATES

It would be impossible to list all the rules and requirements that apply even to one small part of the green technology field. Every city, county, state, region, province, or township in every nation of the world has their own complex set of requirements. For this reason, it is important to check with the appropriate local officials to see what rules apply in a specific location. Even then it may not be entirely clear.

The list of agencies and organizations involved in setting rules and guidelines for the design and installation of "green" products is almost endless, but within the United States, green technology technicians should, at a minimum, be familiar with the following:

- The National Electrical Code (NEC)
- The National Fire Protection Association (NFPA)
- International Building Code (IBC)
- International Energy Conservation Code (IECC)
- Underwriters Laboratories (UL)
- The Environmental Protection Agency (EPA)
- Occupational Safety & Health Administration (OSHA)
- The Army Corps of Engineers
- The American National Standards Institute (ANSI)
- International Organization of Standardization (ISO)
- Construction Specifications Institute (CSI) Master Format
- As well as a host of Federal, state and local programs, laws and regulations.

Additionally, green-technology professionals should also be familiar with specific standards issued by not-for-profit organizations such as:

- Air Conditioning, Heating, and Refrigeration Institute (AHRI)
- American National Standards Institute (ANSI)
- American Society of Heating Refrigerating and Air Conditioning Engineers (ASHRAE)
- American Society for Testing and Materials International (ASTM)
- Illuminating Engineering Society of North America (IESNA)
- Institute of Electrical and Electronics Engineers (IEEE)
- National Fenestration Rating Council, Inc. (NFRC)

U.S. Energy Conservation and Production Act (ECPA)

ANSI/ASHRAE/IESNA Standard 90.1

Energy Standard for Buildings Except Low-Rise Residential Buildings

International Energy Conservation Code (IECC)

International Residential Code (IRC)

The **U.S. Energy Conservation and Production Act (ECPA)** requires that each state certify that it has a commercial building code (includes office, industrial, warehouse, school, religious, dormitories, and high-rise residential buildings) that meets or exceeds **ANSI/ASHRAE/IESNA Standard 90.1 – Energy Standard for Buildings Except Low-Rise Residential Buildings**. ASHRAE 90.1 is the most commonly used energy code for commercial and other non-residential buildings.

The **International Energy Conservation Code (IECC)** is the most commonly used residential energy code by states. The **International Residential Code (IRC)** is also used by some states.

BUILDING CODES

Building codes vary between different municipal and state inspection and regulatory organizations. The preferred guideline for electricians, electrical contractors, engineers, and inspectors, are the **National Electrical Code (NEC)** and **American National Standards Institute (ANSI)** standards. Technical adherence to these codes helps to prevent electrical shock or fire/smoke hazards in buildings. However, in most locations local authorities are responsible for rule interpretation and code enforcement. As such, they have precedence over national NEC and ANSI standards. Because final inspections for residential environments are the responsibility of local authorities, the local city or town electrical inspector should be contacted before any wiring work is undertaken.

National Fire Protection Association

The **National Fire Protection Association (NFPA)** develops, publishes, and disseminates timely consensus codes and standards intended to minimize the possibility and effects of fire and other risks. Virtually every building, process, service, design, and installation in society is affected by NFPA documents. As an insurance industry group, the NFPA's focus on true consensus has helped the association's code-development process earn accreditation from the American National Standards Institute. The NFPA is the sponsoring agency for NFPA 70, which is also called the National Electric Code (NEC).

The National Electrical Code

The National Electrical Code (NEC), also referred to as **NFPA 70**, is a document that outlines practices for the safe installation of electrical wiring and equipment. It is published by the National Fire Protection Association (NFPA) and seeks to "codify" the requirements of safe electrical installations in a single source. The code is written by industry experts through a consensus process (meaning everyone must agree).

It is quite common for governmental bodies within the U.S. and other nations to adopt all or part of the NEC into law. For example, a city may rule that compliance with the NEC is a requirement for buildings located within the city limits. A contractor who does not comply with this ruling may face fines and/or (in extreme cases) imprisonment.

As a consequence, anyone performing green technology services should check with local officials to determine which codes apply to the project. The NEC is updated every three years. Governments, however, do not always keep up with the changes. So even though the NEC 2008 code has been published, a particular city or state may still require compliance with an older version (NEC 2002 for example).

The NEC is divided into eight main chapters, each dealing with a different aspect of electrical system safety. These include:

- Chapter 1: Introduction. Addresses general requirements for electrical installations.
- Chapter 2: Wiring and Protection. This section deals with the safety concerns of wiring a building and protecting occupants and systems. Safe installation methods of circuits, over-current protection, grounding and bonding, are some of the issues addressed here.

- Chapter 3: Wiring Methods and Materials. The installation of various wiring types as well as distribution systems (such as conduit, raceways, etc) are described in this chapter.

- Chapter 4: Equipment for General Use. In this chapter, the NEC addresses how to safely install switches, fixtures, control panels, lights, space heaters, motors, air conditioning equipment, etc.

- Chapter 5: Special Occupancies. This chapter looks into the unique safety issues associated with the electrical needs of specific activities, such as fuel dispensing, health care facilities, theaters, amusement parks, airports, etc.

- Chapter 6: Special Equipment. Equipment that presents unique electrical challenges outside the scope of a normal building project is addressed here. They may include: x-ray equipment, electrified truck-stop parking spaces, elevators, cranes, electric vehicle charging stations, etc.

- Chapter 7: Special Conditions. Emergency systems, such as the powering of 911 call centers have their own unique set of requirements. These, along with other special situations are addressed here.

- Chapter 8: Communications Systems. The NEC addresses the safety concerns associated with the installation of communications, radio and television, broadband systems, along with other low-voltage issues.

Articles

The various chapters within the NEC are further divided into **Articles** that address specific applications within these broad categories. Aside from a good overall understanding of the NEC as it applies to electrical installations, those interested in the design and installation of green technologies should be familiar with:

- Article 100: General Wiring. A good understanding of safe wiring practices is a must.

- Article 240: Overcurrent Protection. This describes the safe installation of fuses, circuit breakers, disconnects and other aspects to overcurrent protection.

- Article 250: Grounding and Bonding.

- Article 410: Luminaires, Lampholders, and Lamps. When addressing the lighting concerns within a building, this section of the NEC is critical.

- Article 424: Fixed Electric Space-Heating Equipment.

- Article 440: Air-Conditioning and Refrigerating Equipment.

- Article 445: Generators. Generators are often installed as part of a sustainable energy powering system (such as photovoltaic or wind). This section outlines the steps necessary to install them safely.

- Article 480: Storage Batteries. There are many requirements associated with the safe installation of stationary batteries incorporated for the storage of power from green energy systems.

- Article 625: Electric Vehicle Charging System. As more people integrate electric vehicles into their lifestyle, buildings must be adapted to provide safe and properly installed charging systems.

- Article 685: Integrated Electrical Systems. Some industrial systems (such as a nuclear power plant, for example) must have a safe and orderly way for systems to be shut down. This article addresses those concerns.

- Article 690: Solar Photovoltaic Systems. Includes all aspects of PV installations, but also goes into more depth (than article 480) on storage battery issues for PV systems.

- Article 692: Fuel Cell Systems.

- Article 700: Emergency Systems. Some systems (such as hospitals, or 911-emergency dispatch) are required by law to have emergency backup systems that automatically supply power if the primary system fails.

- Article 705: Interconnected Electric Power Production Sources. Sustainable power systems, such as wind, solar, hydro and fuel cell often work in parallel with other power systems, such as the utility's electrical grid. This article outlines the requirements associated with interconnecting these system. Exceptions include PV systems (where interconnection issues are outlined in more detail in Article 690) and fuel cell systems (where these issues are addressed in Article 692).

The International Building Code

In the United States, three regional building codes have traditionally been written and adopted. In the eastern and midwest U.S., states have used a set of building codes developed by the **Building Officials Code Administrators International (BOCA)**. In the southeastern U.S., states adopted codes written by the **Southern Building Code Congress International (SBCCI)** and on the west coast, codes published by the **International Conference of Building Officials (ICBO)** were used. This often led to confusion, especially on projects that spanned several states.

In 1994 these three groups decided to join forces to create just one set of building standards. The result was the **International Building Code (IBC)**, first published in 2000 by the combined organization renamed the **International Code Council (ICC)**.

International Energy Conservation Code

The ICC also publishes a standard that focuses exclusively on energy savings within buildings. The **International Energy Conservation Code** (latest edition 2009) addresses the design of energy-efficient building envelopes and the installation of energy-efficient mechanical, lighting and power systems. Heating and cooling load calculations, basic material requirements, insulation and window issues are addressed for multiple climates for commercial and residential buildings.

Codes often reference other standards within their text. For example, the 2009 IECC references the energy-efficiency standards listed in Table 8-1. If a code (such as the IECC) is adopted by a state or municipality, the portions referenced from other standards become part of the adopted code, and then also have the effect of law within that jurisdiction.

Building Officials Code Administrators International (BOCA)

Southern Building Code Congress International (SBCCI)

International Conference of Building Officials (ICBO)

International Building Code (IBC)

International Code Council (ICC)

International Energy Conservation Code

Table 8-1: Standards Referenced in the 2009 International Energy Conservation Code

STANDARDS BODY	TITLE
American Architectural Manufacturers Association (AAMA)	Specifications for Windows, Doors and Unit Skylights
Air Conditioning, Heating, and Refrigeration Institute (AHRI)	Unitary Air-Conditioning and Air-Source Heat Pump Equipment
Air Conditioning, Heating, and Refrigeration Institute (AHRI)	Standard for Packaged Terminal Air-conditioners and Heat Pumps
Air Conditioning, Heating, and Refrigeration Institute (AHRI)	Commercial and Industrial Unitary Air-conditioning and Heat Pump Equipment
Air Conditioning, Heating, and Refrigeration Institute (AHRI)	Commercial and Industrial Unitary Air-conditioning Condensing Units
Air Conditioning, Heating, and Refrigeration Institute (AHRI)	Room Fan-coil
Air Conditioning, Heating, and Refrigeration Institute (AHRI)	Water Chilling Packages Using the Vapor Compression Cycle—with Addenda
Air Conditioning, Heating, and Refrigeration Institute (AHRI)	Absorption Water Chilling and Water Heating Packages
Air Conditioning, Heating, and Refrigeration Institute (AHRI)	Unit Ventilators
Air Conditioning, Heating, and Refrigeration Institute (AHRI)	Water-source Heat Pumps—Testing and Rating for Performance—Part 1: Water-to-air and Brine-to-air Heat Pumps
Air Conditioning, Heating, and Refrigeration Institute (AHRI)	Performance Rating of Heat Pump Pool Heaters
Air Movement and Control Association International (AMCA)	Laboratory Methods for Testing Dampers for Rating
American National Standards Institute (ANSI)	Gas Water Heaters, Volume III - Storage Water Heaters with Input Ratings Above 75,000 Btu per Hour, Circulating Tank and Instantaneous
American National Standards Institute (ANSI)	Gas-fired Low Pressure Steam and Hot Water Boilers
American National Standards Institute (ANSI)	Gas-fired Central Furnaces
American National Standards Institute (ANSI)	Gas Unit Heaters and Gas-Fired Duct Furnace
American Society of Heating, Refrigerating and Air-Conditioning Engineers, Inc (ASHRAE)	Air Leakage Performance for Detached Single-family Residential Buildings
American Society of Heating, Refrigerating and Air-Conditioning Engineers, Inc (ASHRAE)	Standard Method of Test for the Evaluation of Building Energy Analysis Computer Programs
American Society of Heating, Refrigerating and Air-Conditioning Engineers, Inc (ASHRAE)	Testing and Rating Pool Heaters
American Society of Heating, Refrigerating and Air-Conditioning Engineers, Inc (ASHRAE)	Peak Cooling and Heating Load Calculations in Buildings Except Low-rise Residential Buildings
American Society of Heating, Refrigerating and Air-Conditioning Engineers, Inc (ASHRAE)	Water-source Heat Pumps—Testing and Rating for Performance—Part 1: Water-to-air and Brine-to-air Heat Pumps
American Society of Heating, Refrigerating and Air-Conditioning Engineers, Inc (ASHRAE)	Energy Standard for Buildings Except Low-rise Residential Buildings
American Society of Heating, Refrigerating and Air-Conditioning Engineers, Inc (ASHRAE)	ASHRAE Handbook of Fundamentals
American Society of Heating, Refrigerating and Air-Conditioning Engineers, Inc (ASHRAE)	ASHRAE HVAC Systems and Equipment Handbook-2004
American Society of Mechanical Engineers (ASME)	Steam Generating Units
ASTM International	Specification for Load-bearing Concrete Masonry Units.
ASTM International	Test Method for Determining the Rate of Air Leakage Through Exterior Windows, Curtain Walls and Doors Under Specified Pressure Differences Across the Specimen
Canadian Standards Association (CSA)	Specifications for Windows, Doors and Unit Skylights
U.S. Department of Energy (DOE)	Uniform Test Method for Measuring the Energy Consumption of Water Heaters
U.S. Department of Energy (DOE)	Uniform Test Method for Measuring the Energy Consumption of Furnaces and Boilers
U.S. Department of Energy (DOE)	Test Procedures and Efficiency Standards for Commercial Packaged Boilers
U.S. Department of Energy (DOE)	State Energy Prices and Expenditure Report
International Code Council, Inc. (ICC)	International Building Code
International Code Council, Inc. (ICC)	International Fire Code
International Code Council, Inc. (ICC)	International Fuel Gas Code
International Code Council, Inc. (ICC)	International Mechanical Code
International Code Council, Inc. (ICC)	International Plumbing Code
International Code Council, Inc. (ICC)	International Residential Code
Illuminating Engineering Society of North America (IESNA)	Energy Standard for Buildings Except Low-rise Residential Buildings
National Fenestration Rating Council, Inc. (NFRC)	Procedure for Determining Fenestration Product U-factors—Second Edition
National Fenestration Rating Council, Inc. (NFRC)	Procedure for Determining Fenestration Product Solar Heat Gain Coefficients and Visible Transmittance at Normal Incidence—Second Edition

Table 8-1: Standards Referenced in the 2009 International Energy Conservation Code (cont.)

STANDARDS BODY	TITLE
National Fenestration Rating Council, Inc. (NFRC)	Procedure for Determining Fenestration Product Air Leakage—Second Edition
Sheet Metal and Air Conditioning Contractors National Association, Inc. (SMACNA)	HVAC Air Duct Leakage Test Manual
Underwriters Laboratories Inc (UL)	Oil-fired Central Furnaces
Underwriters Laboratories Inc (UL)	Oil-fired Unit Heaters—with Revisions through February 2006
United States - Federal Trade Commission (FTC)	R-value Rule
Window and Door Manufacturers Association (WDMA)	Specifications for Windows, Doors and Unit Skylights

NFPA 5000: Building Construction and Safety Code

In addition to the NEC, the NFPA also publishes the **NFPA 5000: Building Construction and Safety Code**, which also seeks to outline all construction, protection and occupancy features necessary to minimize the danger to life and property within the building construction industry.

First introduced in 2003 (and updated every 3 years), the NFPA 5000 was last updated in 2009, increasing harmonization with global measurements and terminologies. Many of the recent revisions have dealt with building issues raised by the 2001 Twin-Towers terrorist attacks in New York. Special attention has been given to dealing with health and safety issues that may arise when first-responders (police, firemen, paramedics) are called to address incidents within the building.

There have been repeated efforts by groups such as the **American Institute of Architects (AIA)**, **BOMA International** (Building Owners and Managers Association) and the **National Association of Home Builders (NAHB)** to get NFPA and ICC to cooperate and create just one set of uniform standards, but thus far these attempts have failed. As demonstrated in Table 8-2, the subject matter contained in both codes is quite similar.

Table 8-2: Comparison of NFPA 5000 and IBC

NFPA 5000 (2009) TABLE OF CONTENTS	IBC (2009) TABLE OF CONTENTS
Chapter 1: Administration	Chapter 1: Scope and Administration
Chapter 2: Referenced Publications	
Chapter 3: Definitions	Chapter 2: Definitions
Chapter 4: General	
Chapter 5: Performance-Based Option	
Chapter 6: Classification of Occupancy, Classification of Hazard of Contents, and Special Operations	Chapter 3: Use and Occupancy Classification
Chapter 7: Construction Types and Height and Area Requirements	Chapter 5: General Building Heights and Areas
Chapter 8: Fire-Resistive Materials and Construction	Chapter 7: Fire and Smoke Protection Features
Chapter 9: Reserved (placeholder for later version)	
Chapter 10: Interior Finish	Chapter 8: Interior Finishes
Chapter 11: Means of Egress	Chapter 10: Means of Egress
Chapter 12: Accessibility	Chapter 11: Accessibility
Chapter 13: Encroachments into the Public Right-of-Way	Chapter 32: Encroachments into the Public Right-of-Way
Chapter 14: Safeguards During Construction	Chapter 33: Safeguards During Construction
Chapter 15: Building Rehabilitation	Chapter 34: Existing Structures
Chapter 16: Assembly Occupancies	Chapter 4: Special Detailed Requirements Based on Use and Occupancy
Chapter 17: Educational Occupancies	Chapter 4: Special Detailed Requirements Based on Use and Occupancy
Chapter 18: Day-Care Occupancies	Chapter 4: Special Detailed Requirements Based on Use and Occupancy
Chapter 19: Health Care Occupancies	Chapter 4: Special Detailed Requirements Based on Use and Occupancy

Table 8-2: Comparison of NFPA 5000 and IBC (cont.)

NFPA 5000 (2009) TABLE OF CONTENTS	IBC (2009) TABLE OF CONTENTS
Chapter 20: Ambulatory Health Care Occupancies	Chapter 4: Special Detailed Requirements Based on Use and Occupancy
Chapter 21: Detention and Correctional Occupancies	Chapter 4: Special Detailed Requirements Based on Use and Occupancy
Chapter 22: One- and Two-Family Dwellings	Chapter 6: Types of Construction
Chapter 23: Lodging or Rooming House Occupancies	Chapter 4: Special Detailed Requirements Based on Use and Occupancy
Chapter 24: Hotels and Dormitory Occupancies	Chapter 4: Special Detailed Requirements Based on Use and Occupancy
Chapter 25: Apartment Buildings	Chapter 6: Types of Construction
Chapter 26: Residential Board and Care Occupancies	Chapter 4: Special Detailed Requirements Based on Use and Occupancy
Chapter 27: Mercantile Occupancies	Chapter 4: Special Detailed Requirements Based on Use and Occupancy
Chapter 28: Business Occupancies	Chapter 4: Special Detailed Requirements Based on Use and Occupancy
Chapter 29: Industrial Occupancies	Chapter 4: Special Detailed Requirements Based on Use and Occupancy
Chapter 30: Storage Occupancies	Chapter 4: Special Detailed Requirements Based on Use and Occupancy
Chapter 31: Occupancies in Special Structures	Chapter 4: Special Detailed Requirements Based on Use and Occupancy
Chapter 32: Special Construction	Chapter 31: Special Construction
Chapter 33: High-Rise Buildings	Chapter 6: Types of Construction
Chapter 34: High Hazard Contents	
Chapter 35: Structural Design	Chapter 16: Structural Design
Chapter 36: Soils, Foundations, and Retaining Walls	Chapter 18: Soils and Foundations
Chapter 37: Exterior Wall Construction	Chapter 14: Exterior Walls
Chapter 38: Roof Assemblies and Roof Structures	Chapter 15: Roof Assemblies and Rooftop Structures
Chapter 39: Flood-Resistant Design and Construction	Annex G: Flood-Resistant Construction
Chapter 40: Quality Assurance During Construction	Chapter 17: Structural Tests and Special Inspections
Chapter 41: Concrete	Chapter 19: Concrete
Chapter 42: Aluminum	Chapter 20: Aluminum
Chapter 43: Masonry	Chapter 21: Masonry
Chapter 44: Steel	Chapter 22: Steel
Chapter 45: Wood	Chapter 23: Wood
Chapter 46: Glass and Glazing	Chapter 24: Glass and Glazing
Chapter 47: Gypsum Board, Lath, and Plaster	Chapter 25: Gypsum Board and Plaster
Chapter 48: Plastics	Chapter 26: Plastic
Chapter 49: Interior Environment	Chapter 12: Interior Environment
Chapter 50: Mechanical Systems	Chapter 28: Mechanical Systems
Chapter 51: Energy Efficiency	Chapter 13: Energy Efficiency
Chapter 52: Electrical Systems	Chapter 27: Electrical
Chapter 53: Plumbing Systems	Chapter 29: Plumbing Systems
Chapter 54: Elevators and Conveying Systems	Chapter 30: Elevators and Conveying Systems
Chapter 55: Fire Protection Systems and Equipment	Chapter 9: Fire Protection Systems
Annex A: Explanatory Material	Appendix H: Signs
Annex B: Vermin Proofing	Appendix F: Rodentproofing
Annex C: Flood-Resistant Construction	
Annex D: Construction Types and Enhanced Fire Compartment Requirements	
Annex E: Elevators for Occupant-Controlled Evacuation Prior to Phase I Emergency Recall Operations	
Annex F: Supplement Evacuation Equipment	
Annex G: In-Building Radio Systems	
Annex H: Informational References	Chapter 35: Referenced Standards
	Appendix A: Employee Qualifications
	Appendix B: Board of Appeals
	Appendix C: Agricultural Buildings
	Appendix D: Fire Districts
	Appendix I: Patio Covers
	Appendix J: Grading
	Appendix K: Administrative Provisions

Underwriters Laboratories

Underwriters Laboratories (UL) is an independent product safety certification organization that tests products and writes standards for product safety. UL evaluates more than 19,000 types of products, components, materials and systems annually with 20 billion UL Marks appearing on 72,000 manufacturers' products each year.

UL Mark

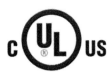

Products that bear the **UL Mark** have been tested and found to meet UL's safety criteria for that specific product. Figure 8-1 shows UL marks common within North America (the mark on the left indicates US only, center mark is for Canada only, and the mark on the right indicates the product has been listed in both countries). Other nations around the world have other listing marks specific to their country.

Figure 8-1: UL Listing Mark

In addition to listing products as meeting UL's safety criteria, UL also lists products for a number of non-safety issues, such as their:

- Energy efficiency
- Effect on drinking water quality
- Impact on the environment and public health

The **UL Classified Mark** indicates that a product has been tested for only certain (but not all) safety hazards. UL also tests products to how they meet specific industry standards, such as their UL Marine Mark, the UL Plumbing Mark, the UL Security Mark, and others.

UL Classified Mark

Governmental Agencies

A number of governmental bodies are involved in the green building industry—writing standards, issuing regulations and ensuring compliance. It would be nearly impossible to list all the agencies involved for every location, but some agencies are encountered within the green building industry more often than others. It is the technician's responsibility to investigate and ensure that the various agencies that may have jurisdiction over a specific project have been contacted.

The Environmental Protection Agency

The **U.S. Environmental Protection Agency (EPA)** is the arm of the Federal government that monitors air, water, land and human health. The goals of the agency (according the their 2006-2011 five-year strategic plan) are to focus on clean air and global climate change, clean and safe water, land preservation and restoration, healthy communities and ecosystems, compliance and environmental stewardship.

U.S. Environmental Protection Agency (EPA)

In attempting to achieve these goals, the EPA promotes a number of programs and issues a vast number of publications and standards that are of interest to green-technology technicians. Some of these include:

- **Energy Star Program**: This is the very successful program to evaluate and label products and homes as to their energy efficiency, giving the public an effective way of comparing the energy efficiency of competing products.

Energy Star Program

Figure 8-2: EPA Design for the Environment Label

Federal Electronics Challenge (FEC)

Green Chemistry

GreenScapes

National Service Center for Environmental Publications (NSCEP)

National Environmental Publications Internet Site (NEPIS)

Indoor Air Quality (IAQ)

- **Pollution Prevention (P2) Programs**: The **Pollution Prevention Act of 1990** was designed to assist in the reduction of industrial pollutants released into the environment.

- The EPA has developed a number of public/private partnership programs to assist in carrying out the goals of this legislation. Some of these include:

  - Design for the environment
  - Federal electronics challenge
  - Green chemistry
  - GreenScapes

Design for the Environment (DfE): This program has worked with more than 200,000 industrial facilities to reduce the number of chemicals used within business processes. The DfE claims to have reduced the amount of chemicals used in 2008 by 335 million pounds. Over 1000 products have been awarded the DfE seal, as shown in Figure 8-2, indicating that the product contains the safest materials available (that are suitable for the manufacture of that product) and that the manufacturer has invested heavily in reducing the amount of "chemicals of concern" used in their processes.

The **Federal Electronics Challenge (FEC)** is a voluntary partnership program that encourages federal facilities and agencies to purchase greener electronic products, reduce the impacts of electronic products while in use, and discard obsolete electronics in an environmentally safe way.

Green Chemistry is another voluntary program administered by the EPA that issues challenges and presents awards in the design of chemical products and processes that reduce or eliminate hazardous substances. Green chemistry reviews the entire life cycle of a chemical product, including its design, manufacture, and use.

The **GreenScapes** program provides cost-efficient and environmentally-friendly solutions for landscaping. It is designed to help preserve natural resources and prevent waste and pollution in the landscaping of residential, commercial and industrial buildings and campuses.

As part of their education and outreach program, the EPA offers a number of helpful publications available to the public. More than 31,000 documents are available (free of charge) from the agency. EPA's print publications can be obtained through the **National Service Center for Environmental Publications** (**NSCEP**), and EPA's digital publications are stored in the **National Environmental Publications Internet Site** (**NEPIS**) database. Some examples of available titles include:

- *Managing Your Environmental Responsibilities: A Planning Guide for Construction and Development* (also referred to as the **MYER Guide**). This document is designed to help building project developers determine what permitting and compliance requirements exist in the areas of: storm water management; the dredging and filling of wetlands; oil spill prevention; solid waste; hazardous substances; air quality (such as dust and the burning of debris); asbestos, and endangered species issues.

- *The Small Business Compliance Policy* that sets out what might cause a small business to be penalized, and how they may be eligible for the elimination or reduction of these penalties if violations are voluntarily discovered, disclosed and corrected.

- *The Indoor airPLUS Construction Specifications.* Developed by the EPA to recognize new homes equipped with a comprehensive set of **Indoor Air Quality** (**IAQ**) features—addressing issues such as moisture control, radon control, pest barriers, HVAC systems, combustion pollutant control, low emission materials and home commissioning (testing and inspecting the systems).

In addition to voluntary programs, the EPA also writes a number of regulations and administers and enforces environmental laws passed by Congress, as well as **Executive Orders (EO)** issued by the President. Many of the laws that are of concern to the green building industry are listed in Table 8-3.

Table 8-3: Selected Laws Administered by the EPA

LAW (DATE ORIGINALLY PASSED)	IMPACT ON GREEN TECHNICIANS
Atomic Energy Act (1946)	Applies to nuclear power plants and gives the EPA the responsibility to set environmental radiation standards.
Clean Air Act (1963)	Gives the EPA broad authority to implement and enforce regulations reducing air pollutant emissions and set maximum acceptable levels of contaminants (including within buildings). The 1990 Amendments placed an increased emphasis on more cost-effective approaches to reduce air pollution.
Clean Water Act (1972)	Under this act, the EPA has implemented pollution control programs such as setting wastewater standards for industry. They have also set water quality standards for all contaminants in surface waters (affecting gray water systems, septic tanks, storm water runoff, etc).
Endangered Species Act (1973)	Protects endangered animals and plants from further harm. May affect building projects if a listed animal or plant is present at the site.
Energy Policy Act (2005)	This act addresses energy production in the United States, including: energy efficiency; renewable energy; fossil fuels; nuclear matters and security; vehicles and motor fuels, including ethanol(increased amounts that could be added to gasoline); hydrogen; electricity; energy tax incentives; hydropower and geothermal energy; and climate change technology. The act provides loan guarantees for entities that develop or use innovative technologies that avoid the production of greenhouse gases.
National Technology Transfer and Advancement Act (1996)	Among its provisions is the requirement that government work with and adopt industry standards whenever practical and when they do not conflict with existing law.
Occupational Safety and Health (1970)	Congress passed the Occupational and Safety Health Act (OSHA) to ensure worker and workplace safety. The goal was to make sure employers provide their workers a workplace free from hazards to safety and health, such as exposure to toxic chemicals, excessive noise levels, mechanical dangers, heat or cold stress, or unsanitary conditions.
Pollution Prevention Act (1990)	The Pollution Prevention Act focused industry, government, and public attention on reducing the amount of pollution through cost-effective changes in production, operation, and raw materials use.
	Pollution prevention covered by this Act also includes other practices that increase efficiency in the use of energy, water, or other natural resources, and protect our resource base through conservation. These practices include recycling, source reduction, and sustainable agriculture.
Resource Conservation and Recovery Act (1976)	This Act gives the EPA the authority to control hazardous waste at all stages, from production to disposal. This includes the generation, transportation, treatment, storage, and disposal of hazardous waste. It also deals with the management of non-hazardous solid wastes as well as underground tanks used to store petroleum or other hazardous substances.
Safe Drinking Water Act (1974)	This law was created to protect the quality of drinking water in the U.S. It focuses on all waters actually or potentially designed for drinking use, whether from above ground or underground sources.
Toxic substance Control Act (1976)	This law gave the EPA control over many of the chemicals and combinations of chemicals used (with the exception of food, cosmetics, drugs and pesticides). For example, this act addresses the production, use and disposal of chemicals used or found in buildings such as radon gas, asbestos, lead-based paint and polychlorinated biphenyls (PCBs).

Occupational Safety and Health Act

People spend a great deal of their day at work, and often the tasks associated with performing the job involve a certain amount of risk. As a result, each year 4.2 million Americans are injured or fall ill while at work. In 2006, 5,703 people were killed in the workplace in the U.S.

While this number may seem high, since the **Occupational Safety and Health Act (OSHA)** was adopted in 1971, workplace deaths have declined 62% and workplace injuries have fallen by 42%. OSHA's mission is to reduce hazards within the workplace, thereby reducing the likelihood or injury or death. The agency performs workplace inspections (about 37,000 firms are inspected each year) and issues fines if they determine that violations of the workplace safety rules are present. Employers with 11 or more employees are required to maintain safety records and have them available for review.

While OSHA requirements are of importance to green technicians during the construction of a project (complying with rules as varied as personal protective equipment, to sanitation, to safety training), it should be kept in mind that the commercial building where these sustainable systems are installed will also be someone else's workplace—so OSHA rules may also affect how the final product is designed.

For example, OSHA defines how a workplace must be ventilated to ensure worker safety. They also have established guidelines for lighting the workplace, especially in areas such as stairwells, where poor lighting could result in accidents and injuries.

Army Corps of Engineers

Within the U.S., the **Army Corps of Engineers** is the agency with regulatory authority over wetlands, dredging and fill issues. Any project that may impact these areas of concern (such as development of a hydropower system) will likely involve compliance with regulations established by this agency.

Construction Specifications Institute Master Format

The construction of a building is a highly complex project, involving many trades and skills. To participate in this process effectively, it is important that each player understand their role and how they fit within the overall project. With this in mind, the **Construction Specifications Institute (CSI)** has, for the past 40 years, organized the various building trades into a kind of "table of contents," or **Master Format** to help facilitate communications between the people working on a project.

In 2004 the Master Format expanded from 16 Divisions to 50, reflecting the many changes (such as increased use of technology and green building techniques) now integrated into commercial buildings. Table 8-4 lists the 50 Divisions (although only 34 are currently used, with 16 divisions reserved for future technologies or organizational revisions) of the current Master Format.

Table 8-4: Comparison between 1995 and 2004 Master Format

MASTER FORMAT 1995	1995 EQUIVALENT	MASTER FORMAT 2004
Division 1 General Requirement	1	Division 00 Procurement and Contracting Requirements
Division 2 Site Work	1	Division 01 General Requirements
Division 3 Concrete	2	Division 02 Existing Conditions
Division 4 Masonry	3	Division 03 Concrete
Division 5 Metals	4	Division 04 Masonry
Division 6 Carpentry	5	Division 05 Metals
Division 7 Moisture Control	6	Division 06 Wood, Plastics, and Composites
Division 8 Doors, Windows	7	Division 07 Thermal and Moisture Protection
Division 9 Finishes	8	Division 08 Openings
Division 1 0 Specialties	9	Division 09 Finishes
Division 11 Equipment	10	Division 10 Specialties
Division 12 Furnishings	11	Division 11 Equipment
Division 13 Special Construction	12	Division 12 Furnishings
Division 14 Conveying Systems	13	Division 13 Special Construction
Division 15 Mechanical	14	Division 14 Conveying Equipment
Division 16 Electrical	13	Division 21 Fire Suppression
	15	Division 22 Plumbing
	15	Division 23 Heating, Ventilating, and Air Conditioning
	New	Division 25 Integrated Automation
	16	Division 26 Electrical
	16	Division 27 Communications
	16	Division 28 Electronic Safety and Security
	2	Division 31 Earthwork
	2	Division 32 Exterior Improvements
	2	Division 33 Utilities
	New	Division 34 Transportation
	New	Division 35 Waterway and Marine Construction
	New	Division 40 Process Integration
	New	Division 41 Material Processing and Handling Equipment
	New	Division 42 Process Heating, Cooling, and Drying Equipment
	New	Division 43 Process Gas & Liquid Handling, Purification, & Storage Equipment
	New	Division 44 Pollution Control Equipment
	New	Division 45 Industry-Specific Manufacturing Equipment
	New	Division 48 Electrical Power Generation

The revised organization of the Master Format provides a convenient way for those preparing green construction project specifications to make sure the various sustainability considerations are contained within them.

For example, Division 1 is the area that describes the general administrative project requirements. *Section 01 35 43 Environmental Procedures* provides a place (and a reminder) within the specifications to state the project's environmental goals. Issues such as resource efficiency, energy efficiency, indoor air quality, environmental construction techniques, building component reuse, and construction recycling can be addressed within the document in this section.

Other areas within Division 1 allow the project developer to state requirements as to how construction waste to dispose of, what materials must be used, etc. *Section 01 80 00 Performance Requirements* spells out the levels at which the finished product must perform. For instance, air quality, energy efficiency and other aspects of sustainable design can be listed in great detail.

Throughout the various divisions, environmental specifications are now fully integrated into the process. There were also several new divisions added in the 2004 version that are of particular interest to those involved in green technology. These include:

- *Division 25 – Integrated Automation:* This section now incorporates specifications for automated environmental controls integrated into the lighting, heating, water and air quality systems.

- *Division 44 – Pollution Control Equipment:* Addresses air, water, and noise pollution within the building as well as solid waste disposal issues.

- *Division 48 – Electrical Power Generation:* Provides specifications for incorporating solar, wind, fuel cell, geothermal, electrochemical (batteries), hydro and even nuclear power within buildings.

State and Local Regulations

State Environmental Law

In general, **State Environmental Law** tends to follow Federal law. States often enact their own legislation governing such things as air pollution, water pollution, and hazardous waste management. The state legislation is, however, generally similar to or perhaps identical to the Federal legislation.

Each state also has the equivalent of an EPA, with authority for overseeing environmental protection issues within that state. In many cases the states have the authority to pass environmental legislation that is more stringent than Federal laws. Typically states cannot set environmental standards that are lower than those established by the Federal government.

States often have significant groundwater protection responsibilities. They may oversee the permitting of wells, as well as pollution concerns generated by underground storage tanks. Additionally, states may have enacted a number of statutes that regulate the discharge of surface water and protect drinking water sources.

Many local authorities have also created rules and guidelines that will affect green energy and construction projects. These include:

- **Building Codes**: Check with local building code officials to determine what requirements are in place for a specific location. Some building inspectors may require that technicians receive a variance or permit from zoning boards for specific projects (such as the installation of a wind turbine or a composting toilet, for example).

- **Easements**: Most states permit easements, which are a voluntary, legally binding agreement between owners of adjacent land regarding the use of the land. For example, two neighbors may agree that they will not build anything or plant any large trees that might interfere with the flow of air to a wind turbine. These agreements are binding regardless of changing land ownership (the easement remains, even if the land is sold).

- **Local Covenants and Ordinances**: Some communities have covenants or other regulations that specify what homeowners can and cannot do with their property. These regulations may prohibit the use of renewable energy systems for aesthetic or noise-control reasons (for example, a homeowners association may prohibit the display of PV panels where they can be seen by neighbors or the installation of a wind turbine). Some municipalities may restrict or prohibit the collection of rainwater from the roof of the structure. Check with local officials, area building professionals and even neighbors to see what rules and regulations may apply to a specific project.

- **Technology-Specific Requirements**: Additional requirements may be in place depending on the technology installed. For example, wind turbine height requirements may be restricted by the local zoning board, or due to the proximity of the site to a nearby airport or other aviation facility. Microhydro systems may require that the project first obtain water rights allowing for the diversion of water through the system.

- **Utility Interconnection Agreements**: For power quality and safety reasons, rules and regulations exist that must be complied with prior to connecting an alternative energy system (such as fuel cell, wind, solar, or microhydro) to the electrical grid. The **Institute of Electrical and Electronics Engineers (IEEE)** has written a standard (IEEE 1547) that addresses all grid-connected distributed generation including renewable energy systems. In addition, Underwriters Laboratories (UL) has developed a standard (UL 1741) to certify inverters, converters, charge controllers, and output controllers for power-producing stand-alone and grid-connected renewable energy systems.

The Final Electrical Inspection

Local building codes require a final inspection of all electrical work in new and remodeled homes. This usually applies to all low voltage installations as well. The state electrician's license may be required to specify that the electrician is qualified for low voltage work, or a low voltage specialty license may be required as well.

Prior to the final inspection of new or remodeled wiring, all devices and fixtures must be installed. In addition, the service equipment must be completely installed and labeled properly. All wiring must be free from short circuits, ground faults, and open circuits.

Industry Standards

Industry standards exist covering a host of processes, from quality assurance throughout the entire design and construction of a building, to the load-bearing capacity of a living roof, and everything in between.

Most standards are written by committees or sub-committees drawn from within the industry they are attempting to define. These committees meet and decide what are the industry's best practices. The focus may be on safety (the standard does not care if it works, as long as nobody gets hurt) or may incorporate performance criteria (defining the best way to put a system together to make sure it works the way it was intended). Standards are meant to be voluntary, but are often referenced in codes and laws, as well as within contracts. Standards are designed to:

- Make the development and manufacturing of products and services more efficient, safer and more environmentally responsible.

- Facilitate fair trade between countries.

- Provide governments with a technical base for health, safety and environmental legislation.

- Share technological advances and good management practices.

- Safeguard those using the products and services.

- Provide common solutions to common problems (everyone does not need to "reinvent the wheel").

The standards process is generally one of consensus, meaning that all parties involved must agree before the standard may be issued. This often means the process can take a very long time and standards can become "watered down" as specific manufacturers attempt to make sure that their particular product is acceptable within the guidelines set forth in the final document.

After the standard has been written, reviewed within the industry and approved, it is then submitted to a national, regional or international standards body. In the United States, this body is the **American National Standards Institute (ANSI)**. In Canada the national standards body is the **Standards Council of Canada (SCC)**. Most nations have a standards body that reviews standards created within that country.

Regional standards bodies also exist, such as **CENELEC** (*Comité Européen de Normalisation Électrotechnique*), which is the European body overseeing standards within the electrical engineering field, or **COPANT**—the Pan American Standards Commission. There are many regional standards bodies focused on a number of specific industries.

There are also quite a number of international standards bodies. The largest of these is the **International Organization for Standardization (ISO)**. The ISO is comprised of a network of over 160 national standards bodies and has published over 15,000 international standards.

American National Standards Institute (ANSI)

Standards Council of Canada (SCC)

COPANT

International Organization for Standardization (ISO)

Once an industry-specific standard is adopted by a national or regional standards body, it is typically assigned a number and published by the standards body (adhering to a very specific format). The title includes the name of the accrediting body (such as ANSI), the names of the organizations involved in writing the standard (such as ASHRAE or IESNA), the number assigned to the standard, as well as the year it was issued. Some full titles of important standards that apply to the green technology industry in the U.S. include:

- ANSI/ASHRAE/IESNA Standard 90.1-2007 – Energy Standard for Buildings Except Low-Rise Residential Buildings

- ANSI/ASHRAE/IESNA 100-2006 – Energy Conservation in Existing Buildings

- ANSI/ASHRAE Standard 105-2007 – Standard Methods of Measuring, Expressing, and Comparing Building Energy Performance

International Residential Code

The **International Residential Code (IRC)** was developed to provide a modern, up-to-date residential code to address the design and construction of one- and two-family dwellings and townhouses. It lists rules for installing and maintaining residential electrical and communications wiring. This comprehensive, stand-alone residential code establishes minimum regulations for these environments using prescriptive provisions. The 2003 edition of the International Residential Code establishes model code regulations that safeguard the public health and safety in both large and small communities. This is the common workplace for residential electronics system installers. Therefore, you must be aware of the specifics of the Residential Code and how it applies to your job.

A committee appointed by the **International Code Council (ICC)**, and representing the *Building Officials and Code Administrators International, Inc. (BOCA)*, the *International Conference of Building Officials* (ICBO) and the *Southern Building Code Congress International (SBCCI)*, as well as representatives from the *National Association of Home Builders (NAHB)* produced the first edition of the International Residential Code (2000) in 1996.

The overall intent was to draft a comprehensive, stand-alone residential code consistent with, and inclusive of, the scope of the existing model codes. Technical content of the 1998 International One- and Two-Family Dwelling Code and the latest model codes promulgated by BOCA, ICBO, SBCCI and the ICC was utilized as the basis for its development, followed by public hearings in 1998 and 1999 to consider proposed changes. Therefore, the 2003 edition of the IRC presents the code as originally issued, with changes approved through the ICC code development process through the year 2002, and the residential electrical revisions based on the 2002 National Electrical Code (NFPA 70). The electrical provisions were included through an agreement with the National Fire Protection Association (NFPA 70). New editions of the IRC are currently produced every three years.

The IRC is founded on broad-based principles that provide for the use of new materials, and new building designs. Its 2003 edition is fully compatible with all of the international codes (I-Codes) published by the ICC, including the *International Building Code*, the *ICC Electrical Code*, the *International Energy Conservation Code*, the *International Existing Building Code*, the *International Fire Code*, the *International Fuel Gas Code*, the *International Mechanical Code*, the *ICC Performance Code*, the *International Plumbing Code*, the *International Private Sewage Disposal Code*, the *International Property Maintenance Code*, the *International Urban-Wildland Interface Code*, and the *International Zoning Code*.

REVIEW QUESTIONS

The following questions test your knowledge of the material presented in this chapter:

1. Explain the difference between an industry standard and a code that has been adopted into law.

2. How can standards be incorporated into codes?

3. List five standards or codes that a green technician working in the U.S. should be familiar with.

4. Explain the role of the NEC (National Electrical Code) in construction and the various articles that apply to the field of green technology.

5. Explain the difference between a product that receives a UL Listing Mark and a product that receives a UL Classified Mark.

6. List five laws enforced by the EPA and their impact on green technology.

7. Discuss the impact local building codes, easements or ordinances may have on the installation of a wind turbine in a gated suburban community.

8. Explain the role of standards within an industry.

9. What is the purpose of the International Residential Code (IRC)?

10. Give four examples of local regulations that may affect the installation of a PV system.

11. Explain the role of OSHA within the U.S. and how a green technician is affected by regulations required under this act.

12. How are NFPA 5000 and the International Building Code related, and how are they different?

13. What do NEC articles 500 through 517 call areas where fire or explosion hazards may exist due to flammable gases or vapors, flammable liquids, combustible dust, or ignitable fibers and flyings?

14. What is the national, regional, or international standards body in the United States to which an approved industry standard is submitted for review?

15. What are the requirements prior to the final inspection of new or remodeled wiring?

1. Which of the following is voluntary, and does not have the force of law?
   a. a local statute
   b. an adopted code
   c. an executive order
   d. an industry standard

2. Which of the following is NOT currently a building code widely in use within the United States?
   a. The International Building Code
   b. The International Energy Conservation Code
   c. The Southern Building Code Congress International
   d. NFPA 5000: Building Construction and Safety Code

3. Which of the following is NOT a program administered by the Environmental Protection Agency (EPA)?
   a. Master Format
   b. Energy Star
   c. Pollution Prevention (P2)
   d. Green Chemistry

4. The 1971 law focused on protecting the health and safety of workers in the workplace is called:
   a. Occupational Safety and Health Act (OSHA)
   b. American National Safety Initiative (ANSI)
   c. National Federal Protection Act (NFPA)
   d. Workplace Protection Act (WPA)

5. The U.S. Army Corps of Engineers would mostly likely be involved in which of the following projects?
   a. Installation of a microhydro power system.
   b. Writing and publishing national electrical standards.
   c. Testing and approving solar photovoltaic systems for large utilities.
   d. Approving the Master Format.

6. In the United States, most industry standards are approved and published by:
   a. ASHRAE
   b. ANSI
   c. CENELEC
   d. SCC

7. The purpose for technician adherence to NEC and NFPA codes is:
   a. to meet local ordinance requirements.
   b. to prevent electrical shock or fire/smoke hazards in buildings.
   c. to comply with the TIA/EIA wiring standards.
   d. to help convince potential customers that your work is superior to competitors'.

8. The International Residential Code (IRC):
   a. is the same thing as the National Electric Code.
   b. is the same thing as the National Fire Protection Code.
   c. lists rules for installing and maintaining residential electrical and communications wiring.
   d. is the supplier of electric power for rural residents.

9. The Construction Specifications Institute is responsible for compiling and publishing:
   a. the Master Format.
   b. the International Building Code.
   c. the NFPA 5000.
   d. all ANSI standards.

10. Since OSHA was enacted in 1971:
    a. the cost of construction has decreased dramatically.
    b. workplace deaths have declined by 62%.
    c. emitted greenhouse gases have increased dramatically, resulting in a major revision of the act in 1996 to address these concerns.
    d. the International Building Code consolidated three pre-existing codes into one document, as required under provisions in OSHA.

CHAPTER
9

UNDERSTANDING BLUEPRINTS

OBJECTIVES

Upon completion of this chapter and its related hands-on procedures, you will be able to:

1. Characterize the various stages leading to the production of finished blueprints.

2. Differentiate between an architectural schematic drawing and a set of preliminary drawings.

3. Establish why a cover sheet is such an important document.

4. Identify the items of information that would normally appear in the title block.

5. Describe the various types of lines and symbols that are typically found on an architectural drawing.

6. Specify the importance of including building material symbols on a drawing.

7. Explain how topographic symbols help the contractor.

8. Contrast the main differences between an architect's scale and an engineer's scale.

9. Clarify the necessity for working drawings to include a detailed set of specifications.

CHAPTER 9

Understanding Blueprints

INTRODUCTION

Personnel involved in energy auditing should have a basic understanding of architectural and mechanical drawings (more commonly known as **Blueprints**). This chapter is designed to provide the reader with a basic knowledge of blueprint reading.

The original process used to create blueprints was actually a photographic process using iron salts, and producing an image in Prussian blue. The process was very expensive and time-consuming, and resulted in the production of prints of architectural and other technical drawings having white images on blue backgrounds. These drawings were very difficult to read, and did not last for any appreciable amount of time. Fortunately, these types of blueprints are no longer manufactured, nor is the type of paper that was required to make them.

Originals, and even reproductions, of architectural drawings are done either by hand, or more often by using computer-based **Computer-Aided Design and Drafting (CADD)** programs. When a rendering is ready to be transferred to a hard copy, the original is printed using a plotter, either on vellum (a heavy off-white fine-quality paper) for normal use or on mylar (a plastic-coated and durable film), which can easily last for 20 or 30 years.

Copies of an original drawing are achieved by placing the translucent vellum against the chemically treated side of a diazo paper, and feeding the combination through a blueprint machine. As the vellum is exposed to light, the chemical side of the diazo paper is burned at areas where light can get through. The burned areas are chemically treated as the paper continues through the machine. The final appearance of the copy is that of blue lines against a white background, hence the name "blueline" to describe this type of copy. These types of architectural drawings are better-looking and longer-lasting than their earlier blueprint cousins. This printing technique, using blue images on white backgrounds, is commonly known as creating "blueline prints." These bluelines can lose their quality over long periods of time, and should therefore be protected from light and other destructive elements.

Bluelines cannot be reproduced from other bluelines. However, copies of blueline prints (called engineer's prints) can be made on large-format Xerox machines, if and when the blueline is all that is available. However, some details in the drawing are certain to be lost using this reproduction method. This problem is only compounded when a copy is made from a copy. For blue-toned photographs produced by the blueprint process, the term "cyanotypes" is used. Today we use the term "blueprints" when referring to reproductions of technical drawings, or "cyanotypes" when referring to camera images or photograms.

It is most important for you, as a energy auditor, to understand that even though most engineers, designers, drafters, and architects use the symbols that have been adopted by the American National Standards Institute (ANSI) for use on plans or drawings, many designers and drafters modify these symbols to suit their own particular requirements. The symbols and abbreviations represented in this chapter may, or may not, represent or resemble the symbols that you will encounter when working with blueprints in the future.

DRAWING STAGES

Finished blueprints are actually the result of several preliminary stages of illustrative work. These preliminary stages provide important opportunities for the various professionals involved with the work to preview the overall ramifications of any ideas that are incorporated in them, and to provide any necessary critical feedback.

Schematic Drawings

Schematic Drawings

The first stage of drawings includes the basic scheme of operation, and normally will present a rough depiction of how the proposed project will work. These illustrations are referred to as **Schematic Drawings**. Schematic drawings are of a theoretical nature, and are usually the first representation of the project owner's needs, requirements, and how he/she expects the various parts of the proposed project to function.

These schematic drawings are first submitted to the project owner for evaluation. Once the project owner has had an opportunity to review the schematics, he/she will be able to knowledgeably offer any changes that may be required to keep the project on track. As you can imagine, this is a very critical first step.

It is important not to confuse these schematic drawings, as we mention them here, with electrical schematic drawings that are used to depict the very detailed electrical circuits of an appliance, machine, or electronic device.

Preliminary Drawings

Preliminary Drawings

Any changes that result from this initial evaluation are incorporated into the following stage of drawings, called **Preliminary Drawings**. The preliminary drawings provide an even more refined and detailed view of how the proposed project will look and function.

Working Drawings

Working Drawings

Working Drawings signify the final stage in the design process. The completed drawings become a "set" that incorporates all of the changes and refinements made by the designer, as he/she turns the preliminary drawings into working drawings.

Working drawings include all the details that the contractor will need to prepare a precise cost estimate. The set of working drawings is organized in such a way that each particular field of work included in the proposed project is represented with its own drawing type.

Various drawing types include:

- **Architectural Drawings**, which show a layout of the proposed project's floor plans, elevations, and details.

- **Structural Drawings**, which characterize how various load-carrying systems will be built.

- **Mechanical/Electrical Drawings**, which show the physical plant of the structure, such as lighting, power, plumbing, fire protection, and HVAC.

- **Site Drawings**, which depict the relationship between the structure and the property it will occupy, including various site improvements, such as sanitary systems, utilities, and so on.

Written instructions, called **Specifications**, are issued by the architect as part of the proposed project. For projects of limited detail, the specifications may be printed on the drawings. We will go into more detail on specifications later in this chapter.

Architectural Drawings

Structural Drawings

Mechanical/Electrical Drawings

Site Drawings

Specifications

Cover Sheet

The very first sheet on any set of plans is the **Cover Sheet**. The cover sheet, shown in Figure 9-1, contains much of the information that the contractor would need in order to intelligently compete in the bidding for the proposed project.

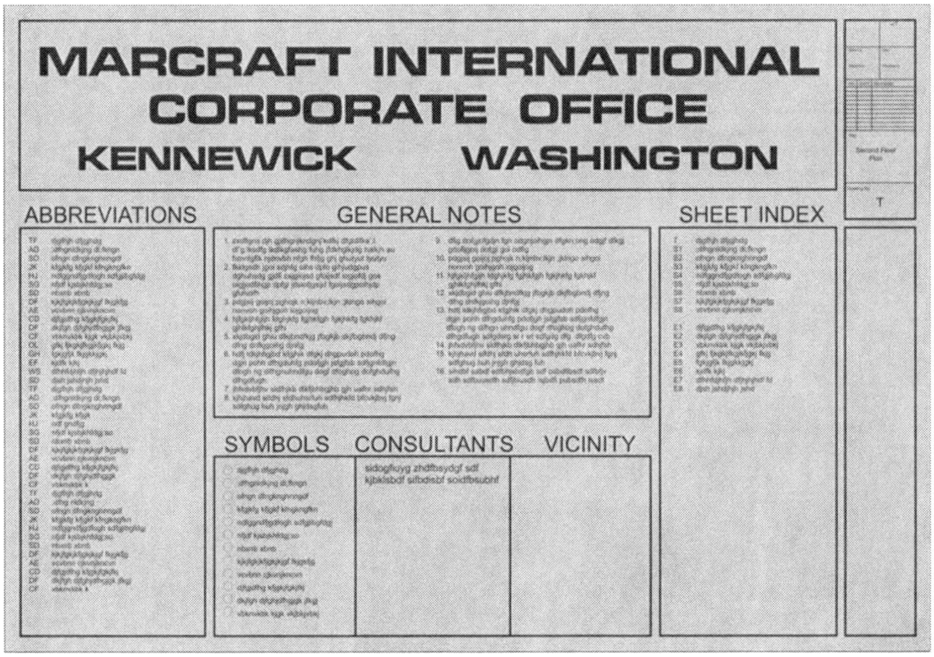

Cover Sheet

Figure 9-1:
Cover Sheet

The cover sheet provides the contractor with information that is crucial to the understanding of the drawings, and of the project as a whole. It generally lists much of the basic information, such as the name of the project, as well as its location, and the names of the architects, engineers, owners, and other notable people or firms that are involved in its design.

The cover sheet lists, in sequential order, the drawings that comprise the set. The drawing list is categorized by the number of drawings, and the title of the page on which each appears. Also listed are the specific requirements of the building codes that apply directly to the design of the proposed project. The required information includes the structure's total square footage, its use group designation, and its constructional type.

Another important element on the cover sheet is the listing of the abbreviations, or graphic symbols, that are used within the drawing set. Additionally, there is usually a section that contains notes specifically for the contractor, such as "All are to the face of the masonry" or "Dimensions shall be verified in the field." If there is not a separate set of specifications, the cover sheet may list the general technical specifications that will govern the quality of the materials used in the work.

Locus Plan

A **Locus Plan** that displays the project's location with respect to preexisting, well-known local landmarks and roadways may be part of the cover sheet. An architectural rendering of the structure may also be included.

Title Block

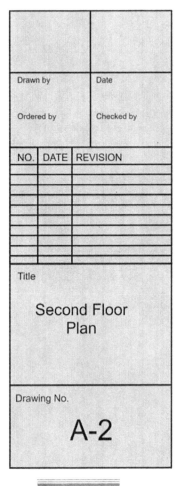

Figure 9-2: Title Block

Title Block

An example of a **Title Block** is shown in Figure 9-2. It is usually located in the lower, right-hand corner of the drawing. In a recent variation of this practice, some architectural firms are using customized layouts that reserve the entire right-hand portion of the sheet. Whichever variation is chosen, the title block should include the following information:

- The sheet or drawing number, identifying the group and order to which it belongs.

- The drawing name or title, such as "Second Floor Plan".

- The date of completion of the drawing.

- The initials of the draftsperson.

- Any revisions to the final set of drawings.

The title block must also define whether the entire drawing is one scale, or, as is the practice in some cases, define the particulars as to how the scale may vary per individual detail.

Revisions

Working drawings are often revised at various times after their initial completion. Various recommendations for the correction, or clarification, of a particular component of the drawing may be needed, or major changes may require the redrafting of an entire sheet.

Small changes or clarifications are shown as revisions on the original sheet, and all revisions must be noted in the title block.

If insufficient space is available within the title block to accommodate all of the notes, they should be placed as close to it as possible. The revision notes should be listed in order, by date and revision number, and the changes must be clearly marked by a **Revision Marker**, and circled with a scalloped line that somewhat resembles a cloud. This revision marker is a triangle, with the number or letter designation of the revision located in the center of it, as shown in Figure 9-3.

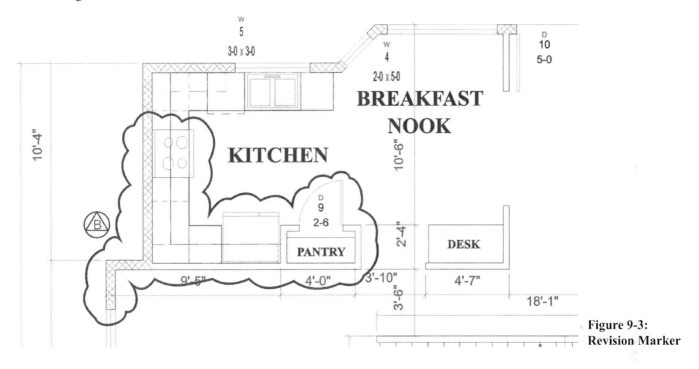

Figure 9-3:
Revision Marker

Registration Stamp

Sets of plans for commercial projects require a **Registration Stamp** of the drafter or design professional, as shown in Figure 9-4. The stamp contains the architect's or engineer's name, and registration number. In addition, the signature of the individual is usually required over the stamp as well.

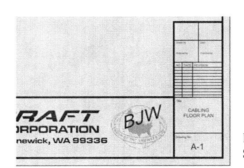

Figure 9-4: Registration Stamp

Lines

Because architectural drawings must provide a great deal of information in a relatively small amount of space, the use of text to provide this information would be extremely impractical. In order to alleviate this problem, various types of lines and symbols have been devised to provide the necessary information without using a great deal of space, as shown in Figure 9-5.

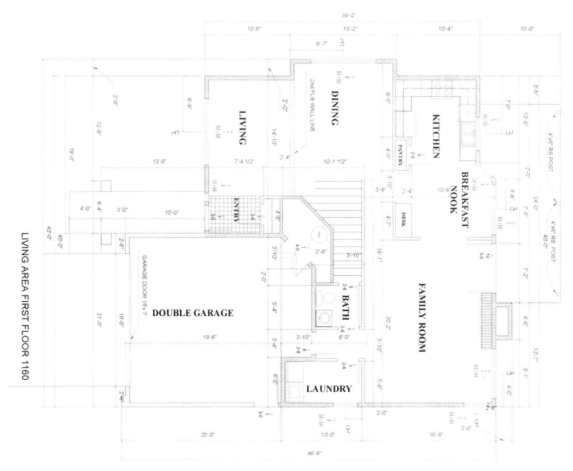

Figure 9-5: Lines and Symbols

The most commonly encountered line types in architectural drawings, as shown in Figure 9-6, are:

Figure 9-6: Line Types

- *Main Object Lines*, which define the outline of the structure, or object. They are thick, unbroken lines that show the main outlines of the walls, floors, elevations, details, or sections.

- *Dimension Lines,* which provide the lengths of the main object lines. They are very light lines with triangles, resembling arrowheads, on each end. The number that appears in the center break of the dimension line represents the measurement of the specific main object line to which it refers.

- *Extension Lines*, which are used together with dimension lines, and are the light lines that extend beyond the main object lines. The arrowheads of the dimension lines usually reach and touch the extension lines.

- *Hidden Lines*, which are light dashes that indicate the outlines of an object normally hidden from view, either under or behind some other part of the structure. The dashes used in this line type are usually of equal length.

- *Center Lines*, which are light lines with alternating long/short dashes, indicating the center of an object, and frequently labeled with the letter C superimposed over the letter L.

Symbols

As already mentioned in the introduction of this chapter, the symbols used by one drafter or designer may not be exactly the same as those used by another. While most of the symbols are widely accepted and practiced, there will always be minor deviations based on local conventions, such as the example shown in Figure 9-7. Although both of these symbols represent a single receptacle outlet, notice that one of them uses an additional line.

However, when you encounter any unfamiliar symbols and abbreviations, these will usually become clear as you study the drawings and check over the cover sheet of the working plans. If there is still some doubt, you will probably have to consult with the drafter or the designer of the proposed project.

Figure 9-7: Single Receptacle Outlet Symbol

Building Material Symbols

Building Material Symbols allow the drafter the opportunity to define the composition of the object being depicted. Various materials must be easily recognizable for the contractor to properly understand what the scope of the proposed project entails (concrete, brick, steel, framing wood, and so on). Table 9-1 presents a building material symbols listing.

Table 9-1: Building Material Symbols

COMMON BRICK	FACE BRICK	CEMENT	CONCRETE
CAST IRON	STEEL	BRASS / BRONZE	ALUMINUM
EARTH	SAND	SOLID INSULATION	QUILTED INSULATION
WOOD FRAME WALL	ROUGH WOOD	PLYWOOD	PLASTIC

Topographic Symbols

Topographic Symbols provide the contractor with a standard format for recognizing the landscape, and objects, located around the outside perimeter of the proposed project. These types of symbols are extremely important to the communications contractor if underground cables are part of the proposed project. If the graphic symbols call for a concrete or paved driveway as part of the proposed project, it would be much more practical to bury the cables before the driveway is actually constructed. Table 9-2 presents a listing of various topographic symbols.

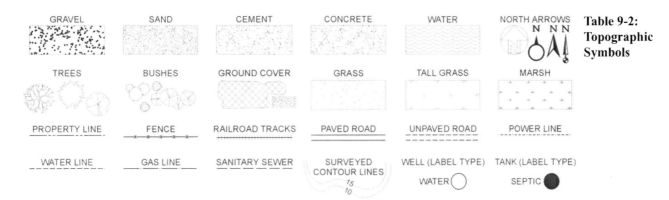

Table 9-2: Topographic Symbols

Electrical Symbols

Construction plans include symbols showing the location and number of electrical outlets, lights, fans, and so on. Table 9-3 displays a listing of several standard **Electrical Symbols**.

Electrical Symbols

Table 9-3: Electrical Symbols

SIMPLEX RECEPTACLE, MOUNT +18" AFF	FAN	CROSSCONNECT JUMPER OR PATCH CORD
DUPLEX RECEPTACLE, MOUNT +18" AFF	PUSH BUTTON	ℓ_1 WORK AREA EQUIPMENT CABLE
QUADRAPLEX RECEPTACLE, MOUNT +18" AFF	BUZZER	ℓ_2 PATCH CORD OR JUMPER
EMERGENCY POWERED DUPLEX RECEPTACLE, MOUNT +18" AFF	BELL	ℓ_3 TELECOMMUNICATIONS CLOSET EQUIPMENT CABLE
EMERGENCY POWERED QUADRAPLEX RECEPTACLE, MOUNT +18" AFF	CH CHIMES	HUB DATA HUB / PATCH PANEL
GFCI PROTECTED RECEPTACLE, MOUNT +18" AFF	D MOTORIZED DAMPER	TELEPHONE TERMINAL CABINET
GFCI PROTECTED RECEPTACLE, MOUNT +48" AFF	LIGHTING FIXTURE	TELEPHONE OUTLET, MOUNT +18" AFF
DUPLEX RECEPTACLE, MOUNT +48" AFF	WALL MOUNTED LIGHTING FIXTURE	W TELEPHONE OUTLET, MOUNT +54" AFF
QUADRAPLEX RECEPTACLE, MOUNT +48" AFF	LIGHTING FIXTURE ON EMERGENCY POWER	DATA OUTLET, MOUNT +18" AFF
DUPLEX RECEPTACLE, MOUNT +7'-6" AFF	RECESSED LIGHTING FIXTURE	COMBO TELEPHONE/DATA OUTLET, MOUNT +18" AFF
DUPLEX RECEPTACLE, FLOOR MOUNTED	VP VAPOR PROOF LIGHTING FIXTURE	$\overset{WP}{S}, S, S_V$ SOUND SYSTEM: CEILING & WALL MOUNTED V - VOLUME CONTROL, WP - WEATHERPROOF
APPLIANCE RECEPTACLE	D LIGHTING DROP CORD	
WIREMOLD SURFACE RACEWAY	S LIGHTING PULL SWITCH - CEILING	$\overset{H}{E}$ WALL MOUNTED SOUND SYSTEM /PAGING HORN. E - EXTERIOR, WATERPROOF
E ELECTRIC CORD REEL	N HOUSE NUMBER LIGHTING	WALL CLOCK
J , J JUNCTION BOX	ELECTRICAL HEATER	DOUBLE-FACE WALL CLOCK
PANELBOARD, 277/480V	EMERGENCY KILL SWITCH	D CABLE TV OUTLET
PANELBOARD, 120/208V	MOTOR & CONNECTIONS	M^2 MICROPHONE OUTLET, 2 - NUMBER OF JACKS
EMERGENCY PANELBOARD, 277/480V	G EMERGENCY GENERATOR	TV TV OUTLET
EMERGENCY PANELBOARD, 120/208V	S^*, S^*_3, S^*_4 SINGLE-POLE, 3-WAY, & 4-WAY LIGHT SWITCH	TP TEACHER'S PANEL
BRANCH CIRCUIT HOMERUN	$S^*_K, S^*_{K3}, S^*_{K4}$ SINGLE-POLE, 3-WAY, & 4-WAY 4-WAY KEY OPERATED LIGHT SWITCH	P.B. FLUSH-MOUNTED PULLBOX
ISOLATED GROUNDED CONDUCTOR GROUNDED CONDUCTOR NEUTRAL CONDUCTOR PHASE CONDUCTOR	S S TWO SINGLE-POLE LIGHT SWITCHES	F FIRE ALARM MANUAL PULL STATION
DISCONNECT SWITCH	S_3, S_3 TWO 3-WAY LIGHT SWITCHES	F FIRE ALARM AUDIO / VISUAL
MANUAL MOTOR STARTER P WITH PILOT LIGHT	FLUORESCENT LIGHT FIXTURE	A FIRE ALARM AUDIO ONLY
MANUAL MOTOR STARTER HOA WITH HAND-OFF-AUTOMATIC	FLUORESCENT LIGHT FIXTURE CONNECTED TO EMERGENCY POWER SUPPLY	V FIRE ALARM VISUAL ONLY
COMBINATION MAGNETIC STARTER	EXIT FIXTURE ON EMERGENCY POWER, CEILING MOUNTED	S FIRE ALARM SMOKE DETECTOR
MAGNETIC STARTER MOTOR	EXIT FIXTURE ON EMERGENCY POWER, WALL MOUNTED	H FIRE ALARM HEAT DETECTOR
SECURITY SYSTEM DIRECTIONAL PASSIVE INFRARED MOTION DETECTOR	S_E EMERGENCY LIGHTING SINGLE-POLE SWITCH	SD FIRE ALARM DUCT SMOKE DETECTOR
SECURITY SYSTEM OMNI-DIRECTIONAL INFRARED MOTION DETECTOR	T LINE VOLTAGE THERMOSTAT	TS FIRE ALARM TAMPER SWITCH
CR SECURITY SYSTEM CARD READER DEVICE	GROUNDING ROD	F FIRE ALARM FLOW SWITCH
SECURITY SYSTEM CCTV CAMERA	K SECURITY SYSTEM REMOTE KEY SWITCH	P FIRE ALARM PRESSURE SWITCH
		M_F FIRE ALARM MAGNETIC DOOR HOLDER
		G FIRE ALARM CONNECTED TO EMERGENCY GENERATOR
		FP FIRE ALARM CONNECTED TO FIRE PUMP CONTROLLER

Plumbing Symbols

In the various trades, there are always symbols that are used to characterize trade-specific items. Table 9-4 displays a listing of **Plumbing Symbols** common to that particular trade.

Table 9-4: Plumbing Symbols

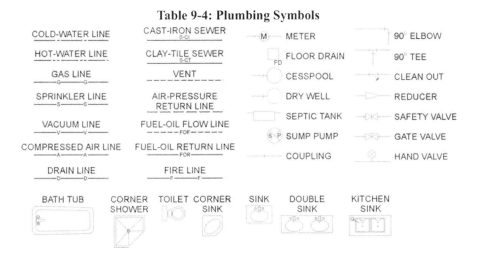

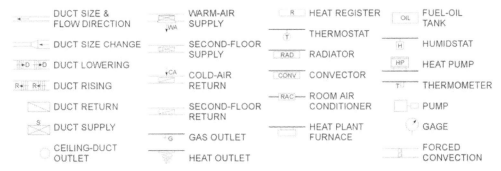

Climate-Control Symbols

Table 9-5 lists several common **Climate-Control Symbols**.

Table 9-5: Climate-Control Symbols

Architectural Symbols

Architectural Symbols make up the shorthand of the building industry. Table 9-6 lists several of the more common architectural symbols.

Table 9-6:
Architectural
Symbols

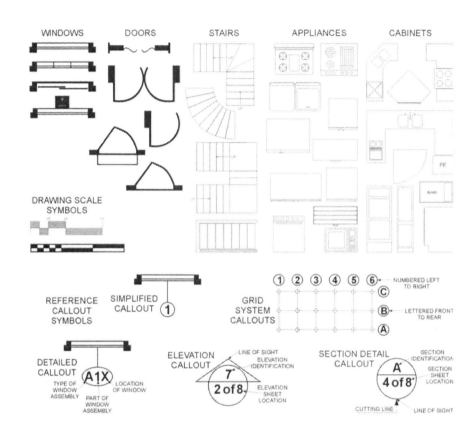

Drawing Scale

Depicting a building to actual size on a piece of paper would be out of the question. The renderings must be smaller than the actual-size buildings that they represent.

Architectural drawings keep their relationship to the actual size of the building by means of a **Ratio**. A ratio is the relationship between two things in amount, size, or degree and is expressed as a proportion. An accepted ratio between full size and what is seen on the drawings is called a **Scale**, and there are two major types of scales used in reading plans.

Architect's Scale

The **Architect's Scale** may either be flat or three-sided. The three-sided version of the scale has ten separate scales, paired in five groups of two. They are:

- 1/8-inch and 1/4-inch

- 1-inch and ½-inch

- 3/4-inch and 3/8-inch

- 3/16-inch and 3/32-inch

- 1 and ½-inch and 3-inch

One side of the scale is marked in inches, similar to a ruler. For example, when using a 1/4-inch architect's scale on a floor plan, each 1/4-inch of length on the drawing represents one foot. This also applies for the 1/8-inch scale, where each 1/8-inch line segment represents one foot of actual size. In fact, the most commonly used scales on floor plans and elevations are in 1/4-inch or 1/8-inch scale. Figure 9-8 illustrates an architect's scale.

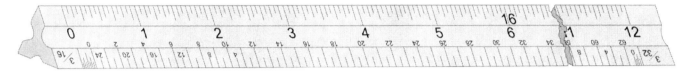

Figure 9-8: Architect's Scale

Engineer's Scale

The **Engineer's Scale** is somewhat similar to the architect's scale. The main differences are the number of scales, and the project size that the scale is capable of depicting. It has six scales (10, 20, 30, 40, 50, and 60) that refer to how many feet per inch the drawing depicts. For example, the 10 scale refers to 10 feet per inch, while the 20 scale refers to 20 feet per inch, and so on.

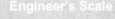

Figure 9-9 illustrates an engineer's scale. Sometimes the architect may insert the letters NTS beside a specific detail in a drawing. The NTS is an abbreviation for "Not To Scale". This tells the contractor that the labeled detail is for illustration purposes only, and is not an accurately scaled part of the drawing.

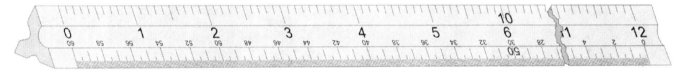

Figure 9-9: Engineer's Scale

Specifications

Working drawings are always issued with a set of specifications. This holds true for even the simplest of projects, which will incorporate the specifications either placed directly on the drawings, or issued as a separate document. The specifications, more commonly called **Specs**, should cover all of the work segments and items shown on the working drawings. It is not uncommon for a set of specifications to cover from fifteen to twenty pages.

For example, considering only the exterior siding to be used on a home or building, such details as material grades, types of fasteners to be used, size and color of individual pieces, manufacturer's name, brick style, mortar joint width, joint dressing style, mortar mix manufacturer, and so on, must all be spelled out, so that there will be no misunderstanding about what is expected.

For interior and exterior doors, details would have to include the exact locations for each one, the manufacturer and model for each, the dimensions, and the model/manufacturer of each handle or door knob to be used.

Consider the sad story of a building client who agreed to having a $500,000 business office built by a contractor who used several pages of yellow legal-sized pad paper to describe the materials that would be used to construct the building. Many thousands of dollars were lost because the contractor felt unconstrained in substituting the cheapest materials possible for those listed and described on the yellow pad paper.

The specs are designed to aid the contractor in the bidding for the proposed project, as well as in the work that is actually performed. If, at any time, a contradiction is discovered between the plans and the specifications, it is generally accepted that the specifications take precedence over the drawings.

ABBREVIATIONS

Architectural
Abbreviations

Table 9-7 provides a comprehensive listing of **Architectural Abbreviations** that are used by designers and drafters on their architectural drawings.

**Table 9-7:
Architectural
Abbreviations**

AB	Anchor Belt	BRG	Bearing
AC	Alternating Current	BRK	Brick
AC	Air-Conditioning	BRZ	Bronze
ACC	Access	BS	Both Sides
ACPL	Acoustical Plaster	BSMT	Basement
ACT	Acoustical Ceiling Tile	BUR	Built-Up Roofing
AD	Auto Damper/Area Drain	BVL	Beveled
ADD	Addendum	BW	Both Ways
ADH	Adhesive	CAB	Cabinet
ADJ	Adjacent	CAM	Closed Circuit TV Camera
ADJT	Adjustable	CB	Catch Basin
A/E	Architect/Engineer	CEM	Cement
AFF	Above Finished Floor	CER	Ceramic
AGG	Aggregate	CF	Cubic Foot
ALUM	Aluminum	CH	Ceiling Height
ALT	Alternate	CI	Cast Iron
ANC	Anchor	CIP	Cast In Place
ANOD	Anodized	CIRC	Circumference
APPROX	Approximate	CJT	Control Joint
APT	Apartment	CLG	Ceiling
ARCH	Architect	CLL	Control Limit Line
ASB	Asbestos	CLO	Closet
ASPH	Asphalt	CLR	Clear
ATS	Automatic Transfer Switch	CMU	Concrete Masonry Unit
BD	Board	CNTR	Counter
BE	Below	CO	Clean-Out
BET	Between	COL	Column
BIT	Bituminous	COMB	Combination
BLDG	Building	COMP	Composition
BLK	Block	CONC	Concrete/Bituminous Concrete
BLKG	Blocking	CONST	Construction
BM	Beam/Benchmark	CONT	Continuous
BOF	Bottom Of Footing	CONTR	Contractor
BOTT	Bottom	CPT	Carpet
BPL	Bearing Plate	CRS	Course

Table 9-7: Architectural Abbreviations (cont.)

CSMT	Casement	FBRK	Fire Brick
CT	Ceramic Tile	FD	Floor Drain
CU FT	Cubic Foot	FE	Fire Extinguisher
CU YD/CY	Cubic Yard	FER	Fire Extinguisher Cabinet
CW	Cold Water	FIN FL	Finish Floor
D	Drain	FFL	Finish Floor Line
DA	Double Acting	FIN	Finish
DC	Direct Current	FJT	Flush Joint
DEM	Demolish	FL	Flashing
DEP	Depressed	FL CO	Floor Clean-Out
DET	Detail	FLG	Flooring/Flashing
DF	Drinking Fountain	FLR	Floor
DH	Double Hung	FLUOR	Fluorescent
DIA	Diameter	FLX	Flexible
DIAG	Diagonal	FN	Fence
DIM	Dimension	FND	Foundation
DIV	Division	FOB	Freight On Board
DL	Dead Load	FOC	Face Of Concrete
DMT	Demountable	FOF	Face Of Finish
DN	Down	FOM	Face Of Masonry
DO	Ditto	FOS	Face Of Stud
DP	Damproofing	FP	Fireproof
DPR	Damper	FPL	Fireplace
DR	Door/Dining Room	FRT	Fire Retardant
DS	Downspout	FS	Full Size
DT	Drain Tile	FTG	Footing
DTL	Detail/Dentil	FUR	Furred
DW	Dishwasher/Dumbwaiter	FUT	Future
DWG	Drawing	G	Gas
DWR	Drawer	GA	Gauge
E	East	GAL	Gallon
EA	Each	GALV	Galvanized
EC	Empty Conduit	GB	Grab Bar
EDH	Electric Duct Heater	GC	General Contractor
EF	Entrance Facilities	GFCB	Ground Fault Circuit Breaker
ELEC	Electric	GFI	Ground Fault Interrupter
ELEV	Elevation/Elevator	GFP	Ground Fault Protector
EMER	Emergency	GI	Galvanized Iron
ENCL	Enclosure	GL	Glass/Glazing
ENT	Entrance	GL BK	Glass Block
EP	Electrical Panel	GRBM	Grade Beam
EQ	Equal	GRD	Grade
EQUIP	Equipment	GRN	Granite
ESC	Escalator	GVL	Gravel
EWC	Electric Water Cooler	GYP	Gypsum
EXC	Excavate	HA	Hot Air
EXG	Existing	HB	Hose Bib
EXH	Exhaust	HBD	Hardboard
EXP	Explosion-Proof	HC	Horizontal Crossconnect
EXP JT	Expansion Joint/Slot	HCP	Handicap
EXT	Exterior	HCWC	Handicap Water Closet
FA	Fire Alarm	HD	Heavy Duty
FAS	Fasten	HDR	Header
FATC	Fire Alarm Terminal Cabinet	HDW	Hardware
FB	Face Brick	HES	High Early Strength
FBE	Fiber Board	HGT	Ceiling Height
FBO	Furnished By Others	HH	Handhole

Table 9-7: Architectural Abbreviations (cont.)

HM	Hollow Metal	MG	Motor-Generated Set
HPT	High Point	MIN	Minimum
HOR	Horizontal	MIR	Mirror
HT	Height	MISC	Miscellaneous
HTG	Heating	MKWK	Millwork
HVAC	Heating, Ventilating, and Air Cond.	MLDG	Molding
HW	Hot Water	MM	Millimeter
HBD	Hardwood	MMB	Membrane
HWH	Hot Water Heater	MO	Masonry Opening
HWT	Hot Water Tank	MON	Closed Circuit TV Monitor
I	Iron	MOR	Mortar
ID	Inside Diameter	MRB	Marble
IN	Inches	MRD	Metal Roof Deck
INCL	Included	MTD	Mounted
INSUL	Insulation	MTL	Metal
INT	Interior	MTL FR	Metal Frame
INV	Invert	MULL	Mullion
IP	Isolated Panel	N	North
IPS	Iron Pipe Size	N/A	Not Applicable
ISI	Isolated Switch	NIC	Not In Contract
JC	Janitors' Closet	NO	Number
JF	Joint Filler	NOM	Nominal
JST	Joist	NRC	Noise Reduction Coefficient
JMB	Jamb	NTS	Not To Scale
JT	Joint	OA	Overall
KD	Knocked Down	OC	On Center
KIT	Kitchen	OD	Outside Diameter
KO	Knock Out	OH	Overhead
KPL	Kick Plate	OJ	Open Web Joist
KW	Kilowatt	OPG	Opening
L	Length	OPP	Opposite
LAB	Laboratory	OPH	Opposite Hand
LAD	Ladder	PAR	Parallel
LAM	Laminated	PBD	Particle Board
LAV	Lavatory	PCC	Precast Concrete
LBL	Label	PCF	Pounds per Cubic Foot
LF	Linear Foot	PERF	Perforated
LH	Left Hand	PL	Plate
LIN	Linen Closet	PLAM	Plastic Laminate
LINO	Linoleum	PLF	Pounds per Linear Foot
LL	Live Load	PNT	Painted
LP	Lighting Panel	PP	Power Panel
LPT	Low Point	PRM	Perimeter
LT	Light	PSF	Pounds per Square Foot
LTL	Lintel	PSI	Pounds per Square Inch
LVL	Laminated Veneer Lumber	PT	Pressure Treated
LVR	Louver	PTD	Painted/Paper Towel Dispenser
LW	Lightweight	PTN	Partition
M	Meter	PVC	Polyvinyl Chloride
MAS	Masonry	PVMT	Pavement
MAX	Maximum	PWD	Plywood
MC	Main Crossconnect/Motor Control	QT	Quarry Tile
MCC	Motor Control Counter	R	Riser/Radius
MDO	Medium Density	RA	Return Air
MECH	Mechanical	RB	Rubber Base
MED	Medium	RBT	Rubber Tile
MFR	Manufacturer	RCP	Reinforced Concrete Pipe

Table 9-7: Architectural Abbreviations (cont.)

RD	Roof Drain	T	Tread
REINF	Reinforced	TB	Towel Bar
REG	Register	TBB	Telephone Backboard
REM	Remove	TC	Telecommunications Closet
REQ'D	Required	TEL	Telephone
RES	Resilient	T&G	Tongue and Groove
RET	Return	THK	Thick
REV	Revised	THR	Threshold
RFG	Roofing	TOL	Tolerance
RFL	Reflected	TPD	Toilet Paper Dispenser
RH	Right Hand	TR	Transom
RM	Room	TSL	Top of Slab
RO	Rough Opening	TOS	Top Of Steel
RVs.	Reverse	TOW	Top Of Wall
RWC	Rain Water Conductor	TYP	Typical
S	South	UC	Undercut
SC	Solid Core	UH	Unit Heater
SCH	Schedule	UNEXC	Unexcavated
SD	Storm Drain	UNF	Unfinished
SEC	Section	V	Volts
SF	Square Foot	VAT	Vinyl Asbestos Tile
SHO	Shoring	VB	Vapor Barrier
SHT	Sheet	VCT	Vinyl Composition Tile
SHTHG	Sheathing	VERT	Vertical
SIM	Similar	VG	Vertical Gain
SKL	Skylight	VIF	Verify In Field
SNT	Sealant	VNR	Veneer
SPEC	Specifications	VPB	Veneer Plywood
SPK	Speaker	VT	Vinyl Tile
SQ	Square	W	West
SS	Sanitary Sewer	WA	Work Area
SST, S/S	Stainless Steel	WC	Water Closet
ST	Steel	WD	Wood
STA	Station	WG	Wire Glass
STC	Sound Transmission Coefficient	WH	Wall Hang
STD	Standard	WI	Wrought Iron
STO	Storage	W/	With
STOR	Storage	W/O	Without
STRUCT	Structural	WP	Weatherproof
SUS	Suspended	WP'G	Waterproofing
SYM	Symmetrical	WSCT	Wainscoting
SYN	Synthetic	WTW	Wall-to-Wall
SYP	Southern Yellow Pine	WWF	Welded Wire Fabric
SYS	System	WWM	Welded Wire Mesh

REVIEW QUESTIONS

The following questions test your knowledge of the material presented in this chapter:

1. What are the various types of working drawings?

2. What do the numbers that appear in the center break of a dimension line represent?

3. Why are topographic symbols important to a communications contractor?

4. How do architectural drawings relate to the actual size of the structure they represent?

5. Which document takes precedence in cases where a contradiction between the blueprint and the specifications exists?

6. What constitutes the main difference between the architect's scale and the engineer's scale?

7. What is the primary use for a revision marker?

8. Where is a title block usually located on an architectural drawing?

9. Which type of drawing depicts the relationship between the proposed structure and its surrounding property?

10. When is a registration stamp required?

11. What do hidden lines on an architectural drawing indicate?

12. Why are building material symbols important?

13. How are the numbers and letters of grid system callouts organized?

14. What is the architectural abbreviation for plywood?

15. Given the detail contained in the specifications issued with each set of drawings, how many pages might be required for a specification set?

EXAM QUESTIONS

1. What are the different drawing stages in the process of design drawings?
   a. abstract, preparatory, and operating
   b. conventional, prefatory, and setup
   c. formal, introductory, and process
   d. schematic, preliminary, and working

2. What drawing stage is first submitted to the project owner for evaluation?
   a. schematic drawings
   b. abstract drawings
   c. operating drawings
   d. introductory drawings

3. hen a drawing is ready to be rendered and transferred to a hard copy, what is the original drawing printed on?
   a. a heavy off-white coarse-quality paper
   b. either vellum or mylar
   c. plastic-coated durable fiber
   d. blue line paper

4. The cover sheet is an important part of the drawing set. What item may be part of the cover sheet that displays the project's location?
   a. pictures of local landmarks
   b. topographical features
   c. local roadway intersections
   d. a locus plan

5. What is the term describing the ratio between a full-size rendering, and what is depicted on an architectural drawing?
   a. series
   b. ratio
   c. share
   d. scale

6. What are the two major types of scales used in reading architectural drawings?
   a. the architect's scale and the engineer's scale
   b. the plumber's scale and the craftsman's scale
   c. the architect's scale and the mechanic's scale
   d. the designer's scale and the manager's scale

7. What does the architectural abbreviation FP represent on architectural drawings?
   a. a fireplace
   b. a fire retardant
   c. a fireproof material
   d. a floor drain

8. Architectural drawings provide a lot of information in a small amount of space. What items enable this information to be provided?
   a. electrical symbols and lines
   b. main lines and typographic symbols
   c. building symbols and dimension lines
   d. lines and symbols

9. How does the engineer's scale differ from the architect's scale?
   a. The number of scales provided is equal to 10.
   b. The project size the scale is capable of depicting is smaller.
   c. It is not actually capable of rendering "to-scale" drawings.
   d. It provides only 6 scales, but is capable of depicting larger-sized projects

10. What drawing item defines the particulars as to how the scale may vary per individual detail?
    a. the specifications
    b. the registration
    c. the title block
    d. the drawing scale

ENERGY-AUDITING
LAB PROCEDURES

Introduction to Lab Procedures

GT-7500 ENERGY AUDITING TECHNOLOGY PANEL ORIENTATION

The GT-7500 Energy Auditing Technology Panel is a training tool to introduce you to the field of energy auditing. The Reconfigurable House can be used to both evaluate insulation and simulate IR camera testing. The panel also demonstrates two different methods to heat water and has a light fixture for evaluating different light bulbs.

Figure 1 depicts the GT-7500 Energy Auditing Technology Panel in its original state.

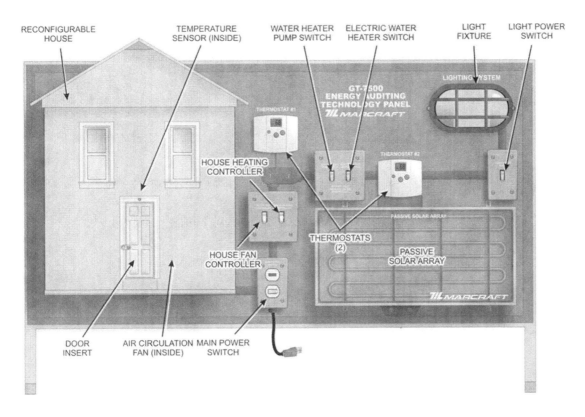

Figure 1: The GT-7500 Energy Auditing Technology Panel

Identify and inventory the components that make up the GT-7500 Energy Auditing training system at this point.

- House Heating Controller
- House Fan Controller
- Air Circulation Fan (inside House)
- Thermostats (2)
- Passive Solar Array
- Light Fixture

- Temperature Sensor (inside House)
- Reconfigurable House
- Electric Water Heater Switch
- Water Heater Pump Switch
- Light Power Switch
- Main Power Switch

Figure 2 depicts the components mounted on the back of the GT-7500 panel.

Identify the components located on the back of the panel:

- Hot Water Tank
- Water Pump
- Electric Water Heater

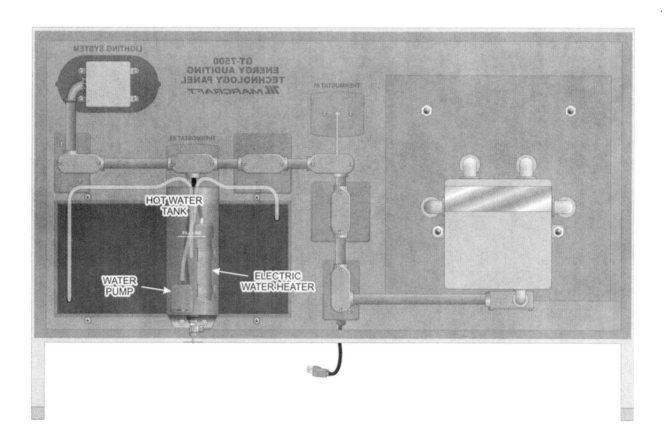

Figure 2: The Back of the GT-7500 Panel

Accessory Components

Many of the GT-7500 components are not pre-mounted on the GT-7500 Energy Auditing Technology Panel. These components are mounted and connected in the process of installing and configuring the system. Figure 3 shows the components of the GT-7500 system that do not come mounted on the panel.

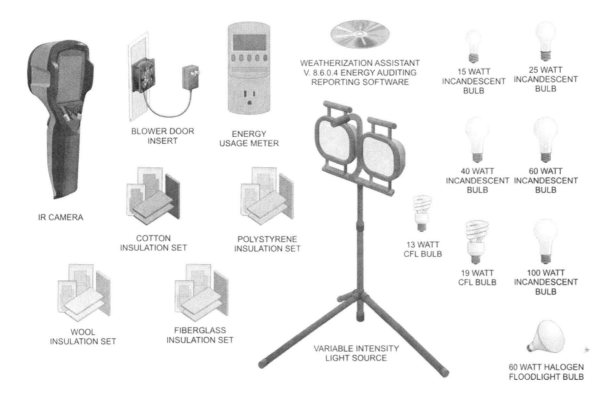

Figure 3: Non-Mounted GT-7500 Energy Auditing Technology Panel Components

Identify and inventory the following non-mounted components. These components should be on hand and available for use at this time:

- Energy Usage Meter

- IR Camera

- Variable Intensity Light Source

- Bulbs

    - 15-Watt Incandescent

    - 25-Watt Incandescent

    - 40-Watt Incandescent

    - 60-Watt Incandescent

    - 100-Watt Incandescent

    - 13-Watt CFL

    - 19-Watt CFL

    - 60-Watt Halogen Floodlight

- Insulation Inserts

    - Polystyrene Insulation Set

    - Fiberglass Insulation Set

    - Wool Insulation Set

    - Cotton Insulation Set

- Weatherization Assistant v.8.6.0.4 Energy Auditing Reporting Software

Introduction to the IR Camera

OBJECTIVES

1. Become familiar with the IR camera's controls and operation.
2. Save, review and delete images from the camera.
3. Measure the temperature of a reflective surface.
4. Find an unknown emissivity value.

Energy Auditing

RESOURCES

1. GT-7500 Energy Auditing Technology Panel
2. IR Camera
3. Clock or Timer
4. Black Electrical Tape
5. Piece of Cardboard About the Size of a Sheet of Paper

DISCUSSION

One of the best ways for energy auditors to test a building's outer shell and insulation is to look for variances in the surface temperature of the structure. Thermal imaging cameras, or IR cameras, are used for this purpose. Photos of the shell of the building reveal areas where heat is escaping (or entering, depending on the relative temperature of indoor versus outdoor air).

All objects emit infrared energy and an object will emit more as its temperature increases. However, this energy is not visible to the human eye. IR cameras are able to detect infrared radiation emitted by objects and convert that information into an image, known as a **Thermogram**.

IR cameras do not directly read the temperature of objects. Instead, they use multiple sources of data based on the areas surrounding an object to give an approximate temperature. This makes thermograms more useful for showing variations in temperature over a given area as opposed to measuring the exact temperature of an object. In addition, the camera is not in contact with objects being measured, so it is necessary for the camera to take into account different variables which can affect the infrared radiation in the space between the camera and the source.

Images produces by IR cameras are composed of incident energy. **Incident energy** is the combination of emitted energy, transmitted energy and reflected energy. **Emitted energy** is the actual thermal energy emitted from an object and is the intended value to be measured. However, energy that passes through an object from remote thermal sources, or **transmitted energy**, and energy that is reflected off the surface of the object, or **reflected energy** will also be visible in a thermal image.

Emissivity

One of the calculations IR cameras make is to correct the temperature of an object based on its reflected energy compared to its emitted energy. The emissivity, or ε, of a material will need to be entered into the camera. **Emissivity** is the ratio of the actual amount of radiation emitted by an object as compared to the amount emitted by an ideal **blackbody**, or a theoretical object that absorbs 100% of radiation that strikes it and emits 100% of the radiation it absorbed. The emissivity of a blackbody is 1, so objects that do not reflect thermal energy well will have a higher emissivity value. Objects that reflect a large amount of thermal energy, like silver, have an emissivity value closer to zero, as shown in Table 1-1.

**Table 1-1:
Emissivity Values
for Common
Materials**

MATERIAL	EMISSIVITY
Aluminum, polished	0.05
Concrete	0.92
Electrical Tape	0.97
Glass, smooth	0.92
Glass	0.82
Granite	0.45
Human Skin	0.98
Silver, polished	0.01
Wood, oak	0.90

When using an IR camera, it is important to be able to identify when an object is reflecting thermal energy. To get a more accurate temperature reading off reflective surfaces, like metals or windows, it is easiest to adhere a material with a known emissivity to the surface of the reflective object. Electrical tape is generally used, but there are emissivity sprays manufactured for this specific purpose. Situations do exist where it becomes necessary to compare surface temperature of a large reflective surface. The emissivity value and the reflected energy of the IR camera will need to be entered into the camera. Emissivity tables are available and provide expected emissivity values for common materials. Finding the value to enter for the reflected energy can be a little more work. If the thermal background energy is constant, like an overcast sky, the reflected temperature can be obtained by aiming the camera away from the object, in the direction of the reflected angle and with the emissivity set to 1, as shown in Figure 1-1. If there are heat sources or constant background radiation changes, it may be necessary to use a large flat surface, like a piece of cardboard, to block out the background thermal energy. The value for the reflected temperature can be obtained by aiming the camera directly at the reflected object (not the reflection) with the emissivity set to 1.

However, when using an IR camera for more accurate temperature measurements, using values found in an emissivity table may not be accurate or specific for your conditions and the condition of the material to be measured. There are two methods to find an emissivity value. The first method involves evenly heating the material to a specific temperature, at least 24 degrees higher than the ambient temperature. Since the temperature of the material is known, the emissivity setting in the camera can be adjusted until the temperature reading is correct.

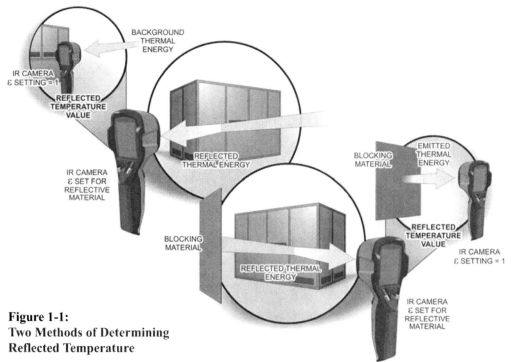

**Figure 1-1:
Two Methods of Determining
Reflected Temperature**

The second, more practical method to determining emissivity is to adhere a material with a known emissivity value, like electrical tape, to the reflective surface. With the emissivity value for the known material set in the camera, measuring the temperature of the known material gives the actual surface temperature of the reflective surface. Then, the reflected temperature is determined and controlled, if needed. The camera is then aimed at the reflective surface, near the affixed material with the known emissivity. The emissivity value is adjusted until the temperature reads correctly. It is important to note that the lower the emissivity value, the more difficult it is to achieve accurate surface temperature measurements. More advanced thermal imaging cameras are better suited for this purpose because users can account for more variables, like relative humidity, distances and atmospheric temperature.

PROCEDURES

1. Examine the IR camera. Use Figure 1-2 to locate and identify the important components.

2. On the side of the camera, lift the protective rubber cover and reveal the USB input, power cord input and memory card. Ensure there is a memory card in your camera and close the cover.

3. Use Figure 1-3 to locate and press the **Power** button. Identify the remainder of the buttons and graphics in the figure.

4. Release the Lens Cover by pressing the switch on the front of the camera.

5. Press the **Left Selection** button to open the Menu.

6. Use the +/- buttons to highlight **Color palette** and then press the **Right** button.

7. Use the +/- buttons to highlight **Iron** and then press the **Right** button.

8. Press the **Left Selection** button to open the Menu.

9. Use the +/- buttons to highlight **Settings** and then press the **Right** button.

10. Use the +/- buttons to highlight **Unit** and then press the **Right** button.

11. Use the +/- buttons to highlight **Fahrenheit** and then press the **Right** button.

12 Press the **Left Selection** button to open the Menu.

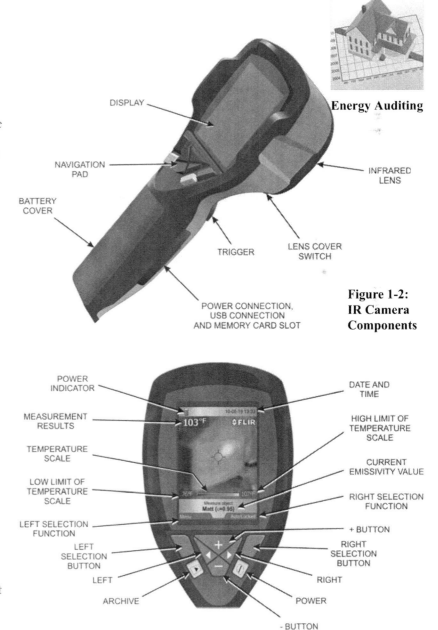

Energy Auditing

DISPLAY

NAVIGATION PAD

BATTERY COVER

INFRARED LENS

TRIGGER

LENS COVER SWITCH

POWER CONNECTION, USB CONNECTION AND MEMORY CARD SLOT

Figure 1-2: IR Camera Components

POWER INDICATOR

MEASUREMENT RESULTS

TEMPERATURE SCALE

LOW LIMIT OF TEMPERATURE SCALE

LEFT SELECTION FUNCTION

LEFT SELECTION BUTTON

LEFT

ARCHIVE

DATE AND TIME

HIGH LIMIT OF TEMPERATURE SCALE

CURRENT EMISSIVITY VALUE

RIGHT SELECTION FUNCTION

+ BUTTON

RIGHT SELECTION BUTTON

RIGHT

POWER

- BUTTON

Figure 1-3: IR Camera Buttons and Graphics

13. Highlight **Measure Object** and then press the **Right** button.

14. Highlight **Matt** and then press the **Right** button.

15. Press the **Left Selection** button to open the Menu.

16. Highlight **Measure Object** and then press the **Right** button.

17. Highlight **Advanced** and then press the **Right** button.

18. Highlight **Reflected temperature** and then press the **Right** button.

19. Use the +/- buttons to change the number to the ambient room temperature. Press the **Right** button when finished.

20. Find an empty area of a wall around 1 square foot in size. With the camera positioned 1-2 feet away, aim the IR camera at the wall. Observe the IR camera's display and record the color of the wall shown along with the high and low limits of the temperature scale on the following lines:

Wall color: _____

Low limit of temperature scale: _____

High limit of temperature scale: _____

21. Move your hand to where your fingers are visible in the display of the IR camera. Record the new color of the wall, the color of your fingers, and the new high/low limits of the temperature scale on the following lines:

Wall color: _____

Color of your hand: _____

Low limit of temperature scale: _____

High limit of temperature scale: _____

22. With your fingers still visible, press the **Right Selection** button. Small padlocks should appear below the high and low limits of the temperature scale indicating that their values will be locked.

23. Remove your hand from the view of the IR camera. Record the color of the wall on the following line:

Wall color: _____

24. Press the **Right Selection** button. The padlocks will disappear from below the high and low limits of the temperature scale. Record the color of the wall changes on the following line:

Wall color: _____

25. Press the **Right Selection** button again. The Temperature Scale should be locked again.

26. Move your fingers back into view of the IR camera. Record their color as seen using the IR camera on the following line:

Color of fingers: _____

27. Press the **Right Selection** button to unlock the Temperature Scale.

28. Record the color of your fingers as seen through the IR camera on the following line:

Color of fingers: _____

29. Move your fingers back into view of the IR camera.

30. Press the trigger on the front of the camera.

31. Press the **Archive** button on the IR camera. The image just saved should be visible. Record the name of the image on the following line:

Image Name: _____

32. Press the + button. The images in the camera's memory card will be displayed. Use the navigation pad to highlight the image just created and open it by pressing the **Right Selection** button.

33. Press the **Left Selection** button to delete the image, and then press the **Right Selection** button to confirm this.

34. Press the **Right Selection** button to exit the image review mode.

35. Go to the rear of the GT-7500 Energy Auditing Technology Panel. Position the camera about a foot away from the center of the top of the panel. Move your free hand to where it is visible on the other side of the panel.

36. Use the IR camera to determine whether it is possible to see your hand through the panel. Record the result on the following line:

_____

37. Move to the rear of the panel and position the IR camera 2 feet away from the side of the Hot Water Tank. Aim the IR camera at the Tank. Notice how the temperature reading in the upper-left corner of the IR camera's display fluctuates.

NOTE: If you are having trouble locating an object because there is no temperature difference between the object and the surroundings, briefly touch the object with your finger to mark the object.

38. For the next minute watch the temperature fluctuate. Record the highest temperature displayed and the lowest temperature displayed on the following lines. Next, try to determine the exact temperature of the tank and record its value on the following line: (Pay careful attention as the camera pauses and clicks when it recalibrates.)

Highest temperature: _____

Lowest temperature: _____

Temperature of the Tank: _____

39. Record the temperature displayed on Thermostat #2. Compare this temperature to the values you recorded in the previous step. How much variance exists between the thermostat reading and the IR camera readings?

Thermostat #2 temperature: _____

Variance between readings: _____

Energy Auditing

Reading the Temperature of a Reflective Surface

It is important to be aware of heat reflective surfaces when using an IR camera. Objects like heat ducts and windows can be misleading when comparing surface temperatures to non-reflective surfaces. One of the easiest solutions for this situation is to affix a material with a known emissivity to the reflective surface.

1. Locate the reflective tape on the rear of the GT-7500 Energy Auditing Panel. Position the IR camera 18 inches away and 30 degrees to one side of the tape. Record the approximate temperature of the tape on the following line:

Approximate temperature: _____

2. Raise your free hand and move it 18 inches away and to the opposite side of the reflective tape so you can view the reflected heat of your hand. Aim the IR camera at the reflection of the center of your hand and record the approximate temperature on the following line:

Approximate temperature: _____

3. Place a 1" piece of electrical tape over the reflective tape so it blocks part of the heat reflected from your hand. Try to touch the tape as little as possible.

4. Wait 2 minutes for the electrical tape to cool to the same temperature as the reflective tape.

5. Press the **Left Selection** button to open the Menu.

6. Highlight **Measure Object** and then press the **Right** button.

7. Highlight **Advanced** and then press the **Right** button.

8. As shown in Figure 1-4, highlight **Emissivity** and press the **Right** button. Use the +/- buttons to change the emissivity value to 0.97, the expected emissivity value of electrical tape. Press the **Right** button when finished.

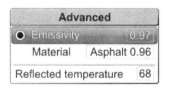

Figure 1-4: Changing the Emissivity Value

9. Aim the IR camera at the electrical tape. (You can use the heat reflection of your hand to help find it.) Record the temperature reading of the electrical tape on the following line:

Temperature: _____

10. Move the Main Power Switch of the GT-7500 Energy Auditing Technology Panel to its **On** position.

11. Turn the House Fan Controller to its **On** position and move the speed control slide all the way to the top.

12. Turn the House Heating Controller to its **On** position and move the temperature control slide all the way to the top. Look inside the house to confirm that the fan is running and there is a light on behind the fan.

13. Return to the rear of the panel and use the IR camera to watch both pieces of tape for the next 2 minutes as they warm up. Record the approximate temperature of both pieces of tape after 2 minutes along with the surface temperature of the grey box next to the tape on the following lines:

    Temperature of reflective tape: _____

    Temperature of electrical tape: _____

    Temperature of grey box: _____

14. Turn the House Fan Controller and the House Heating Controller to their **Off** positions.

15. Based on the temperatures you recorded in the previous step, when you use the IR camera to directly measure the temperature of the reflective tape, describe what are you actually measuring on the following lines:

    _____

    _____

Energy Auditing

Finding an Unknown Emissivity Value

1. Allow the GT-7500 panel to cool for 5 minutes.

2. Use the IR camera to read the temperature of the black electrical tape and record it on the following line:

    Temperature of electrical tape (actual temperature of reflective tape): _____

3. Using the IR camera, measure the temperature of the piece of cardboard and record its temperature on the following line:

    Temperature of cardboard: _____

4. Move the IR camera back to where it is 18 inches from the reflective tape and 30 degrees to one side.

5. Position the cardboard so its heat is reflected off the reflective tape. The cardboard serves to provide a controlled amount of background infrared radiation being picked up by the IR camera and block any other background sources.

6. On the IR camera, press the **Left Selection** button to open the Menu.

7. Highlight **Measure Object** and then press the **Right** button.

8. As shown in Figure 1-5, highlight **Advanced** and then press the **Right** button.

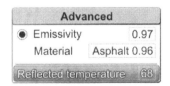

Advanced	
● Emissivity	0.97
Material	Asphalt 0.96
Reflected temperature	68

Figure 1-5: Setting the Reflected Temperature

9. Highlight **Reflected temperature** and then press the **Right** button.

10. Use the +/- buttons to change the current value to the temperature of the cardboard. Press the **Right** button when finished. The IR camera will now account for the reflected energy of the cardboard when displaying a temperature.

11. Press the **Left Selection** button to open the Menu.

12. Highlight **Measure Object** and then press the **Right** button.

13. Highlight **Advanced** and then press the **Right** button.

14. As shown in Figure 1-6, highlight **Emissivity** and then press the **Right** button.

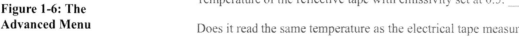

Advanced	
● Emissivity	0.50
Material	Asphalt 0.96
Reflected temperature	68

Figure 1-6: The Advanced Menu

15. Use the +/- buttons to change the value to **0.50**. Press the **Right** button when finished.

16. Use the IR camera to read the temperature of the reflective tape again. Record the temperature on the following line:

    Temperature of the reflective tape with emissivity set at 0.5: _____

    Does it read the same temperature as the electrical tape measured in Step 2? _____

17. Continue to adjust the emissivity value in the IR camera until the camera reads the same temperature for the reflective tape as the electrical tape measured in Step 2. Record the emissivity value on the following line:

    Emissivity value of the reflective tape: _____

18. Move the Main Power Switch of the GT-7500 Energy Auditing Technology Panel to its **Off** position.

19. Delete any images you have saved on the IR camera. Turn the camera **Off** and press the switch on the front of the camera to close the lens cover. Return the camera to its protective case.

20. Return all materials and tools to their designated areas. Clean up your work area.

LAB QUESTIONS

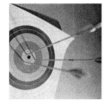

Feedback

1. What is a thermal image produced by an IR camera called?

2. Do IR cameras directly measure the temperature of an object?

3. What types of energy make up incident energy?

4. Just by glancing at the display of the IR camera, how can you tell if the values for the temperature scale are locked?

5. On the IR camera, what two settings need to be adjusted to allow the camera to give corrected temperature measurements for a material?

Evaluating Lighting and Heating Systems

Energy Auditing

OBJECTIVES

1. Measure and record the amperage of various light bulb types and ratings.
2. Determine the kilowatts per hour (kWh) of various light bulbs.
3. Heat a tank of water using the active water heater.
4. Use the passive water heater to reheat a tank of water.
5. Calculate the energy used by both systems and evaluate the costs of the water heaters.

RESOURCES

1. Energy Usage Meter
2. Bulbs

   - 15-Watt Incandescent
   - 25-Watt Incandescent
   - 40-Watt Incandescent
   - 60-Watt Incandescent
   - 100-Watt Incandescent
   - 13-Watt CFL
   - 19-Watt CFL
   - 60-Watt Halogen Floodlight

3. GT-7500 Energy Auditing Technology Panel
4. Passive Solar Array Module
5. Electric Water Heater
6. IR Camera
7. Variable Intensity Light Source
8. Watch or Timer
9. Water

DISCUSSION

The modern building has evolved over many thousands of years to become how we know it today. The addition of light, heat and running water brought comfort, safety and convenience into the structures man created. As technology advanced, so did these systems.

In every commercial and residential building there are environmental convenience systems like heating, ventilation, air conditioning, lighting and hot water. Each of these systems has a major impact on the energy usage and efficiency of the structures they are installed in and it is important that these systems are implemented and maintained to ensure they operate as efficiently as possible.

Electrical Lighting Systems

Architects and interior designers commonly mix natural and artificial lighting sources to help people see while inside buildings. Sunlight is utilized as the primary source of lighting, and electric powered light bulbs are used when natural lighting is insufficient or unavailable.

Because electrical lighting traditionally accounts for up to 10% of the energy consumption in a residential setting, efficient lighting represents a significant opportunity to save on energy costs. This is also one of the easiest and least expensive ways to improve energy efficiency. Lighting fixtures typically consist of replaceable units and do not require a license to replace. Therefore, it is relatively quick and inexpensive to upgrade an inefficient lighting fixture.

Another lighting-related opportunity for conserving energy and saving money is to change the usage habits of artificial lighting. Historically, electricity has been relatively inexpensive, so people are not always concerned with the amount of energy one light bulb consumes. However, when all the minutes and hours that a single light bulb is unnecessarily left on are added to the unnecessary use of all the other bulbs in a residence, the yearly cost becomes relevant. This cost increases exponentially when these occurrences are applied to a high occupancy building such as a large office, high-rise apartment building, or large commercial site. These larger buildings have long employed automated methods of turning off lighting and other resources in unoccupied areas to reduce energy costs without impacting safety of comfort.

Hot Water Systems

Another 10% of energy consumption in residential structures is used to generate hot water. The hot water is used for cooking, cleaning, washing clothes and bathing. Traditionally, water is collected in a large tank and then heated by electricity, natural gas or fuel oils. To keep the water available at all times, it will need to be reheated periodically, using additional energy. Table 2-1 shows the average amount of hot water used for different activities in a typical US home.

ACTIVITY	USAGE
Clothes Washing, typical washing machine (Hot Water on all cycles)	32 Gallons
Clothes washing, modern energy efficient machine (Hot water on all cycles)	18-24 Gallons
Showering	20 Gallons
Bathing	20 Gallons
Dishwasher, automatic	12 Gallons
Food preparation	5 Gallons
Dishwashing, hand	4 Gallons

Table 2-1: Average Hot Water Usage for Various Activities

One of the easiest ways to increase the efficiency of hot water systems is to identify long periods of time when hot water is not needed. During these times, the temperature of the water can be decreased. However, if the energy needed to maintain the temperature is more than is needed to reheat the water, the water heater can be turned off for maximum energy savings. Demand or tankless water heaters can also be employed when smaller amounts of hot water is needed. These types of water heaters turn on when hot water is needed, saving the energy needed to maintain an unnecessary supply of hot water.

Another way to improve hot water system efficiency is to add a second, less-expensive method to heat the water, like a simple solar thermal collector. A solar thermal collector is a dark-colored box with a clear lid and tubes circulating through it. Sunlight heats the air inside the collector which then heats the water as it runs through the tubes. These panels are typically mounted on the roof of a building and are ideal for heating swimming pools.

PROCEDURES

Evaluating Lighting Systems

Energy Auditing

The GT-7500 provides an Energy Usage Meter to measure the power use of various electrical devices. In this lab procedure you will use the Energy Usage Meter to measure and record the power usage of various light bulb types and ratings and then input that data into a formula to determine the **kilowatts per hour (kWh)** of each bulb.

You will also use the Internet to find the kWh cost of your local utility company and determine the cost difference between each bulb. Once the power usage has been determined for each of the different bulb types, the overall cost effectiveness of using different bulb types will be determined.

1. Ensure that the Main Power Switch and the Light Power Switch are both in their **Off** positions.

2. Unplug the Main Power Cord of the GT-7500 from the power source. Plug the Power Cord into the Energy Usage Meter, then plug the Energy Usage Meter into the AC power outlet, as shown in Figure 2-1.

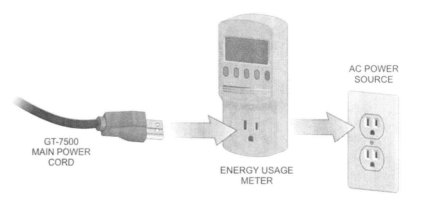

Figure 2-1:
Installing the Energy
Usage Meter

3. Remove the screws from the lighting fixture and carefully remove the cover. Store the cover in a safe location and install the screws back in the fixture base.

> ### CAUTION
>
> You will be inserting light bulbs into the fixture and removing them shortly afterwards. It is not necessary to tighten the bulbs all the way. Instead, secure them only far enough to receive power while you examine them and take readings. If a bulb should happen to break off inside the fixture, IMMEDIATELY switch **Off** the Main Power Switch and unplug the panel until the broken bulb can be removed.

4. Using a protective glove or cloth, carefully insert the 15-Watt Incandescent Bulb into the light socket of the fixture.

> ### CAUTION
>
> The light fixture is live and there is a risk of electric shock. Never insert anything other than the light bulbs into the socket.

5. Move the Main Power Switch to the **On** position. Move the Light Power Switch to its **On** position. The light bulb should light up.

6. On the Energy Usage Meter, press the **Amp** button to display the current that the bulb is using. Record the current level in the *AMPS* column of Table 2-2.

Table 2-2

BULB	AMPS	VOLTS	ACTUAL WATTS	TEMP OF BULB
15-Watt Incandescent				
25-Watt Incandescent				
40-Watt Incandescent				
60-Watt Incandescent				
100-Watt Incandescent				
13-Watt CFL				
19-Watt CFL				
60-Watt Halogen Floodlight				

7. Press the **Volt** button on the Energy Usage Meter. Record the voltage reading in Table 2-2.

8. Press the **Watt** button once, so that the display shows the watts being used. Record the Watts being used in Table 2-2.

9. Let the bulb warm up a minute and then stand 2-3 feet from the center of the panel and use the IR camera to read the temperature of the hottest area of the bulb. Record this in Table 2-2.

10. Turn the Light Power Switch to its **Off** position and, using a protective glove or cloth, remove the 15-Watt Incandescent Bulb.

> **CAUTION**
>
> The light bulb may be hot! Always use your protective glove or cloth to handle the bulbs.

11. Repeat Steps 5-11 for each of the other bulbs listed.

12. Remove the screws from the lighting system, replace the cover on the fixture base and secure it in place with the screws.

Table 2-3

13. Calculate the Actual Kilowatts for each bulb by dividing the Actual Watts recorded in Table 2-2 by 1000. Record the results in the appropriate box in the *ACTUAL KILOWATTS* column of Table 2-3.

BULB	ACTUAL KILOWATTS	KWH USED PER DAY	MONTHLY COST
15-Watt Incandescent			
25-Watt Incandescent			
40-Watt Incandescent			
60-Watt Incandescent			
100-Watt Incandescent			
13-Watt CFL			
19-Watt CFL			
60-Watt Halogen Floodlight			

14. Using an estimate of 6 hours as the number of hours each bulb will be powered on every day, calculate the kilowatt hours (kWh) each bulb will consume. Record your answer in the *KWH USED PER DAY* column of Table 2-3.

15. Using the Internet (or a current electrical bill), find the cost per kilowatt hour for your local utility or power company. Record the information on the following line:

Current Cost per KWh: _____

16. Determine the total monthly cost of operating each bulb and record the result in the *MONTHLY COST* column of Table 2-3. Use the formula:

kWh used per day x 30 days x Cost per kWh = Monthly Cost

17. Remove the screws from the lighting fixture and carefully remove the cover. Store the cover in a safe location and install the screws back in the fixture base.

18. Using a protective glove or cloth, insert the 15-Watt Incandescent bulb and turn the Light Power Switch to its **On** position. Examine the amount of light that is given off.

19. Turn the Light Power Switch to its **Off** position and, using a protective glove or cloth, remove the 15-Watt Incandescent bulb.

20. Using a protective glove or cloth, insert the 13-Watt CFL bulb and turn the Light Power Switch to its **On** position. Examine how much light is given off. Compare that to the 15-Watt Incandescent Bulb. Which one was brighter?

_____

21. Turn the Outlet Power Switch to its **Off** position and, using a protective glove or cloth, remove the 13-Watt CFL bulb.

22. Using a protective glove or cloth, insert the 60-Watt Incandescent bulb into the socket and turn the Light Power Switch to its **On** position. Observe the amount of light produced and try to compare it to the light given off by the 13-Watt CFL. How much brighter is this bulb?

_____

23. Turn the Light Power Switch to its **Off** position and, using a protective glove or cloth, remove the 60-Watt Incandescent bulb.

24. Move the Main Power Switch to its **Off** position. Unplug the Energy Usage Meter.

25. Remove the screws from the lighting system, replace the cover on the fixture base and secure it in place with the screws.

26. Return all materials and tools to their designated areas. Clean up your work area.

Passive and Active Solar Heating

Energy Auditing

The GT-7500 includes both an active (electric) water heater and a passive solar array system that can be used to heat water in a **hot water tank**. The passive solar array includes a submerged pump in the tank to circulate the water through the system. As the array is heated, the water in the tubes is heated as well.

The remote temperature sensor for Thermostat #2 is located in the tank and measures the water temperature. Before beginning this procedure, make sure Thermostat #2 is equipped with good batteries and that its probe is not touching the active water heater.

In this procedure you will use the active water heater to heat the tank of water. Then, you will heat the water to the same temperature using the passive solar water heater. Finally, the cost to operate the active system will be calculated and then compared to the cost of the same system when supplemented with the passive system.

1. Ensure that all switches on the GT-7500 Energy Auditing Panel are in their **Off** position.

2. Plug the GT-7500's Main Power Cord into the front of the Energy Usage Meter. Then, plug the Energy Usage Meter into an AC power outlet.

3. Make sure the drain valve on the Hot Water Tank is closed and fill the tank with cold water to the fill line.

NOTE: When the water is circulated through the Passive Solar Array, the water level in the tank will fall below the Fill Line. This is OK.

4. Make sure the dial on the top of the Electric Water Heater is set to the maximum and replace the lid on the tank.

5. Move the Main Power Switch to its **On** position.

6. Record the temperature displayed on Thermostat #2 on the following line:

Initial temperature: _____

7. Move the Electric Water Heater switch to its **On** position and begin keeping track of time.

8. On the Energy Usage Meter, press the **Watt** button and record the power used by the electric water heater on the following line:

_____ Watts

9. As shown in Figure 2-1, move the Water Heater Pump Switch to its **On** position. Water should begin circulating through the Passive Solar Array. If water does not begin circulating through the system within 60 seconds, turn the Water Heater Pump Switch **Off** and check the tubing for obstructions. If necessary, remove the loose tube from the Hot Water Tank and try sucking the water through the system.

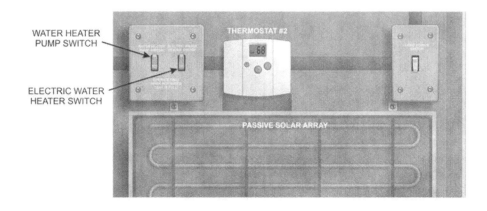

Figure 2-1:
The Water Heater
Pump Switch

10. Track the time it takes for the electric water heater to increase the temperature of the water 5 degrees. Record this time in Table 2-4.

Table 2-4:
Heating Water
with the Electric
Water Heater

	TIME	HOURS	KWH USED	COST
Initial +5 degree increase				
From +5 to +10 degree increase				
+10 degree increase				

11. Continue tracking time until the water increases another 5 degrees. Record the time in Table 2-4. Then record the overall time taken to heat the water 10 degrees.

12. Turn the Electric Water Heater Switch to its **Off** position.

13. Record the temperature displayed in Thermostat #2 on the following line:

_____

14. Drain ½ of the warm water from the tank and replace with cold water. Remember to refill the tank to the **Fill Line**.

15. Record the temperature displayed on Thermostat #2 on the following line:

_____

16. Position the Variable Intensity Light Source 18"- 24" inches from the Passive Solar Array. Turn on all four bulbs of the Light Source and focus them on the array.

17. Track the time it takes for the temperature of the water in the tank to increase to the temperature recorded in Step 13. Record the time on the following line:

_____

18. Convert the times you recorded in Table 2-4 into units of hours. Use the following formula:

[(Seconds/60) + Minutes]/60 = Hours

Record your answer in the *HOURS* column of Table 2-4.

19. Calculate the Kilowatt hours used to initially heat the water and to reheat the water by dividing the Watts by 1000 then multiplying that number by the number of hours. Use the formula:

(Watts/1000) x Hours = KWh

Record your answer in the *KWH USED* column of Table 2-4.

20. Using the Internet or a current electrical bill, find the cost per kilowatt hour for your local utility or power company. Record the information on the following line:

Current cost per KWh: _____

21. Use the Kilowatt hours you've recorded in Table 2-4 and the cost of electricity from the previous step, to calculate the cost of the energy used to heat the water from room temperature. Record that cost in Table 2-4. Do the same for reheating the water.

22. Calculate the cost required to heat one tank of water with the electric water heater every day for 30 days. To find this, multiply (cost to heat the tank of water 10°) x 30. Record the cost on the following line:

_____

23. On average, it takes 2.5 hours for the water in the tank to cool down 5 degrees and need to be reheated. Calculate the total hours it takes for the water to cool down and then be reheated with the electric water heater. Record the total hours on the following line:

_____

24. Calculate the number of times per day this cycle occurs. Record the number of cycles per day on the following line:

Cycles per day: _____

25. Multiplying the number of times a day this occurs by the cost to heat the water from 5 to 10 degrees to find the daily cost of keeping the water warm. Record the daily cost on the following line:

Daily cost: _____

Multiply this by 30 to calculate the approximate monthly cost. Record the monthly cost on the following line:

Monthly cost: _____

26. Calculate the total monthly cost to keep the water warm and heat a tank of water every day. Record the cost on the following line:

Total monthly cost: _____

27. What would be the total monthly cost if the solar water heater was used to heat a half a tank of water and keep the water warm for 6 hours every day? Use the following formulas and record your answer on the following line:

Monthly cost to heat ½ tank of water daily = Cost to heat the water from +5° to +10° x 30 days

Monthly cost to keep the water warm = [18 hours / (Hours for the water to cool + Hours to reheat the water)] x Cost to heat the water from 5° to 10° x 30 days

Total Monthly Cost = Monthly cost to heat ½ tank of water daily + Monthly cost to keep the water warm

Total monthly cost: _____

28. Find the percentage of decrease for the monthly cost between using only the electric water heater (amount figured in Step 26) and using the electric water heater with the solar water heater (amount figured in Step 27). Use the formula and record your answer on the following line:

Percentage of cost decrease = 1 – (Monthly cost using the electric water heater and the solar water heater / Monthly cost of using only the electric water heater)

Percentage of cost decrease: _____

29. Unplug the Energy Usage Meter. Drain the water from the Hot Water Tank.

30. Return all materials and tools to their designated areas. Clean up your work area.

Feedback

LAB QUESTIONS

1. Based on the model used for determining monthly cost of a light bulb, how much would it cost if you had twelve (12) 60-watt light bulbs and the utility company charged $0.084 / kWh?

2. Using the same scenario from the previous question, how much money per month would you save if you switched all twelve bulbs to 13-watt CFL bulbs?

3. Which bulb consumed the least energy and which bulb consumed the most energy?

4. Which bulb gave off the most heat?

5. Which bulb gave off the least heat?

6. If you compared a 19-Watt CFL bulb to a 75-Watt Incandescent bulb the light emitted should be comparable. Which would be hotter after 10 minutes of use and why?

7. Which heated the water faster, the passive solar array or the electric water heater?

8. What is the major drawback of a solar water heater when compared to a traditional water heater?

Evaluating Insulation Materials

OBJECTIVES

1. Evaluate the effectiveness of various types of insulation with the Reconfigurable House.
2. Examine the effects of different materials on how the interior and exterior of the Reconfigurable House heats and cools.
3. Evaluate the condition of installed insulation using the IR camera.

Energy Auditing

RESOURCES

1. GT-7500 Energy Auditing Technology Panel
   - Reconfigurable House
     - Fixed Reconfigurable House Base
     - Door & Window Side Wall
     - Plain Side Wall
     - Removable Front Wall
     - Removable Roof Piece
     - Front Door Insert
2. IR Camera
3. Screwdriver
4. Watch or Timer
5. Tablespoon

6. Insulation Inserts
   - Polystyrene Insulation Set
   - Fiberglass Insulation Set
   - Wool Insulation Set
   - Cotton Insulation Set

DISCUSSION

Buildings generally consume large amounts of energy. This energy is used to provide comfort and convenience for the inhabitants of the building. Of these comforts, the largest portion of the energy used is for temperature control. It makes sense when designing buildings for maximum efficiency, to focus on improving this area, and to do this, two predominate properties need to be considered — *thermal mass* and *thermal efficiency*.

Thermal mass (also referred to as *thermal capacity* or *heat capacity*) is the ability of a material or object to hold heat. In sustainable architecture designs, thermal mass is a gauge of how well a building can maintain a constant temperature during the normal temperature fluctuations of the surrounding environment throughout the day. During warm periods of the day, the building's thermal mass absorbs heat from the surrounding atmosphere and releases the heat during cooler periods.

Optimizing thermal mass involves selecting proper materials for the prevailing climate of a building's location and utilizing passive solar design techniques when selecting locations. When thermal mass is optimized, the efficiency of any active heating and cooling systems will improve, saving energy and reducing costs.

Concrete is one of the primary materials used to help structures increase their thermal mass. Other materials with a high thermal mass are adobe, stone and compacted (rammed) earth. Water also has a high thermal mass and can be used in passive solar heaters or heat exchanging ponds

Insulation

The other major energy consumption aspect the building designer must consider is the building's **thermal efficiency**—or insulation efficiency. In structural terms, insulation is the ability to control thermal (heat/cold) transfers through a barrier. Buildings with high thermal efficiency can achieve higher temperature differences between its interior and exterior and maintain that difference for longer periods. This allows for greater control of interior temperatures, providing comfort for the inhabitants, less work for heating and cooling systems, and protection of internal materials and systems from temperature related damage. All of the materials used to construct a building factor into its thermal efficiency. This includes the outer shell materials, the inner wall coverings, doors, windows and insulating materials inserted into walls, attics and crawlspaces.

Each material has a different insulation value and is expressed as an **R-value**. On the **R-scale**, higher values mean a material is better at insulating against heat and cold transfers than materials with lower values. In addition, a material's R-value increases with the material's thickness. However, to achieve better thermal efficiency, inferior insulation may need to be replaced with a better material as opposed to just adding more.

There are a number of different insulation materials that can be added to the structures to improve insulation and include:

- Blanket or rolled fiber materials

- Loose-fill, blown-in materials

- Spray-in, expanding foam

- Rigid sheet materials

- Reflective, radiant barrier materials

When choosing insulation, selecting materials with highest R-values will give the highest performance, but there are other factors that need to be considered that include:

- Local climate
- Price and availability of materials
- Accessibility to insulation spaces
- Space available for insulation

In the United States, the Department of Energy has developed recommended minimum levels of insulation for buildings located within different geographical zones, as depicted in Figure 3-1.

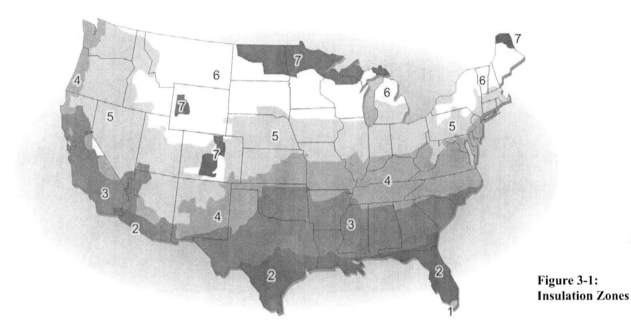

Figure 3-1:
Insulation Zones

Table 3-1 provides the recommended R-value ratings for the insulation zones in the figure.

ZONE	ATTIC	CATHEDRAL CEILING	WALL CAVITY	FLOOR
1	R30 (RSI 5.0)	R22 (RSI 3.9)	R13 (RSI 2.2)	R13 (RSI 2.2)
2	R30 (RSI 5.0)	R22 (RSI 3.9)	R13 (RSI 2.2)	R13 (RSI 2.2)
3	R30 (RSI 5.0)	R22 (RSI 3.9)	R13 (RSI 2.2)	R25 (RSI 4.4)
4	R38 (RSI 6.7)	R30 (RSI 5.0)	R13 (RSI 2.2)	R25 (RSI 4.4)
5	R38 (RSI 6.7)	R30 (RSI 5.0)	R13 (RSI 2.2)	R25 (RSI 4.4)
6	R49 (RSI 8.6)	R30 (RSI 5.0)	R13 (RSI 2.2)	R25 (RSI 4.4)
7	R49 (RSI 8.6)	R30 (RSI 5.0)	R13 (RSI 2.2)	R25 (RSI 4.4)
8	R49 (RSI 8.6)	R30 (RSI 5.0)	R13 (RSI 2.2)	R25 (RSI 4.4)

Table 3-1:
Minimum Recommended Insulation Levels for Insulation Zones

Energy Auditing

PROCEDURES

The Marcraft GT-7500 can be used to evaluate a material's relative R-value, or its ability to resist heat transfer. The Reconfigurable House can be fitted with inserts made of different materials that can be installed in the attic, walls, and crawlspace. As the heat is distributed throughout the house, the different insulation materials affect the temperature inside the house, as well as the time it takes to heat up and cool down. In the following procedures, you will evaluate the effectiveness of insulation and use an IR camera to evaluate the integrity of installed insulation.

Evaluating Insulation with an IR Camera

1. Ensure that all the switches on the panel are in their **Off** positions.

2. Turn the screw on the top of the Front Door Insert ½ turn in either direction to unlock it from the Front Wall. As shown in Figure 3-2, gently tilt the top of the Front Door Insert out from the Front Wall and then slide the insert up and out.

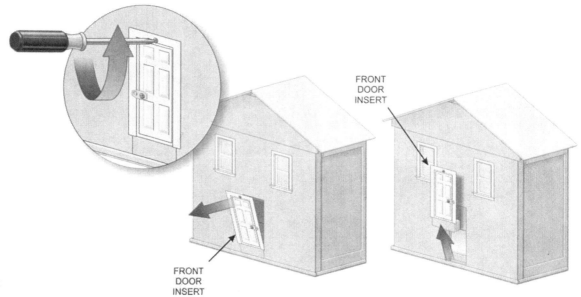

**Figure 3-2:
Removing the
Front Door Insert**

3. Remove the Roof from the Reconfigurable House.

4. Remove the Front Wall from the Reconfigurable House Base by lifting it up and out, as shown in Figure 3-2.

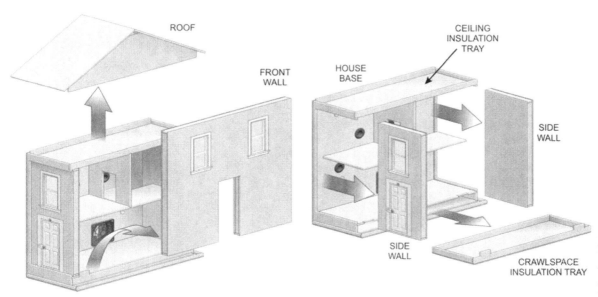

Figure 3-2: Disassembling the Reconfigurable House

5. Slide the two Side Walls and the Crawlspace Insulation Tray out of the Reconfigurable House Base.

6. Remove any insulation inserts from the Ceiling Insulation Tray and the Crawlspace Insulation Tray. Replace the Crawlspace Insulation Tray in the Reconfigurable House Base.

7. As shown in Figure 3-3, ensure the side walls are empty.

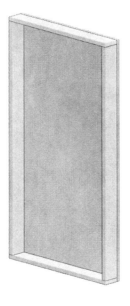

Figure 3-3: The Empty Side Walls

8. Slide the plain Side Wall into the right side of the Reconfigurable House Base with the open side on the inside of the house. Insert the other Side Wall into the left side of the base, as illustrated in Figure 3-4. Lock the door on the Side Wall shut.

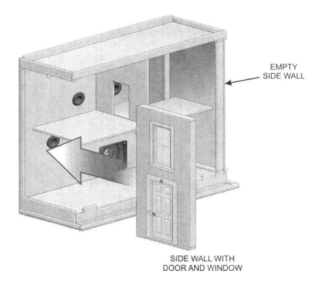

**Figure 3-4:
Replacing the
Side Walls**

9. Remove any insulation found inside the Front Wall.

10. Replace the Front Wall on the front of the Reconfigurable House Base with the interior of the wall open to the interior of the house. The bottom of the Front Wall should fit into the channel on the bottom of the house base.

11. As shown in Figure 3-5, replace the roof onto the top of the Reconfigurable House. The back of the roof will slide between the back of the house base and the panel. The front of the roof will slide over the exterior of the Front Wall and hold it in place.

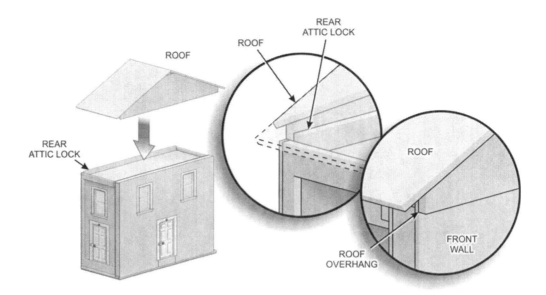

**Figure 3-5:
Replacing the
Roof**

Table 3-2: Heating the House with No Insulation

12. Look at Thermostat #1 and record the temperature inside the Reconfigurable House as the *Initial INTERNAL TEMPERATURE* in Table 3-2.

MINUTES	INTERNAL TEMPERATURE	EXTERNAL TEMPERATURE	MINUTES	INTERNAL TEMPERATURE	EXTERNAL TEMPERATURE
Initial			08		
01			09		
02			10		
03			11		
04			12		
05			13		
06			14		
07			15		

13. Turn on the IR camera. Lift the protective rubber cover on the side to reveal the USB input, power cord input and memory slot. Ensure there is a memory card in the slot and close the cover. Use the switch on the front of the camera to release the lens cover. Make sure the emissivity is set to "**Matt**".

14. Position the IR camera 2-3 feet away from the front of the house and aim the IR camera at the space in between the windows, the top of the door and the top of the Front Wall. Record this as the *Initial EXTERNAL TEMPERATURE* in Table 3-2.

15. Move the Main Power Switch to its **On** position.

16. Turn the House Fan Controller to its **On** position and move the speed control slide all the way to the top.

17. Look inside the house to confirm that the fan is running. If it is, move the speed control slide on the House Fan Controller down to the middle. The fan should slow down, but not stop.

18. Turn the House Heating Controller to its **On** position and move the slide all the way to the top. Observe the inside of the house to confirm that there is a light on behind the fan.

CAUTION

Do not turn the House Fan Controller **Off** or move the slide all the way down. This will prevent the air from circulating inside the house and may damage the panel.

---

19. As shown in Figure 3-6, slide the Front Door Insert into place on the bottom of the Front Wall. Turn the screw on the top of the door ½ turn in either direction to secure it to the Front Wall. Lock the door shut.

PROCEDURE - 3

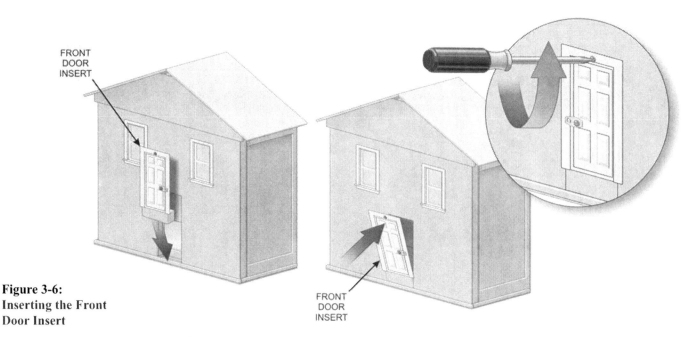

**Figure 3-6:
Inserting the Front
Door Insert**

20. Start keeping track of time. Every minute, record the internal temperature of the house and use the IR camera to record the external temperature in the same spot in the center of the Front Wall.

**Table 3-3: Cooling
the House with
No Insulation**

21. After 15 minutes, turn the House Heating Controller to its **Off** position, but continue tracking the time and recording the interior and exterior temperature of the house in Table 3-3.

MINUTES	INTERNAL TEMPERATURE	EXTERNAL TEMPERATURE	MINUTES	INTERNAL TEMPERATURE	EXTERNAL TEMPERATURE
01			14		
02			15		
03			16		
04			17		
05			18		
06			19		
07			20		
08			21		
09			22		
10			23		
11			24		
12			25		
13					

22. After the table is complete, move the speed control slide on the House Fan Controller all the way up so the fan is running at full power. This will help speed the cooling of the Reconfigurable House so it will be ready for the next experiment.

23. Turn the screw on the top of the Front Door Insert ½ turn in either direction to unlock it from the Front Wall. Gently tilt the top of the Front Door Insert out from the Front Wall and then slide the insert up and out.

24. Disassemble the Reconfigurable House by removing the Roof and then removing the Front Wall. Next, slide the Side Walls and the Crawlspace Insulation Tray out.

25. Using the empty chart for the interior temperature, plot the data for the internal temperature you recorded in Table 3-2 and Table 3-3. Connect each point to create a line chart. Label this line as **No Insulation**. Repeat this process for the Exterior Temperature Chart.

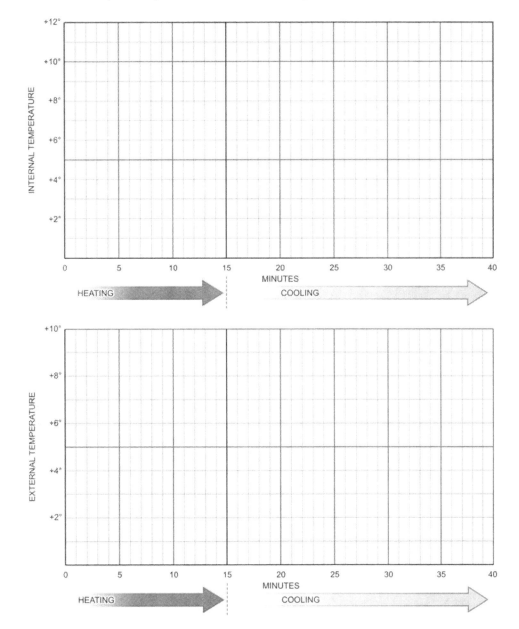

Comparing the Use of Insulation versus Not Using Insulation

26. After 30 minutes of cooling, obtain the Cotton Insulation Insert Set for the Reconfigurable House. As shown in Figure 3-7, place the ceiling insert piece into the tray on top of the Reconfigurable House Base.

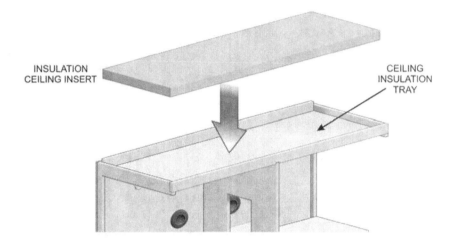

Figure 3-7: Inserting Insulation into the Ceiling Insulation Tray

27. Place the crawlspace insert piece into the Crawlspace Insulation Tray.

28. Place the large side wall insert piece into the plain Side Wall.

29. Fill the side wall with the door and window with the small side wall insulation pieces.

30. Fill the Front Wall with the front wall insulation pieces.

31. Reassemble the house, as illustrated in Figure 3-8.

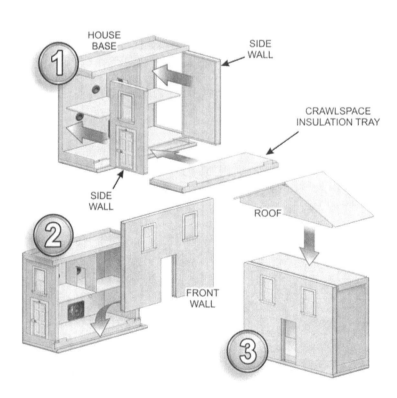

Figure 3-8: Reassembling the Reconfigurable House

32. Observe at Thermostat #1 and record the temperature inside the Reconfigurable House as the *Initial INTERNAL TEMPERATURE* in Table 3-4. Use the IR camera to read the temperature of the Front Wall between the windows and above the door. Record this as the *Initial EXTERNAL TEMPERATURE*.

Table 3-4: Heating the House with the Cotton Insulation Installed

MINUTES	INTERNAL TEMPERATURE	EXTERNAL TEMPERATURE	MINUTES	INTERNAL TEMPERATURE	EXTERNAL TEMPERATURE
Initial			08		
01			09		
02			10		
03			11		
04			12		
05			13		
06			14		
07			15		

33. Look inside the house to confirm that the fan is still running. If so, move the speed control slide on the House Fan Controller down to the middle. The fan should have slowed, but not stopped.

34. Turn the House Heating Controller to its **On** position and move the temperature control slide all the way to the top. Look inside the house to confirm that there is a light on behind the fan.

35. Slide the Front Door Insert into place in the bottom of the Front Wall. Turn the screw on the top of the door ½ turn in either direction to secure it to the Front Wall. Lock the door shut.

36. Begin tracking the time. Every minute, record the internal and external temperature of the house.

37. After 15 minutes, turn the House Heating Controller to its **Off** position, but continue tracking the time and recording the interior temperature of the house in Table 3-5.

Table 3-5: Cooling the House with Cotton Insulation Installed

MINUTES	INTERNAL TEMPERATURE	EXTERNAL TEMPERATURE	MINUTES	INTERNAL TEMPERATURE	EXTERNAL TEMPERATURE
01			14		
02			15		
03			16		
04			17		
05			18		
06			19		
07			20		
08			21		
09			22		
10			23		
11			24		
12			25		
13					

38. After the table is complete, move the speed control slide on the House Fan Controller all the way up so the fan is running at full power. This will help speed the cooling of the Reconfigurable House so it will be ready for the next experiment.

39. Turn the screw on the top of the Front Door Insert ½ turn in either direction to unlock it from the Front Wall. Gently tilt the top of the Front Door Insert out from the Front Wall and then slide the insert up and out.

40. Disassemble the Reconfigurable House by removing the Roof and then removing the Front Wall. Next, slide the Side Walls and the Crawlspace Insulation Tray out.

41. Using the charts in Step 25, plot the data for the internal temperatures you recorded in Table 3-4 and Table 3-5. Connect each point to create a line chart. Label this line with the type of insulation you used. Then do the same for the External Temperature Chart.

42. Turn the House Fan Controller **Off**, then move the Main Power Switch to its **Off** position.

43. Remove the insulation inserts from the Reconfigurable House and carefully set them aside.

44. Repeat steps 26-43 for the Wool Insulation Set. Use Table 3-6 to record the heating and cooling data.

HEATING					
Minutes	Internal Temperature	External Temperature	Minutes	Internal Temperature	External Temperature
Initial			08		
01			09		
02			10		
03			11		
04			12		
05			13		
06			14		
07			15		
COOLING					
Minutes	Internal Temperature	External Temperature	Minutes	Internal Temperature	External Temperature
01			14		
02			15		
03			16		
04			17		
05			18		
06			19		
07			20		
08			21		
09			22		
10			23		
11			24		
12			25		
13					

Table 3-6: Heating and Cooling Data for the Wool Insulation Set

45. Repeat steps 26-43 for the Fiberglass Insulation Set. Use Table 3-7 to record the heating and cooling data.

Table 3-7: Heating and Cooling Data for the Fiberglass Insulation Set

HEATING					
Minutes	Internal Temperature	External Temperature	Minutes	Internal Temperature	External Temperature
Initial			08		
01			09		
02			10		
03			11		
04			12		
05			13		
06			14		
07			15		
COOLING					
Minutes	Internal Temperature	External Temperature	Minutes	Internal Temperature	External Temperature
01			14		
02			15		
03			16		
04			17		
05			18		
06			19		
07			20		
08			21		
09			22		
10			23		
11			24		
12			25		
13					

46. Repeat steps 26-43 for the Polystyrene Insulation Set. Use Table 3-8 to record the heating and cooling data.

HEATING					
Minutes	Internal Temperature	External Temperature	Minutes	Internal Temperature	External Temperature
Initial			08		
01			09		
02			10		
03			11		
04			12		
05			13		
06			14		
07			15		
COOLING					
Minutes	Internal Temperature	External Temperature	Minutes	Internal Temperature	External Temperature
01			14		
02			15		
03			16		
04			17		
05			18		
06			19		
07			20		
08			21		
09			22		
10			23		
11			24		
12			25		
13					

Table 3-8: Heating and Cooling Data for the Polystyrene Insulation Set

47. Reassemble the Reconfigurable House.

48. Delete any images you saved on the IR camera, turn the camera Off and close the protective lens cover. Return the camera to its protective case.

49. Return all materials and tools to their designated areas. Clean up your work area.

Energy Auditing

Applying the IR Camera to Evaluate Insulation Quality

1. Ensure that all the switches on the panel are in their **Off** positions.

2. Observe at Thermostat #1 and record the ambient room temperature inside the house and the start time on the following lines:

Ambient Room Temperature: _____   Time: _____

3. Turn the screw on the top of the Front Door Insert ½ turn in either direction to unlock it from the Front Wall. As shown in Figure 3-9, gently tilt the top of the Front Door Insert out from the Front Wall and then slide the insert up and out.

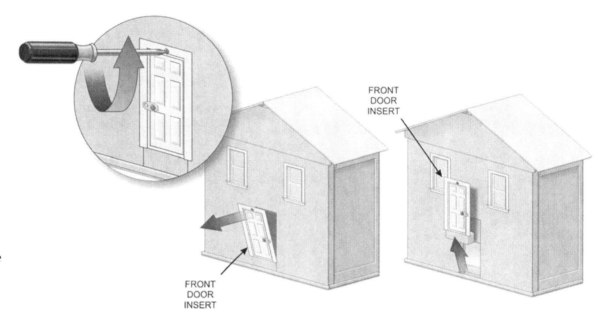

**Figure 3-9:
Removing the
Front Door
Insert**

4. Disassemble the Reconfigurable House by removing the Roof and then removing the Front Wall. Then slide the Side Walls and the Crawlspace Insulation Tray out.

5. Move the Main Power Switch to its **On** position.

6. Turn the House Fan Controller to its **On** position and move the speed control slide all the way to the top.

7. Observe at the fan inside the house and confirm it is running. If it is, move the slide on the House Fan Controller down to the middle. The fan should have slowed down, but not stopped.

8. Turn the House Heating Controller to its **On** position and move the temperature control slide all the way to the top. Look inside the house to confirm that there is a light on behind the fan.

9. Insert the Fiberglass Crawlspace Insert into the Crawlspace Insulation Tray. Insert the tray back into the slot on the bottom of the house base.

10. Insert the Fiberglass Ceiling insert into the tray on the top of the house base.

11. Fill the Side Wall with the door and window with the small Fiberglass Side Wall Insulation pieces. Make sure the door is locked shut and slide the Side Wall into the left side of the house base, with the open side of the wall facing the inside of the house.

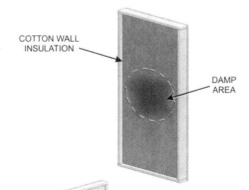

Figure 3-10: The Damp Area Inside the Side Wall

12. Insert the large Cotton Side Wall Insert into Side Wall without the door and window.

13. As illustrated in Figure 3-10, dampen the center of the insulation by adding 1 tablespoon of water until there is a wet area about 2-3 inches wide.

14. Slide the Side Wall into the right side of the Reconfigurable House Base.

15. Insert the Polystyrene Front Wall Insert pieces into the Front Wall, but as shown in Figure 3-11, leave the area to the left of the left window empty.

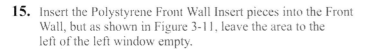

16. Replace the Front Wall on the house base so the insulation is open to the inside of the house.

Figure 3-11: Leaving a Hole in the Front Wall Insulation

17. Replace the Roof on top of the Reconfigurable House Base. The back of the Roof should slide in between the house base and the panel and the front of the Roof should slide over the front of the Front Wall.

18. As shown in Figure 3-12, slide the Front Door Insert into place on the bottom of the Front Wall. Turn the screw on the top of the door ½ turn in either direction to secure it to the Front Wall. Lock the door shut.

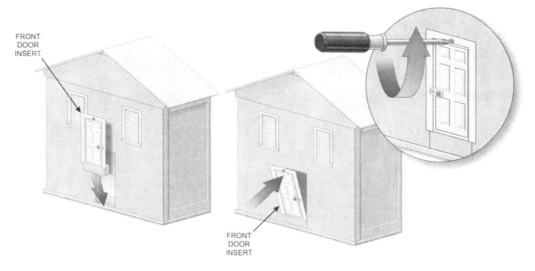

Figure 3-12: Inserting the Front Door Insert

19. Turn on the IR camera. Lift the protective rubber cover on the side of the camera to the USB input, power cord input and memory card slot. Ensure there is a memory card in your camera and close the cover. Use the switch on the front of the camera to release the lens cover.

20. Using the IR camera, examine the right Side Wall of the Reconfigurable House. On the following lines, record the temperatures of the center of the wall where the insulation was wet and the area above it, where the insulation is dry.

Temperature of Wall with Wet Insulation: _____ Dry Insulation: _____

21. Allow the house to heat up for at least 20 minutes. Use the IR camera to examine the Front Wall of the Reconfigurable House. Record the temperature of three different locations of the exterior wall on the second floor of the house on the following lines:

    Temperature of the wall between the left edge and left window: _____

    Temperature of the wall between the windows: _____

    Temperature of the wall between the right edge and the right window: _____

22. Delete any images you saved on the IR camera. Turn the IR camera **OFF** and use the switch on the front of the camera to close the protective lens cover. Return the camera to its protective case.

23. Turn the House Heating Controller to its **OFF** positions.

24. Slide the House Fan Controller all the way up so the house can begin cooling down.

25. Unlock the Front Door Insert from the Front Wall by turning the screw on top of the door ½ turn in either direction. Remove the Front Door Insert by gently pulling the top forward and lifting the insert up and out.

26. Disassemble the Reconfigurable House by removing the Roof then removing the Front Wall. Then, slide the Side Walls and the Crawlspace Insulation Tray out.

27. Remove the insulation from the house parts. Set the wet piece of cotton insulation out to dry. Use a paper towel or cloth to dry the inside of the Side Wall.

28. When the Side Wall is dry, reassemble the Reconfigurable House.

29. Return all materials and tools to their designated areas. Clean up your work area.

30. Move the Main Power Switch to its **OFF** position.

Feedback

LAB QUESTIONS

1. Describe how the interior of the house heated up and cooled down when using insulation versus not using insulation?

2. How did the use of insulation affect the temperature inside the house as compared to using no insulation?

3. How did the use of insulation affect the surface temperature of the exterior of the house as compared to using no insulation?

4. Using any insulation, what is the best way to increase its effectiveness?

5. If this were a real house, what might be the cause of the wet insulation found in the side wall?

6. If this were a real house and blown cellulose insulation was used instead of polystyrene, what might be possible causes of an entire area missing insulation?

Energy Auditing Tests

OBJECTIVES

1. Prepare the Reconfigurable House for testing using a blower door.
2. Examine the house for areas of heat loss and air penetration using the IR camera.
3. Create a summary of your test and provide advice on improving the energy efficiency of the building.

Energy Auditing

RESOURCES

1. GT-7500 Energy Auditing Technology Panel
   - Reconfigurable House
     - Fixed Reconfigurable House Base
     - Door & Window Side Wall
     - Plain Side Wall
     - Removable Front Wall
     - Removable Roof Piece
     - Front Door Insert
     - Blower Door Insert
2. Watch or Timer
3. Screwdriver
4. Polystyrene Insulation Set
5. IR Camera

DISCUSSION

An important part of living with future energy demands and maintaining a high living standard involves making existing structures as energy efficient as possible. All buildings were not created equal. Some existing buildings use energy more effectively than others either through their original design and construction techniques, or through renovations and upgrades taken through the building's **life cycle**. The chart in Figure 4-1 describes the Energy Usage Consumption in a typical residential building in the United States.

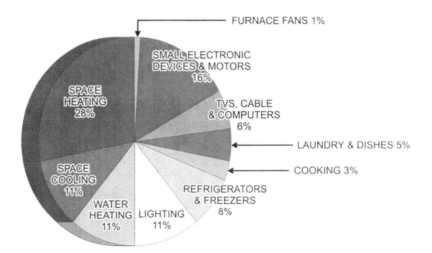

Figure 4-1:
Residential Energy
Usage

To determine what steps will be effective for making a given building more efficient requires an **energy audit**. An energy audit is a systematic investigation of the building's true energy usage and potential for improvement. A good audit will evaluate each of these areas:

- **Evaluate the Physical Structure** — Buildings are constructed in different ways and using different materials. An energy audit will identify the different parts of a structure, how they are constructed and what materials were used. Insulation materials are also identified. Each part of a structure is then evaluated.

- **Evaluate the Outer Shell** — A basic check of a building's outer shell will reveal obvious areas of air leakage or poor insulation. Areas around doors, windows and pipes or cables that enter a building are checked for gaps. IR cameras can be utilized to identify major areas of air intrusion and bad insulation, but for more comprehensive testing, a blower door should be used to test how airtight a building is and to enhance the effectiveness of IR cameras.

- **Evaluate the Heating and Cooling Systems** — Heating and cooling systems account for 40% of a home's energy usage, so it is important that these systems are operating as efficiently as possible. Each of these systems and their energy sources must be identified and evaluated along with the control system (thermostat). In addition, the distribution system should be tested for air leakage.

- **Evaluate Water Heating Systems** — The water heating system and its energy sources should be identified, and the efficiency of the system should be determined. Solar water heaters need to be identified and details about its size, orientation and tilt should be recorded and evaluated. Hot water tanks and piping should be checked for insulation and evaluated.

- **Evaluate Lighting** — An energy audit will identify and evaluate each type of lighting used in a building. In addition, usage habits and control systems are also checked. One of the easiest and cost effective ways to improve energy efficiency of a building is to upgrade to energy efficient light bulbs and turn off lights when leaving a room.

- **Evaluate Other Large Appliances** — Other large appliances, like washers, dryers, fridges and ovens should be evaluated for energy efficiency.

After the energy audit is performed, a report is generated. This report will include the results of the audit and provide an overall rating of the home. The estimated overall usage and cost of energy for a home should also be included along with suggestions for improving a home's energy efficiency. Each suggestion should include the estimated energy savings, implementation costs, useful life of the improvements and the overall financial savings.

PROCEDURE

The Marcraft GT-7500 can be used to simulate tests used during an energy audit to evaluate a building's outer shell and insulation quality. Just as in a real blower door test, the front door of a house is opened or removed and replaced with fans. This fan will pull air out of the house and exaggerate any air leaks present so they are easier to identify using IR cameras.

1. Ensure that all the switches on the panel are in their **Off** positions.

2. Observe Thermostat #1 and record the ambient room temperature inside the house and the starting time on the following line:

   Ambient Room Temperature: _____ Time: _____

3. Turn the screw on the top of the Front Door Insert ½ turn in either direction to unlock it from the Front Wall. As shown in Figure 4-2, gently tilt the top of the Front Door Insert out from the Front Wall and then slide it up and out.

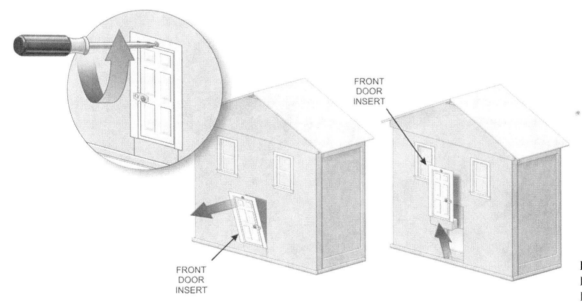

FRONT DOOR INSERT

FRONT DOOR INSERT

FRONT DOOR INSERT

**Figure 4-2:
Removing the
Front Door Insert**

4. Disassemble the Reconfigurable House by removing the Roof and then removing the Front Wall. Next, slide the Side Walls and the Crawlspace Insulation Tray out.

5. Move the Main Power Switch to its **On** position.

6. Turn the House Fan Controller to its **On** position and move the speed control slide all the way to the top.

7. Observe at the fan inside the house and confirm it is running. If so, move the slide on the House Fan Controller down to its mid range point. The fan should slow, but should not have stopped.

8. Move the House Heating Controller switch to its **On** position and move the temperature control slide all the way to the top. Look inside the house to confirm that there is a light on behind the fan.

> ## CAUTION
>
> Do not turn the House Fan Controller **Off** or move the slide all the way down. This will prevent the air from circulating inside the house and may damage the panel.

9. As shown in Figure 4-3, place the Polystyrene Ceiling Insert into the tray on top of the Reconfigurable House Base.

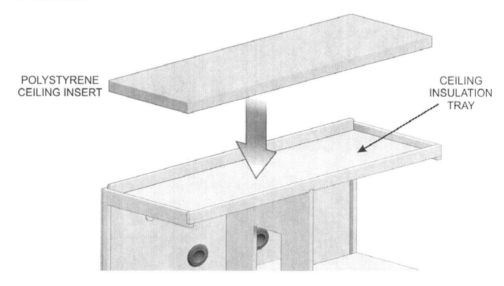

POLYSTYRENE CEILING INSERT

CEILING INSULATION TRAY

**Figure 4-3:
Inserting Insulation
into the Ceiling
Insulation Tray**

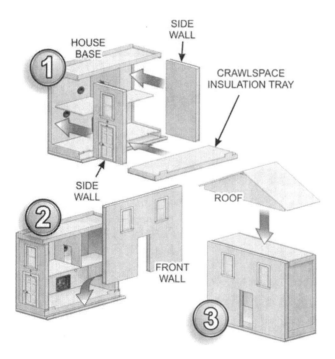

HOUSE BASE

SIDE WALL

CRAWLSPACE INSULATION TRAY

SIDE WALL

FRONT WALL

ROOF

**Figure 4-4:
Reassembling the
Reconfigurable
House**

10. Place the Polystyrene Crawlspace Insert into the Crawlspace Insulation Tray.

11. Place the large Polystyrene Side Wall Insert into the plain Side Wall.

12. Remove the cover from the Side Wall with the door and window. Fill it with the small Polystyrene Side Wall Insert pieces.

13. Fill the Front Wall with the Polystyrene Front Wall Insert pieces.

14. Reassemble the house as illustrated in Figure 4-4.

15. Turn on the IR camera. Lift the protective rubber cover on the side of the camera to the USB input, power cord input and memory card slot. Ensure there is a memory card in your camera and close the cover. Use the switch on the front of the camera to release the lens cover.

16. Using the IR camera, save images of the items listed in Table 4-1. Record the name of the image in the table.

17. Wait for the interior temperature inside the house to increase by 15° from the Ambient Room Temperature recorded at the beginning of the lab. This should take approximately 20-25 minutes from starting this procedure.

TARGET	IMAGE NAME
Right Side Wall	
Left Side Wall	
Left Side Wall Door only	
Left Side Wall Window only	
Full Front Wall	
Front Door	
Front Wall, Left Window	
Front Wall, Right Window	
Front Gable	

Table 4-1: Initial Exterior Survey of the House

18. Using the IR camera, save images of the items listed in Table 4-2. Record the name of the image in the table. Make note of areas that show more than 1° difference in temperature from the rest of the wall (such as the window panes).

TARGET	IMAGE NAME	VISIBLE AREAS OF HEAT LOSS
Right Side Wall		
Left Side Wall		
Left Side Wall Door only		
Left Side Wall Window only		
Full Front Wall		
Front Door		
Front Wall, Left Window		
Front Wall, Right Window		
Front Gable		
Roof		

Table 4-2: Exterior Survey of the House After Warming Up

19. Turn the screw on the top of the Front Door Insert counterclockwise to unlock it from the Front Wall. Gently tilt the top of the Front Door Insert out and then slide the insert up and out.

PROCEDURE - 4

20. Obtain the Blower Door Insert. With the fan facing the outside of the house, slide the bottom of the Blower Door Insert into the hole where the Front Door Insert was removed from. Push the top of the Blower Door Insert against the Front Wall. Turn the screw on top of the insert ½ turn in either direction to lock it in place.

21. Plug the Blower Door Insert's power cord into an AC power source. The fan should begin pulling warm air out of the house.

22. Wait 10-15 minutes for the blower door to reveal any air leaks in the house.

23. Using the IR camera, save images of the items listed in Table 4-3. Record the name of the image in the table. Make note of areas that show more than a 2° decrease in temperature from the area around it. Also record any areas that have cooled since taking pictures 10 minutes ago (such as the upper window pane on the Side Wall). Use the Archive Button on the IR camera to review the saved images.

Table 4-3: Exterior Survey of the House After using the Blower Door

TARGET	IMAGE NAME	VISIBLE AREAS OF AIR LEAKS
Right Side Wall		
Left Side Wall with Door and Window		
Left Side Wall Door only		
Left Side Wall Window only		
Full Front Wall		
Front Wall, Left Window		
Front Wall, Right Window		
Front Gable		
Roof		

24. Disconnect the Blower Door Insert's power cord from the AC power supply. Remove the insert from the Front Wall.

25. Remove the Roof and the Front Wall from the Reconfigurable House.

26. Using the IR camera, save images of the items listed in Table 4-4. Record the name of the image in the table. Make note of areas that show more than a 2° decrease in temperature from the area around it.

TARGET	IMAGE NAME	VISIBLE AREAS OF AIR LEAKS
1st Floor, where left Side Wall meets the back wall		
1st Floor, where the left Side Wall meets the floor		
1st Floor, Door and Frame		
1st Floor, where the right Side Wall meets the back wall		
1st Floor, where the right Side Wall meets the floor.		
1st Floor, right vent		
1st Floor, left vent		
1st Floor, air return (fan)		
2nd Floor left room, where the Side Wall meets the back wall		
2nd Floor left room, where the Side Wall meets the ceiling		
2nd Floor left room, Window and Frame		
2nd Floor left room, air vent		
2nd Floor right room, where the Side Wall meets the back wall		
2nd Floor right room, where the Side Wall meets the ceiling		
2nd Floor right room, air vent		

Table 4-4: Interior Survey of the House After using the Blower Door

27. Move the House Heating Controller to its **Off** positions.

28. Move the House Fan Controller speed control slide all the way up so the house can begin cooling down.

29. Remove the Side Walls and the Crawlspace Insulation Tray.

30. Remove the Polystyrene Insulation Inserts from the walls, ceiling tray and crawlspace tray of the Reconfigurable House.

31. Using Table 4-5, List 5 areas of the house where improvements are needed most and list the image(s) that show the problem. In the SUGGESTED SOLUTION(S) column, list possible ways a homeowner can fix each problem found.

Table 4-5:
Results of
Thermographic
Survey

	PROBLEM	IMAGE REFERENCES	SUGGESTED SOLUTION(S)
1			
2			
3			
4			
5			

32. Delete any images you saved on the IR camera. Turn the IR camera **Off** and use the switch on the front of the camera to close the protective lens cover. Return the camera to its protective case.

33. Reassemble the Reconfigurable House.

34. Return all materials and tools to their designated areas. Clean up your work area.

35. Turn the House Fan Controller to its **Off** position.

36. Move the Main Power Switch to its **Off** position.

Feedback

LAB QUESTIONS

1. Of the total energy used by a typical US residential home, what percentage is used by heating and cooling?

2. In a typical US residential home, if the energy used to heat the building is decreased by 50%, how much should the overall energy usage decrease?

3. Where on the Reconfigurable House did you find the worst Heat Loss?

4. How did the blower door allow you to see the air leaks in the Reconfigurable House?

Energy Auditing Research

OBJECTIVES

1. Search for energy auditing strategies.
2. Research the various components used to conduct energy auditing.
3. Locate applicable energy auditing regulations and legislation.

Energy Auditing

RESOURCES

1. Books
2. Newspapers
3. Magazines
4. Computer with Internet access and graphic capture software

DISCUSSION

Effective research skills are necessary for students hoping to participate in successful scholarship. These skills are well within reach thanks to the current availability of numerous information sources. Although the ability to research a given subject is often underrated, it is not wise to do so. Although traditional research avenues are still available (library card files, books, newspapers, and microfilmed magazines, the advent of Internet browsing has resulted in their gradual abandonment. Perceived as a superior source of information, the Internet now accounts for the majority of modern research from both home computers and library terminals.

Taking advantage of the Internet as an information source involves developing a number of basic research skills. Otherwise, the prodigious supply of Internet information may overwhelm the inquisitive mind. It's important for the modern scholar to locate relevant information quickly, without spending limited time sifting through endless amounts of data. While researching the subject of Energy Auditing, the student must effectively utilize his or her time regardless of which Internet search engine is being used. Using the advanced searching methods described in the following paragraphs will help in locating the required information quickly.

To locate documents containing an exact phrase, type the phrase, surrounded by quotation marks, into the search field. For example, typing *"energy auditing"* (with the quotation marks) will locate documents that contain the phrase *energy auditing*, but not Web pages that contain only *energy* or *auditing*. To locate documents containing these words, but not necessarily together, type the words separated by the Boolean operator *AND* in all caps. For example, typing *energy AND auditing* (without the quotation marks) will return Web pages that contain *energy*, *auditing*, and *energy auditing*.

To locate documents containing either one word or the other, type the words separated by the Boolean operator *OR* in all caps. For example, typing *energy OR auditing* (without the quotation marks) will return documents that contain *energy*, or *auditing*, or both.

You can deliberately exclude certain words from a search by typing the word to be excluded into the search field, preceded by the Boolean operator *NOT* in all caps. Using this approach, typing *energy NOT auditing* (without the quotation marks) will return only documents that do contain the word *energy*, and do not contain the word *auditing*. To zero in on documents that contain two terms separated by between 10 to 25 words, type the two terms separated by the Boolean operator *NEAR*, in all caps, into the search field. If the search expression is lengthy or complicated, use parentheses to separate the different parts. For example, typing *energy OR auditing NOT (ventilation OR infiltration)* will get you entries that have the words *energy*, or *auditing*, or both, but do not have the words *ventilation* or *infiltration*.

Considering the fact that thousands of additional files have probably been added to the Internet's total during the time you've taken to read this far, it should be obvious that there is no way to identify, catalog, or retrieve all of the billions of files the Internet contains. Add to this the fact that many Internet addresses are frequently changed, relocated, or even removed. Various data delivery services are routinely employed to help organize these files, including electronic mail, file transfers, Internet groups, interactive collaborations, and multimedia displays. The uncertainty regarding the future status of any source Internet site places a major responsibility upon the student for copying and storing any relevant research information (text and graphics) that may be found.

This holds true even when product vendor websites format their online proprietary information in such a way as to prevent it from being copied. In order to save the relevant text, the student may be required to use a word processor to type it manually. Whenever various pictures and illustrations cannot be copied directly, third-party graphics tools can be used to capture and convert them into usable picture formats.

Due to the fact that Internet information can be posted by anyone, for a variety of reasons, the student must assume the responsibility for verifying the correctness and integrity of any information gathered. Although data gathered using library-based researching formats has already undergone a certain amount of verification by its publishers, the safe approach is to never assume the veracity of any information you gather from a single Internet site, newspaper, or magazine/book article. When information can be supported from a variety of sources, it becomes more reliable!

Energy Auditing

PROCEDURES

Energy auditing involves the inspection, survey, and analysis of energy flows in a building, process, or system to reduce the amount of energy input into the system without negatively affecting the system's overall operations. Its main goal is the attainment of meaningful energy conservation. When an energy audit is conducted on an occupied building, the primary concern becomes the reduction of its energy consumption. However, this goal must be met while maintaining or improving the comfort, health, and safety of the building's human occupants. In addition to identifying the sources of energy use, an energy audit can help to prioritize the way in which the building uses energy. In this way, energy savings can be realized by taking advantage of the greatest to least cost effective opportunities.

For example, the energy audit of a home may involve recording various characteristics of the building envelope including its walls, ceilings, floors, doors, windows, and skylights. Area measurements are taken or estimated for each of these components regarding the resistance to heat flow (R-value). These readings depend to a large extent on the infiltration of air through the building's envelope, and is of primary concern. Air leakage is strongly affected by window construction and the quality of door seals such as weather-stripping. The energy audit can be used to quantify the building's overall thermal performance. The audit may also assess the efficiency, physical condition, and programming of such equipment as the thermostat, heating, ventilation, and air-conditioning components.

1. R-values for exterior walls depend primarily on what type of insulation material is utilized. For the insulation material listed in Table 5-1, list its expected R-value per inch of thickness.

Table 5-1: Typical R-Values for Exterior Wall Insulation

MATERIAL	R-VALUE PER INCH OF THICKNESS
Wood Chips	
Rigid Foam	
Fiberglass	
Cellulose	
Polyurethane Foam	

2. In multi-pane windows, the air-cavity conductivity and R-values for various gases differ substantially. Factors that affect a window's R-value include the type of glazing material (glass, or plastic treated glass), the layers of glass, the size of the glass, the thermal resistance or conductivity of the frame and spacer materials, and the tightness of the installation. Low conductivity presents a higher resistance to heat flow. Standard single-pane glass windows have very little insulating value (approximately R-1), and provide only a thin barrier to the outside for considerable heat loss and gain. Table 5-2 lists inert gases such as argon, krypton, xenon typically used in multi-pane windows. They are preferred due to their lower conductivity and a correspondingly higher R-values when compared with air. For each gas listed, locate conductivity and R-value data to fill in the table. Alternative Energy technicians will need to be familiar with the details of these values, and how they relate to the energy efficiency of a building.

Table 5-2: Typical Air-Cavity Conductivity and R-Values for Various Gases in Multi-Pane Windows

GAS	CONDUCTIVITY	TOTAL R-VALUE
Air		
Argon		
Krypton		
Xenon		

PROCEDURE - 5

3. Use Tables 5-3 through 5-9 to organize the specified details about the following energy auditing certification strategies. For each subject, try to locate at least two information sources.

Table 5-3: Energy Auditing Certification Sources

SOURCE	CERTIFICATION	CONCLUSION

Table 5-4: Energy Performance Standards Organizations

ORGANIZATION	STANDARDS	DETAILS

Table 5-5: Energy Auditing Software

SOURCE	SOFTWARE	DETAILS

Table 5-6: Energy Auditing Materials and Resources

SOURCE	MATERIAL OR RESOURCE	DETAILS

Home owners can find out how their families uses energy by maintaining an energy log similar to that shown in Table 5-7. At the end of four weeks, add up the kWh used each week and divide this number by the number of days (28) to get the weekly average use. For example, if 960 kWh are consumed in 28 days, then 960/28 = 34 kWh of electricity is consumed each day. Use Table 5-7 to calculate how much energy per day is being used in your home. Don't forget to include the meter's multiplier (usually 10).

Table 5-7: Monthly Home Energy Audit Log

WEEK	METER READING	CALCULATION
Begin		Begin
Weekly Average		

One of the biggest wasters of electricity in residential dwellings involves the leakage of air between the indoor and outdoor environments. Research various indoor and outdoor locations and attempt to identify sources of air leakage. Document the results in Table 5-8.

Table 5-8: Searching for Indoor or Outdoor Air Leaks or Drafts

LOCATION	TYPE	DETAILS

Table 5-9: Searching for Ceiling and Wall Insulation Weaknesses

LOCATION	TYPE	DETAILS

Energy costs and production constraints make the construction of energy-efficient architectural systems more and more imperative. To make your remaining research time more productive, concentrate on information about the energy auditing strategies listed below. This type of research will be of benefit for learning how energy audits take place in various buildings, including the particular requirements of the local and national governing agencies. Information gathered here will help when considering and comparing specific energy audits, and whether or not they make sense.

4. Examine the following list. It identifies various energy auditing strategies that lend themselves to a reduction in energy use. The Alternative Energy technician should be familiar with these strategies and how they contribute to a sustainable environment.

    - Residential energy audits
    - Weatherization
    - Environmental building programs or strategies
    - Energy star new home auditing benefits
    - Energy star new home auditing features
    - Energy star qualified heating equipment for new homes
    - Energy star qualified cooling equipment for new homes
    - Energy star qualified mechanical ventilation

5. Use Tables 5-10 through 5-17 to organize the specified details about the energy auditing strategies listed. For each item, try to locate at least two information sources.

Table 5-10: Residential Energy Audits

ORGANIZATION	STANDARDS	DETAILS

Table 5-11: Weatherization

STRATEGY	DESCRIPTION	DETAILS

Table 5-12: Environmental Building Programs or Strategies

PROGRAM OR STRATEGY	DESCRIPTION	DETAILS

Table 5-13: Energy Star New Home Auditing Benefits

BENEFIT	DESCRIPTION	DETAILS

Table 5-14: Energy Star New Home Auditing Features

FEATURE	DESCRIPTION	DETAILS

Table 5-15: Energy Star Qualified Heating Equipment for New Homes

FEATURE	DESCRIPTION	DETAILS

Table 5-16: Energy Star Qualified Cooling Equipment for New Homes

FEATURE	DESCRIPTION	DETAILS

Table 5-17: Energy Star Qualified Mechanical Ventilation

FEATURE	DESCRIPTION	DETAILS

Residential or rural farm clients seeking to audit their own energy use usually require some practical information and advice on obtaining an accurate auditing of home and farm energy requirements. For example, they need to understand when and how to audit their energy consumption and to view this consumption the way local boards and state agencies do. It may be necessary for them to consult closely with their energy providers in order to achieve the targeted energy reductions.

Applicable Regulations

Energy Auditing

Various local, state, or federal regulating bodies have jurisdiction over residential energy auditing providers. A completed energy audit must satisfy specific requirements; otherwise, it testifies to the ignorance of the Residential Alternative Energy technicians who performed it.

Local

Local coding authorities are often very sensitive about being ignored. This is because Residential Alternative Energy technicians usually make a greater effort to strictly adhere to the federal and state regulations with which they are most familiar. This adherence is often good enough to result in the performance of a locally compliant energy audit, but not always. Although local codes usually involve local commercial enterprises rather than residential installations, they must also be taken into account before any auditing begins! Keep in mind that city or county energy auditing criteria are often revised to match the circumstances of the communities to which they apply. These realities have periodically resulted in the subsequent prosecution for chronic violators of local energy regulations.

Applicable power consumption information can be obtained from local planning commissions or coding departments. These bodies are usually responsible for controlling the development of both residential and commercial growth in the local community. Specific information about residential energy auditing activity and/or equipment requirements not otherwise addressed by state or federal codes can be gathered by contacting your local planning commission, or the city/county agencies responsible for code enforcement. For example, environmental conditions could place unique restrictions on the local use of energy auditing materials and equipment.

6. Examine the following list. It identifies specific areas of concern regarding energy auditing activities that may be strictly controlled by your local codes.

    - Local energy auditing legislation
    - Local energy audit incentive programs

7. Use Table 5-18 to organize the specified details about any local legislation regarding energy auditing activities. Use Table 5-19 to organize the specified details of any local energy auditing incentive programs. Try to locate more than one source of information for each area of concern.

Table 5-18: Local Energy Auditing Legislation

CITY/COUNTY	LEGISLATION/CODE	DATE	TITLE	DETAILS

Table 5-19: Local Energy Auditing Incentive Programs

LOCATION	PROGRAM	DESCRIPTION	DETAILS

State

State-sponsored regulations are aimed at appropriate use of state resources in the development of energy auditing programs. Although state regulations normally restrict the use of state resources to legitimate government or college business, support for various residential energy auditing mandates are often included. Although they may at first be voluntary, state governmental or university offices will soon be required to comply with these mandates as energy audits become the normal way in which buildings are rated for suitability.

State governmental jurisdictions usually limit the legitimate uses of their energy resources to official legislative and administrative functions. Legal interagency agreements dictate that such resources must not be used for personal, commercial, or for-profit purposes without some form of official written approval. This makes it important to recognize the legitimate use of state resources in the energy auditing of buildings used for state business and/or governmental activities. Information regarding the results of such energy auditing can be located by browsing your state government's web pages.

8. Examine the following list. It identifies specific areas of concern regarding energy auditing legislation and incentive programs that may be strictly controlled by your state laws and programs.

   - State energy auditing legislation
   - State energy auditing incentive programs

9. Use Table 5-20 to organize the specified details about any state legislation regarding the use of energy audits. Use Table 5-21 to organize specific data about state authorized incentive programs related to energy auditing. Try to locate more than one source of information for each area of concern.

Table 5-20: State Energy Auditing Legislation

STATE	LEGISLATION/CODE	DATE	TITLE	DETAILS

Table 5-21: State Energy Auditing Incentive Programs

STATE	PROGRAM	DESCRIPTION	DETAILS

Federal

Alternative energy manufacturers and consumers around the world recognize certain research facilities and/or governmental agencies that have been consulted in order to determine the suitability of a specified energy audit. As the construction of commercial and residential buildings continues, standards designed to reduce their energy consumption have recently emerged. The recognition of energy auditing as a reliable building industry rating tool has helped to achieve some control over the perceived waste of energy resources by these buildings.

The federal organizations and programs listed here can be consulted regarding the suitability of various auditing criteria related to gaining the desired energy efficiency for a building. The Residential Alternative Energy technician can depend on the information provided by these organizations and programs to provide guidance as to how the various energy auditing criteria for a particular building are defined and applied.

U.S. Green Building Council (USGBC)

The USGBC is a nonprofit organization based in Washington, D.C. that is committed to a prosperous and sustainable future for our nation through cost-efficient and energy-saving green buildings. USGBC works toward its mission of market transformation through its LEED green building certification program, robust educational offerings, a nationwide network of chapters and affiliates, the annual Greenbuild International Conference & Expo, and advocacy in support of public policy that encourages and enables green buildings and communities.

Leadership in Energy and Environmental Design (LEED)

The Leadership in Energy and Environmental Design (LEED) green building certification program is a successful and independent operation developed by the U.S. Green Building Council (USGBC). Its LEED Green Building Rating System is a voluntary, consensus-based national standard for development of buildings with high-energy performance and environmentally sustainable features. The LEED rating system for new construction and renovation projects is based on lists of specific green building features that, if included in a project, accrue points toward a rating. To obtain a LEED rating, building owners must submit detailed, defined technical documentation to USGBC for review. The LEED rating system has stimulated a tremendous amount of voluntary interest across the United States. Private organizations and federal and state agencies have made commitments to LEED certification for new construction and major renovation projects.

LEED Green Building Certification Program

The LEED green building certification program is a voluntary, consensus-based national rating system for buildings designed, constructed, and operated for improved environmental and human health performance. LEED addresses all building types and emphasizes state-of-the-art strategies in five areas: sustainable site development, water savings, energy efficiency, materials and resources selection, and indoor environmental quality.

Green Building Certification Institute (GBCI)

The Green Building Certification Institute (GBCI) was established in January of 2008, with the support of USGBC, to allow for objective, balanced management of the credential program LEED Professional Credentials (LEED AP and Green Associate). The LEED Professional Credentials program recognizes professionals who have demonstrated a thorough understanding of green building techniques, the LEED green building rating systems, and the certification process.

U.S. Department of Energy (DOE)

The Department of Energy's overarching mission is to advance the national, economic, and energy security of the United States. In order to do this, it promotes scientific and technological innovation, while working to ensure the environmental cleanup of the national nuclear weapons complex. Strategic goals to achieve the mission are designed to deliver results along five strategic themes, including:

- Energy security. The DOE's philosophy is that America's energy security should be achieved through the production of reliable, clean, and affordable energy.

- Nuclear security. Ensuring America's nuclear security is also a critical component of DOE's working agenda.

- Scientific discovery and innovation. The DOE works to strengthen scientific discovery, economic competitiveness, and to improve the quality of life in the United States through innovations in science and technology.

- Environmental responsibility. The DOE helps to protect the environment by providing a responsible resolution to the environmental legacy of nuclear weapons production.

- Management excellence. The DOE believes in enabling its mission through sound management.

DOE Weatherization Assistance Program

In the three decades since its founding in 1976, U.S. Department of Energy (DOE) Weatherization Assistance Program has provided weatherization services to more than 6.4 million low-income families. It is a record of service to some of society's neediest citizens that also benefits our nation by reducing our energy dependency, improving the environment, and stimulating economic development in low-income communities. Through this program, weatherization service providers install energy efficiency measures in the homes of qualifying homeowners free of charge. These are not expensive upgrades—the average expenditure limit is $6,500 per home—but they are effective, and energy savings pay for the upgrades within a few years. DOE documents the savings and compares them against costs, so that over the years it can determine the efficacy of these measures.

Environmental Protection Agency (EPA)

The U.S. Environmental Protection Agency (EPA, or sometimes USEPA) is an agency of the federal government of the United States charged to protect human health and the environment, by writing and enforcing regulations based on laws passed by Congress. It employs 17,000 people in headquarters program offices, 10 regional offices, and 27 laboratories across the country. More than half of its staff are engineers, scientists, and environmental protection specialists; other groups include legal, public affairs, financial, and computer specialists.

Conducting environmental assessment, research, and education, the EPA has the primary responsibility for setting and enforcing national standards under a variety of environmental laws, in consultation with state, tribal, and local governments. It delegates some permitting, monitoring, and enforcement responsibility to U.S. states and Native American tribes. EPA enforcement powers include fines, sanctions, and other measures. The agency also works with industries and all levels of government in a wide variety of voluntary pollution prevention programs and energy conservation efforts.

ENERGY STAR

ENERGY STAR is a joint program of the U.S. Environmental Protection Agency and the U.S. Department of Energy helping us all save money and protect the environment through energy efficient products and practices. Results are already adding up. Americans, with the help of ENERGY STAR, saved enough energy in 2009 alone to avoid greenhouse gas emissions equivalent to those from 30 million cars—all while saving nearly $17 billion on their utility bills.

For the home, energy efficient choices can save families about a third on their energy bill with similar savings of greenhouse gas emissions, without sacrificing features, style or comfort. ENERGY STAR helps you make the energy efficient choice. If looking for new household products, look for ones that have earned the ENERGY STAR. They meet strict energy efficiency guidelines set by the EPA and US Department of Energy. If looking for a new home, look for one that has earned the ENERGY STAR.

If looking to make larger improvements to your home, EPA offers tools and resources to help you plan and undertake projects to reduce your energy bills and improve home comfort.

Because a strategic approach to energy management can produce twice the savings—for the bottom line and the environment—as typical approaches, EPA's ENERGY STAR partnership offers a proven energy management strategy that helps in measuring current energy performance, setting goals, tracking savings, and rewarding improvements. EPA provides an innovative energy performance rating system which businesses have already used for more than 130,000 buildings across the country. EPA also recognizes top performing buildings with the ENERGY STAR.

Green Advantage

Established with grant funding from the EPA and the Nature Conservancy, Green Advantage was developed in collaboration with Science Applications International Corporation (SAIC), and the University of Florida. Its green building Environmental Certification program brings consumers together with certified building practitioners, who have proven knowledge about green building techniques and approaches. Its vision is to see that buildings throughout the world are constructed in an environmentally sensitive manner that supports social and economic sustainability. It seeks to be the preeminent certifier of building organizations and practitioners nationally and internationally, by producing certification programs, benefits, services for building sector practitioners and organizations, and promoting green building education.

Environmental Technology Verification (ETV) Program

As an important partner with the EPA is the Environmental Technology Verification (ETV) program, which helps to direct activities involving more than 800 public and private individuals representing federal, state, and local government agencies. These include academics and technology experts, not-for-profit organizations, associations, and a broad group of technology purchasers, users, developers, and vendors. The ETV program develops testing protocols and verifies the performance of innovative technologies with the potential to improve protection of human health and the environment. The program partners with private-sector testing organizations, federal agencies such as the Department of Defense (DOD), the Department of Energy (DOE), the National Oceanic and Atmospheric Administration (NOAA), and the Coast Guard. It helps numerous states to accelerate the entrance of new environmental technologies into their domestic and international marketplaces.

Residential Energy Services Network's (RESNET)

The Residential Energy Services Network's (RESNET®) mission is to ensure the success of the building energy performance certification industry, set the standards of quality, and increase the opportunity for ownership of high performance buildings. RESNET is a membership 501-C-3 non profit organization.

RESNET's standards are officially recognized by the U.S. mortgage industry for capitalizing a building's energy performance in the mortgage loan, certification of "White Tags" for private financial investors, and by the federal government for verification of building energy performance for such programs as federal tax incentives, the Environmental Protection Agency's ENERGY STAR program and the U.S. Department of Energy's Building America Program.

Energy Savings Performance Contracts (ESPCs)

Energy Savings Performance Contracts (ESPCs) allow Federal agencies to accomplish energy savings projects without up-front capital costs and without special Congressional appropriations. An ESPC is a partnership between a Federal agency and an energy service company (ESCO). The ESCO conducts a comprehensive energy audit for the Federal facility and identifies improvements to save energy. In consultation with the Federal agency, the ESCO designs and constructs a project that meets the agency's needs and arranges the necessary financing. The ESCO guarantees that the improvements will generate energy cost savings sufficient to pay for the project over the term of the contract. After the contract ends, all additional cost savings accrue to the agency. Contract terms up to 25 years are allowed.

Rural Energy for America Program

Run by the Department of Agriculture, the Rural Energy For America Program provides grants and loan guarantees to farmers, ranchers (agricultural producers), and rural small businesses to promote energy efficiency improvements and renewable energy systems development in rural areas. The program provides grants of up to 25 percent of project costs, and/or loan guarantees of up to 75 percent of project costs to purchase and install energy efficiency improvements and renewable energy systems. It also provides grants to agricultural producers and rural small businesses to help fund up to 25 percent of the cost for a feasibility study for a renewable energy system. In addition, it provides grants to government entities, educational institutions, rural electric cooperatives, and public power entities to assist with the cost of performing energy audits and renewable energy development assistance for agricultural producers and rural small businesses. Recipients of energy audits or renewable energy development assistance must pay at least 25 percent of the cost of the service.

Energy Management and Audit Services (EMAS)

To reduce energy consumption, legislation and mandated goals for reducing federal energy consumption are on the rise. As a division of the U.S. General Services Administration (GSA), Energy Management and Audit Services provides agencies with contractors offering such services as: comprehensive energy management, energy audits to establish baseline assessments, metering and advanced metering services, building commissioning, energy management training, water conservation, installation and site preparation for power distribution equipment, and power systems engineering support.

Federal Energy Management Program (FEMP)

FEMP supports energy efficiency and water conservation in the Federal sector by assisting agencies in obtaining SAVEnergy Audits and Action Plans for their facilities. The SAVEnergy Audit is a comprehensive, thorough examination of the energy systems in a specified Federal facility or building. The audit is conducted by engineers specializing in building energy systems, and evaluates such things as the condition of the building envelope (windows, walls, floors, and roof) and the performance of the building's energy-consuming equipment (lighting, furnaces, chillers, pumps), and so on. A SAVEnergy Audit reveals the operating condition of a specified building, assesses its energy use, identifies cost-effective energy conservation measures (ECMs) that can be implemented, and recommends cost-effective operation and maintenance (O&M) activities. The audit also includes a screening of the facility for opportunities to conserve water and to use renewable energy systems that benefit the environment.

10. Search the information pages of various federal governmental agencies and locate any related energy auditing information regarding the subjects listed below.

- Federal energy auditing legislation
- Federal energy auditing incentive programs

11. Use Table 5-22 to organize the specified details about any federal legislation regarding the application of energy auditing. Use Table 5-23 to organize the specified details of federal energy auditing incentive programs. Try to locate more than one source of information for each area of concern.

Table 5-22: Federal Energy Auditing Legislation

AGENCY	LEGISLATION/CODE	DATE	TITLE	DETAILS

Table 5-23: Federal Energy Auditing Incentive Programs

LOCATION	DESCRIPTION	ANALYSIS	CONCLUSION

12. This concludes the hands-on lab procedure. Have your instructor review your results before moving on to the next procedure.

LAB QUESTIONS

1. What is the main reason for conducting an energy audit on an occupied building?

2. What is the term used to describe the resistance of a building's walls, ceilings, floors, doors, windows, and skylights to heat flow?

3. How is a building's overall thermal performance quantified?

4. For exterior wall insulation, which of the materials listed in Table 4-1 provides the best resistance to heat flow?

5. List the factors that affect a multi-pane window's R-value.

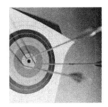

Feedback

Energy Auditing Design

OBJECTIVES

1. Become familiar with an energy auditing software program.
2. Determine the actions necessary to conduct an energy audit of a single-story structure.

Energy Auditing

RESOURCES

1. Marcraft GT-750 Energy Auditing Text/Lab
2. Computer System
3. Weatherization Assistant Energy Auditing Software
4. Completed Lab # 5 – Energy Auditing Research

ABOUT THE AUTHOR

Whitney G. Freeman is a curriculum developer with more than 25 years of experience in the creation of technical education courses. Following military service in the United States Air Force as a radio relay technician, Whitney spent 20 years in the recording and entertainment industry as a bass player, band leader, and songwriter. After several years working as a electronics repair technician, Whitney found himself back in the classroom, this time teaching electronics and creating digital electronics curriculum for the National Education Corporation. His work caught the attention of Marcraft International Corporation (now called Educational Technologies Group, Incorporated), where he helped to produce many of their well-received Knowledge Transfer Projects, which combined the excitement of kit building with the exposure to technical electronics innovation and development. During his years with ETG Marcraft, he helped produce the popular Enhanced Data Cabling Installers Certification textbook, as well as the Fiber Optic Cable Installers Certification textbook.

In addition to various projects for ETG Marcraft, Whitney found time to develop three training courses for the employees at Framatome ANP, designed to keep workers aware of their safety responsibilities while working with and around nuclear materials. He also created the training manual used by the Spokane School District in preparing their employees and students for emergency response situations. Other safety materials developed by Mr. Freeman help to keep employees at the Department of Energy up-to-date regarding safety issues and qualifications at various nuclear and non-nuclear workstations.

Whitney currently researches green technology and the attention being paid to developing renewable energy sources. Green technology offers the possibility of producing one's own energy needs, reducing those needs, and running a smart home that uses energy in the most efficient manner possible.

▬▬▬▬▬▬▬▬▬▬▬▬

DISCUSSION

Read the following scenario:

> You and your spouse have been reviewing the family's utility bills for the preceding year and have become concerned about increased rates and usage. With an eye towards energy conservation, you are looking to reduce the amount of energy being consumed by your residential system. However, neither of you can identify precisely where the greatest amounts of energy are being consumed.

> An ongoing energy audit (an inspection, a survey, and an energy consumption analysis) could help to identify operations requiring the implementation of energy conservation practices. The goal is to reduce the amount of energy input into the system or process, without negative repercussions. Before turning this chore over to professional auditors, you and your spouse want to use an energy auditing software program to gain some understanding about your home's energy consumption.

> The Weatherization Assistant Energy Auditing Software is provided free of charge by the Department of Energy to aid homeowners in identifying areas in their homes requiring improved weatherization to reduce the amount of energy being consumed. The program is capable of determining the cost of energy consumption for any given residential or commercial building. You will use the Weatherization Assistant program to conduct several auditing chores. However, you should be prepared to spend a certain amount of time exploring the program's screens and parameters to more fully understand the scope of its operations.

Energy Auditing

When a home energy audit is conducted, professional equipment (blower doors and infra-red cameras) is deployed within the targeted residence in order to evaluate its energy efficiency. The person conducting the audit will use the evaluation to suggest various ways to improve the home's energy efficiency with respect to heating and cooling requirements. The audit may involve recording various aspects of a home's envelope, including the walls, ceilings, floors, doors, windows, and skylights. Resistance to heat flow (R-value) is measured or estimated for each of these component areas, with particular concern to the infiltration of air through the building envelope. This infiltration is strongly affected by the weather seals around windows and doors. The audit will quantify the building's overall thermal performance by assessing its efficiency, physical condition, and HVAC programming.

The energy audit may include a written report suggesting energy use criteria for the given local climate, thermostat settings, roof overhang, and solar orientation. The monthly or yearly impact of suggested energy use improvements may also be provided. When coupled with the homeowner's billing history showing the quantities of electricity, natural gas, fuel oil, or other energy sources consumed over a specified time period, an estimate of possible energy savings can be calculated. Because the greatest effects on energy use are directly related to user behavior, climate, and the age of a home, energy audits often result in meaningful changes in attitudes and habits. Homeowners often take actions that greatly reduce energy consumption patterns, while making their homes less susceptible to air infiltration.

PROCEDURES

During this procedure, you will become familiar with an energy auditing software program and explore its various screens. You will use the program to investigate the steps involved with auditing a single-story structure, such as the one shown in Figure 6-1.

Energy Auditing

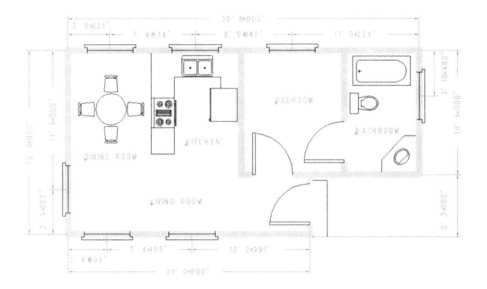

**Figure 6-1:
A One-Story
Floorplan**

Using the Weatherization Assistant Energy Auditing Software

1. Turn the computer system **ON**, and wait for the opening screen to appear.

2. At the opening screen, click on the **WA** icon to start the Weatherization Assistant program.

3. Observe the opening screen appears as shown in Figure 6-2.

4. From the *Weatherization Assistant Program* window, click on the **Help** button to get to the *USDOE Weatherization Assistant Help* screen.

5. Read the text provided about the USDOE Weatherization Assistant selection.

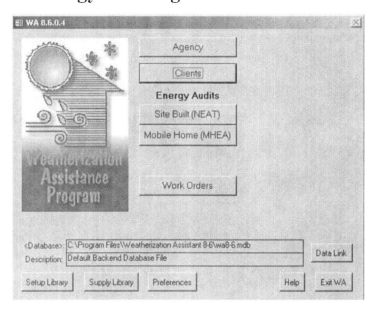

Figure 6-2: The Weatherization Assistant Opening Screen

6. Which two types of residential structures can be audited using the Weatherization Assistant?

_____

_____

7. Determine which type of residential structure applies to the one-story floorplan shown earlier and record it on the following line:

_____

NOTE: It is necessary to become familiar with the various screens provided with the Weatherization Assistant. They are designed to gather the required information for correctly processing energy auditing data. Keep the floorplan depicted in Figure 6-1 in mind throughout this procedure.

8. Click on the **Agency** button at the top of the *WA* window to get to the *AGENCY* screen shown in Figure 6-3.

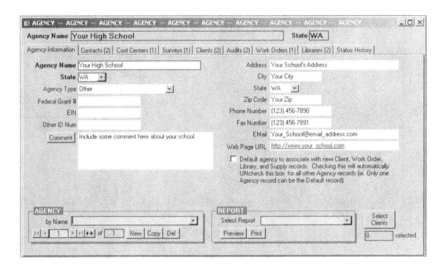

Figure 6-3: The Weatherization Assistant Agency Screen

9. At the *AGENCY* screen, click on the **Agency Name** text entry box and type in the name of your school.

10. Click on the **State** text entry box and use its drop-down list to select your state.

11. For the *Agency Type* drop-down list, select **Other**.

12. At the *Comment* text entry box, type in some text describing your school.

13. In the right column of the *AGENCY/Agency Information* screen, type in the necessary information in the boxes provided, including valid EMail and Web Page URL addresses.

NOTE: Because your school name will be associated with all subsequent Client, Work Order, Library, and Supply records, it becomes the defacto Agency name. Check this box only if this is the first record to be created for your school.

14. Once all information has been entered into the *Agency Information* screen, click on the **Contacts** button.

15. Type your name into the *Contact Name* text entry box using the Last, First naming convention. Then, type your name the way you normally do into the *User Name* text box.

16. In the *Company* text entry box type in the name of your school. Then, place a checkmark in the *Auditor* checkbox.

17. Fill in the applicable address, telephone, fax, email, and web page information in the spaces provided.

18. Click on the **Cost Centers** button and enter the following information:

- Cost Center Name: **DOE Weatherization Program**

- Cost Center Type: **DOE**

- Program Year: **2010**

- Description: **Sponsored by the DOE, a database computer software tool.**

- Comment: **All information for clients, energy audits, work orders, and setup information for the Weatherization Assistant is stored in a single Microsoft Access database file.**

19. Close the screen and return to the *WA* window. From the *WA* window, click on the **Clients** button to get to the *CLIENT* screen shown in Figure 6-4.

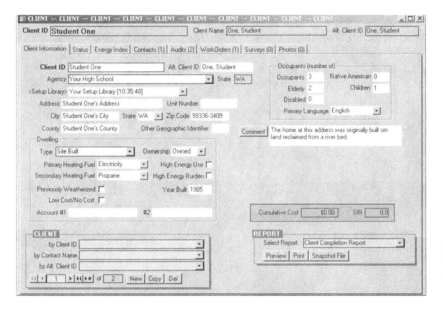

Figure 6-4: The Weatherization Assistant Client Screen

20. At the *CLIENT* screen, click on the **Client ID** text entry box and type in your name. In the *Alt. Client ID* text entry box, type in any alternate name by which you are known.

21. Enter appropriate address information in the text boxes provided.

NOTE: The name of your school can be entered for the Agency.

22. Enter appropriate information in the *Dwelling* and *Occupants (number of)* text boxes.

23. Include any relevant *Comment* in the appropriate section.

24. Once appropriate information has been entered into the *CLIENT* screen, close the screen and return to the *WA* window.

25. Recalling your answer for Step 7, click on the **Site Built (NEAT)** button.

26. At the *NEAT AUDIT* screen, click on the **Audit Name** text entry box and type in **Residential House**.

27. At the *Client ID* drop-down text box, make sure your name appears. If not, click on the arrow and then click on your name so that it appears in the box.

28. In the *Auditor* drop-down text box, select the one shown for the **CompanyName** listed.

29. In the *Conditioned Stories* text entry box, type in **1**.

30. For the *Floor Area (sq ft)* text entry box, type in **400**.

NOTE: This value is roughly based on the interior floor area shown in Figure 6-1. Realistically, the floor area would equal 30 x 15 or 450 square feet, minus 5 x 10 or 50 square feet. This gives us an approximate interior floor area of 450 – 50, or 400 square feet.

31. Include any relevant *Comment* in the appropriate section.

32. Under *Libraries and Other Options*, select an appropriate **Weather File** from the drop-down listing.

33. Once appropriate information has been entered into the *NEAT AUDIT* screen, close the screen and return to the *WA* window.

34. From the *WA* window, click on the **Work Orders** button to get to the *WORK ORDER* screen.

35. In the *Work Order* text entry box, type **Procedure 9 - Energy Auditing Design**.

36. In the *Client ID* drop-down text box, make sure your name appears. If not, click on the arrow and then click on your name so that it appears in the box.

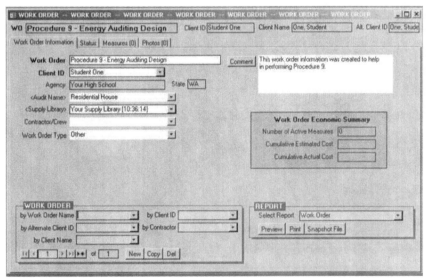

37. Examine the remaining text entry boxes to make sure that *Residential House* is the entry for <Audit Name>, and the remaining entries match the information provided to the program previously.

38. If necessary, place text in the Comment text entry box. The *Work Order* text entry box should now appear similar to that shown in Figure 6-5.

39. Once appropriate information has been entered into the *WORK ORDER* screen, close the screen and return to the *WA* window.

Figure 6-5: The Weatherization Assistant Work Order Screen

Conducting an Energy Audit

Energy Auditing

The Weatherization Assistant software program is capable of performing an energy audit of any building whose size and physical dynamics are known. Using the measurements already calculated for the single-story Residential House, you will use the Weatherization Assistant software to determine its energy requirements according to several considerations.

Prior to using the NEAT engine, specific information must be entered before any meaningful results can be produced. Audits not meeting the required specification will cause NEAT to stop the run and request the needed information.

1. From the *WA* window, click on the **Site Built (NEAT)** tab.

2. In order to prevent the NEAT engine from requesting additional information, make sure that the **Audit Information** tab is completely filled out, including the selection of the setup library and the weather file for the run.

3. Define at least one wall under the *Walls* tab under *NEAT AUDIT/Shell*.

4. For the *Wall Code*, type in **WLS** (an abbreviation for the south wall).

5. In the *Wall Type* drop-down text entry box, select **Concrete Block**.

6. In the *Exterior Type* drop-down text entry box, select **Stucco**.

7. In the *Exposed To* drop-down text entry box, select **Outside (Ambient)**.

8. In the *Orientation* drop-down text box, select **South**.

9. Using a height of **10 feet** for the front wall, determine its overall size and type this information in the *Gross Area (sq ft)* text box.

10. In the *Measure #* text entry box, select **1**.

11. Move to the *Existing Insulation* section, click on the **Type** drop-down text entry, and select **Polystyrene Board**.

NOTE: The Extruded Polystyrene Board (XEPS) used with this course is 5/8 of an inch thick and carries an R-value of 5.00 per inch.

12. Calculate the R-value of the XEPS insulation and record your answer in the *R Value* text entry box.

13. In the *Added Insulation* drop-down text entry box, select **None**.

14. Click on the **Windows** subtab under the *Shell* tab, and in the *Window Code* text box, type **WLS**.

15. Make selections for **Window Type**, **Glazing Type**, **Interior Shading**, **Exterior Shading**, and **Leakiness** in the appropriate boxes.

16. Fill in accurate data for the **Average Size** and **Number** on this *Wall* text boxes.

17. In the *Retrofit Options* drop-down text entry box, select **Weatherize**.

18. Obtain some reasonable data on window weatherization, and enter the estimated cost per window in the *Weatherization ($/window)* text box.

NOTE: In addition, a heating system must also be defined.

19. Click on the **Heating** tab. A screen similar to Figure 6-6 appears.

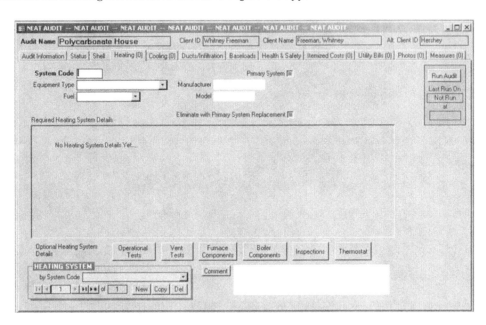

Figure 6-6: The Weatherization Assistant Heating System Details

20. In the *System Code* text box, type **HTG**.

21. In the *Equipment Type* drop-down, select **Heat Pump**.

NOTE: Observe that the Fuel drop-down automatically inputs the Electricity entry.

22. For the *Location* drop-down entry, select **Heated Space**.

23. For the *Manufacturer* text entry box, type in **Fedders**.

24. For the *Model* text entry box, type in **CH42ACD1VF**.

25. In the H*EAT PUMP DETAILS* information area, enter **7.7** as the *Heating Seasonal Performance Factor (HSPF)* in the appropriate box.

NOTE: HSPF is a measure of a heat pump's energy efficiency over one heating season. It represents the total heating output of a heat pump (including supplementary electric heat) during the normal heating season (in Btu) as compared to the total electricity consumed (in watt-hours) during the same period. HSPF is based on tests performed in accordance with AHRI Standard 210/240.

26. In the *Replacement System/Options* drop-down, select **Don't Replace - Evaluate None**.

27. Click on the **Cooling** tab, and in the *AC Code* text box, type **CLG**.

28. In the *Equipment Type* drop-down, select **Heat Pump**.

29. For the *Manufacturer* text entry box, type in **Fedders**.

30. For the *Model* text entry box, type in **CH42ACD1VF**.

31. For the *Floor Area Cooled (sq ft)* text entry box, type in **400**.

32. For the *Capacity (kBtu/hr)* text entry box, type in **42**.

33. For the *SEER* text entry box, type in **13**.

34. Click on the **Ducts/Infiltration** tab and observe the *Air and Duct Leakages* section.

NOTE: Most HVAC systems suffer from leakage around seams, joints, and access doors. The information required by the software's Air and Duct Leakages section requires the use of sophisticated testing equipment both before and after any weatherization takes place. In addition, the duct system must be sealed during testing, as depicted in Figure 6-7. To move through this procedure, you need to input values into the Whole House Blower Door Measurements section just as if an actual weatherization activity is taking place at the Residential House depicted in Figure 6-1. Imagine that this house uses a 3-ton system with a 75,000 BTU furnace.

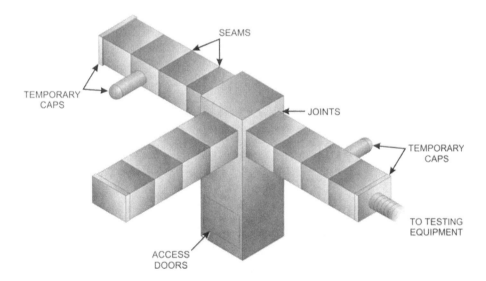

Figure 6-7: Determining CFM Leakage

35. If the system moves 400 cubic feet of air per minute for each ton of system cooling, how many cubic feet of air per minute will the cooling system move?

36. If the standard multiplier of .0217 is used to estimate the air movement of the 75,000 BTU heating system, how many cubic feet of air per minute will the furnace move?

37. According to the standard leakage multiplier for a heating system of 0.15, what is the allowable leakage for this system?

_____

NOTE: At this point a leakage test would be performed on the house in order to determine if its actual leakage is greater than that calculated in Step 37.

38. Imagine that a leakage test Before Weatherization (Existing) indicates that the system is leaking 663 CFM at a House Pressure Difference (Pa) of 50. Input **663** in the *Air Leakage Rate (cfm)* text box and **50** in the *House Pressure Difference (Pa)* text box under Whole House Blower Door Measurements.

39. Calculate the leakage reduction by subtracting 176.7 from 663 and record this value on the following line:

_____

NOTE: This would obviously be an unacceptable leakage value and the system would require sealing. Now imagine that in addition to sealing the system, you also replace the furnace condenser and evaporator coil. The leakage test is performed once again, indicating that the leakage is reduced to 176.7 CFM and the House Pressure Difference (Pa) is reduced to 23. Record these values in the After Weatherization (Target or Actual) text boxes under Whole House Blower Door Measurements.

40. Calculate the percentage of leakage reduction by dividing 486.3 by 663, multiplying by 100, and recording your value on the following line:

_____

NOTE: If the system equals or surpasses the normal leakage reduction requirement of 60 percent, it will undoubtedly pass inspection. Keep in mind that energy audits vary in price depending on the square footage of the home, and whether or not the audit includes a blower door test and infrared scan.

41. Examine Table 6-1 for an example of residential energy audit pricing that includes blower door tests and infrared scans.

Table 6-1: Pricing for Energy Audits with Blower Door Testing and Infrared Scanning

SIZE	STANDARD PRICING	WITH COMPUTER ANALYSIS
Up to 2000 sq ft	$300	$500
From 2001 to 3000 sq ft	$350	$550
From 3001 to 4000 sq ft	$400	$600
From 4001 sq ft or more	$450	$650

42. Blower door tests can be conducted without auditing and without infrared scanning. Examine the pricing schedules listed in Table 6-2.

SIZE	PRICING
Up to 2000 sq ft	$200
From 2001 to 3000 sq ft	$250
From 3001 to 4000 sq ft	$300
From 4001 sq ft or more	$350

Table 6-2: Pricing for Blower Door Testing Only

43. Sometimes homeowners merely wish to have an analysis of their electrical usage performed. Examine the pricing for these tests based on the size of the home, as shown in Table 6-3.

SIZE	PRICING
Up to 2000 sq ft	$150
From 2001 to 3000 sq ft	$200
From 3001 to 4000 sq ft	$250
From 4001 sq ft or more	$300

Table 6-3: Pricing for Electrical Usage Analysis

NOTE: Companies that perform the energy audits and testing are also capable of performing the necessary air-sealing weatherization to help reduce the costs of energy for a particular residence or building. These services normally run $400 for three hours of site time (including labor and blower door testing), with additional charges for the materials used.

44. Examine the following list of materials commonly used for residential weatherization and conduct the necessary research to record the pricing data for each in the space provided.

- V-seal type weather-stripping:
  - Kerf-mounted vinyl: _____
  - Polypropylene, 7/8-inch wide: _____
- Siliconized acrylic latex caulking:
  - DAP acrylic latex caulk w silicone: _____
  - BOSS siliconized acrylic latex caulk: _____
- High temperature caulking:
  - BRAMEC RTV silicone sealant: _____
  - MEECO Hi-heat silicone sealant: _____
  - DAP high heat mortar: _____
  - Rutland RTV silicone sealant: _____

- Plastic and Aluminum door sweeps:
  - M-D Building Products aluminum w 36in vinyl sweep: _____
  - M-D Building Products aluminum heavy duty 36in sweep: _____
  - Frost King white 36in reinforced rubber sweep: _____
  - W. J. Dennis adjustable U-shaped PVC door sweep: _____
- Aluminum tape:
  - Polyken tape w butyl rubber adhesive, 3in x 100ft: _____
  - Intertape Polymer aluminum foil tape, 2.5in x 50yds: _____
  - 3M high temperature aluminum flue tape, 1-1/2in x 15ft: _____
- Metal flashing:
  - Amerimax aluminum flashing, 0.0092 mill, 20in x 10ft: _____
  - NW Metal galvanized edge flashing, 1in x 1-1/2in x 10ft: _____
- Outlet and Switch Plate foam gaskets: _____
- Air sealing board materials:
  - Foam Board:
    - Molded expanded polystyrene (MEPS), 4ft x 8ft: _____
    - Extruded expanded polystyrene (XEPS), 4ft x 8ft: _____
    - Polyiso and polyurethane, 2ft x 4ft x 1.5in: _____
  - Cardboard:
    - Single-wall corrugated sheets, 36in x 72in, bundle of 20: _____
    - Double-wall corrugated sheets, 36in x 72in, bundle of 20: _____
  - Fiberglass:
    - Crane Composites Sequentia panels, 26in x 12ft, white: _____
    - Structoglas liner panel, 4ft x 8ft x 0.90in thick, white: _____
  - Drywall:
    - SHEETROCK Firecode (X) core gypsum, 4ft x 8ft x 0.625in: _____
    - SHEETROCK Mold Tough regular core, 4ft x 8ft x 0.625in: _____
    - SHEETROCK Mold Tough Ultracode gypsum, 4ft x 8ft x 0.75in: _____
  - Ductboard:
    - EnduraGold fiberglass ductboard, 48in x 120in x 1in sheet: _____
    - M-Ke flexible HVAC R6.0 duct, 14in diameter, 25ft : _____

45. Review the material list in Step 44 and select the materials that could be used in weatherizing the *Residential House.*

46. Use the pricing data to determine the overall cost of the materials that could be used to weatherize the *Residential House.*

NOTE: Don't get carried away with this. Price only those materials that could actually be used in this scenario, and be sure to include adequate amounts (quantity, feet, ounces) to complete the job. For example, rigid ductboard is primarily used in commercial applications, where HVAC systems distribute conditioned air through overhead ducts. Residential ducting often utilizes flexible material, which requires no fittings between the trunk duct and the outlet, offering substantial labor reductions. As such, flexible ducting would be a more sensible choice for use with the Residential House. Keep in mind the fictitious scenario in which we previously reduced the residential house leakage from 663 CFM to 176.7 CFM. Its area footage (single floor) was merely 400 sq ft. The interior wall area is roughly 1,000 sq ft.

47. Using the residential energy audit pricing that includes blower door tests and infrared scans, estimate the overall cost of the audit and the required materials/labor to completely weatherize the *Residential House.*

_____ Audit

_____ Weatherization

_____ Materials

_____ Total

48. Input the total costs of conducting an energy audit of the *Residential House* into the *Costs/Infiltration Reduction ($)* text entry box in your *NEAT AUDIT/Ducts/Infiltration/Air and Duct Leakages* sheet.

49. Type in some appropriate text into the *Comment* text entry box.

50. At the upper-right of the *NEAT AUDIT* sheet, click on the **Run Audit** button to generate a WA Report. Once the WA Report has been generated, print the report and give it to your instructor.

NOTE: Although the WA Report is somewhat limited in scope, it provides a good example of the calculations and information provided by the Weatherization Assistance Program.

Feedback

LAB QUESTIONS

1. If the cooling system for the *Residential House* depicted in Figure 6-1 moves 525 cubic feet of air per minute for each ton of system cooling, how many cubic feet of air per minute will the cooling system move?

2. How long will it take the cooling system described in Question 1 to replace all the air in the proposed *Residential House* depicted in Figure 6-1?

Understanding Blueprints

OBJECTIVES

1. To understand how to identify standard blueprinting symbols.

Energy Auditing

RESOURCES

1. Industry standard blueprint*

* The blueprint supplied with this course, depicted in Figure 7-2, is not printed on vellum or mylar. Instead, it consists simply of a large foldout paper diagram with no protection against markings or moisture.

DISCUSSION

This procedure provides an opportunity to locate and identify various symbols and abbreviations used on an industry standard blueprint.

PROCEDURE

Before beginning this procedure, read through all of the following steps at least once, thoroughly.

1. Examine Figure 7-1 carefully.

TIP: Notice that the conceptual plan includes several different buildings separated by two crossing streets. You can be assured that the master set of blueprints will include detailed drawings for each of the buildings shown, in addition to the building-to-building cabling specification being used.

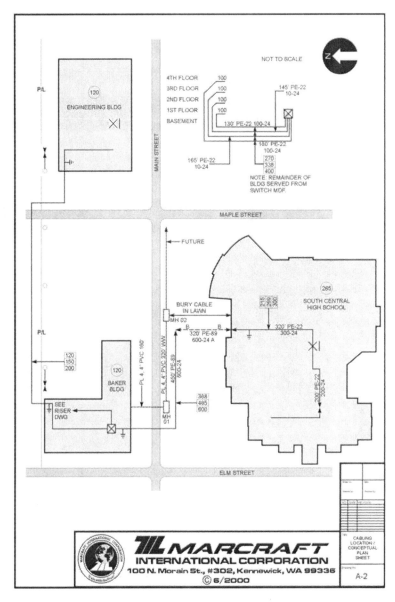

Figure 7-1:
Conceptual Plan

2. Identify which of the buildings depicted in the conceptual plan of Figure 7-1 is featured in the copy of the industry standard blueprint shown in Figure 7-2.

3. Locate the industry standard blueprint, and unfold it so that it lies flat on your work surface.

TIP: Notice that Figure 7-2 is a miniature version of the industry standard blueprint that you just unfolded. It may be necessary to place objects on the corners of the industry standard blueprint to keep it flat.

4. Try to identify various acronyms used to denote the components associated with the data communications equipment located in this building. Record each item you identify in your Energy Auditing Worksheets.

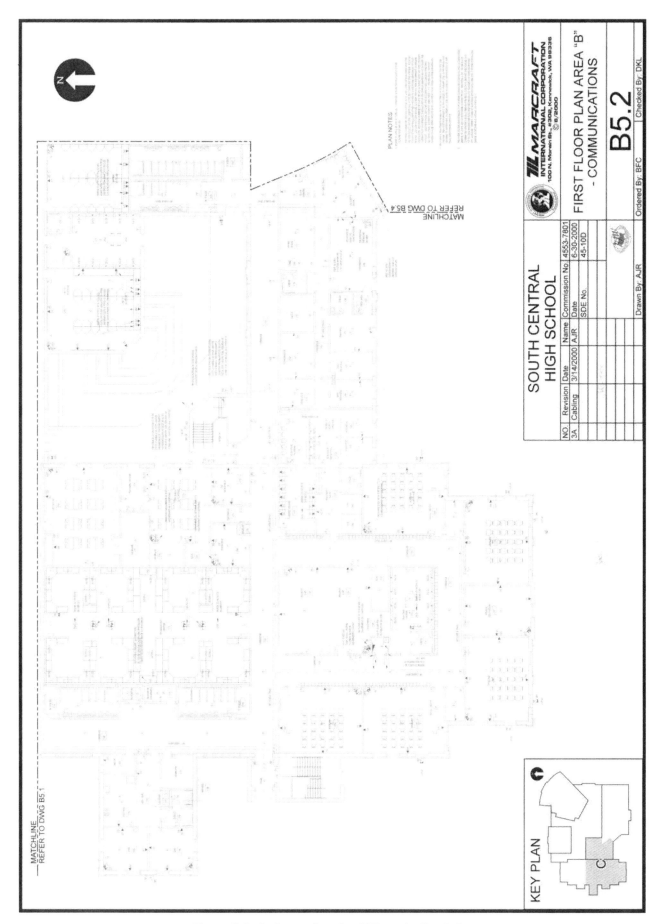

Figure 7-2: Industry Standard Blueprint Depiction

5. Using the information supplied by the previously given tables, see how many of the architectural symbols and abbreviations you can locate and identify from the industry standard blueprint.

6. Record each item you identify in your Energy Auditing Worksheets.

TIP: It would be a good idea to split your list into two list categories, one for symbols and one for abbreviations.

7. When you feel you have identified as many of the symbols or abbreviations contained in the industry standard blueprint as you can, fold the blueprint back up and return it to its designated storage area.

8. When all of the blueprints have been returned to the storage area, get together with your instructor to determine which hands-on procedure team successfully located and identified the greatest number of symbols and abbreviations from the industry standard blueprint.

9. Before leaving your work area, check to be sure that you are leaving it in a clean and orderly condition.

Feedback

LAB QUESTIONS

1. Do all of the symbols shown in the blueprint relate to cable installations?

2. Why could the architectural abbreviation MC possibly be confusing?

3. List the different types of lines that may occur on an architectural drawing, and indicate which ones existed on the blueprint you used for this procedure.

Let's Take It Outside — Energy Auditing

Energy Auditing

OBJECTIVES

1. Understand the scope of an assigned energy audit and properly prepare for the work.
2. Perform an audit and any other additional testing as directed.
3. Compile the results of the audit and prepare a report.

RESOURCES

1. Blank audit form
2. Other blank testing forms (optional)
3. Utility bills for previous 12 months (optional)
4. Blueprints (optional)
5. Tape measure
6. Energy usage meter
7. IR camera
8. Any equipment needed to perform additional tests
9. A Personal Computer with Weatherization Assistant Software (or a similar energy auditing or reporting program) installed
10. Digital camera (optional)

DISCUSSION

This procedure is designed to apply the knowledge acquired in the theory and lab portions of this course towards performing a simulated energy audit.

PROCEDURES

Preparing for the Audit

1. Receive a work order from your instructor. Examine the work order and discuss the scope of the work to be performed with your instructor.

2. Record the location of where the audit is to be performed on the following line:

   _____

3. What additional tests besides the audit will be performed? List the additional tests to be performed on the following lines:

   _____   _____

   _____   _____

Discuss these testing procedures with your instructor.

4. Obtain a blank Audit form and any additional paperwork required for any additional tests specified by your instructor.

5. Examine the blank Audit and testing forms. Create a list of the tools and materials you will need to perform the work on the following lines:

   _____   _____

   _____   _____

   _____   _____

   _____   _____

   _____   _____

6. Examine the blank audit and testing forms and determine whether any tests have already been completed. List the tests that have already been completed on the following lines:

   _____   _____

   _____   _____

7. What other documents concerning the location of the audit will need to be obtained?

    _____

8. Begin filling out the blank audit list by entering the information about the location of the audit and the occupants.

9. Are there blueprints or plans available for location of the audit? If so, what information needed for the audit can be obtained from these documents and recorded now?

    _____

    _____

    _____

Performing the Audit

1. Gather all the paperwork, tools and materials you will need.

2. Go to the location of the audit.

3. Review any safety rules or restrictions that need to be followed while at the location.

4. Continue filling out the audit list.

5. If available, use a digital camera to document any immediate problems.

6. Perform any additional tests, such as Thermography testing, specified by your instructor and record the data on the appropriate forms.

7. Gather all the tools, materials and paperwork brought to the audit location. Clean up the site.

8. Return to your classroom location.

Preparing the Report

1. Evaluate each item in the audit and identify areas and systems that could be improved or replaced to make the building more energy efficient. Record each item in Table 8-1.

2. For each item listed in Table 8-1, research suggested improvements or replacements

3. Research the costs associated with each improvement and record them in Table 8-1. Be sure to include costs for materials, installation and maintenance.

4. Calculate the energy cost savings associated with each suggested improvement. Record them in the far right column of Table 8-1.

5. Access the personal computer with the Weatherization Assistant software installed (or a similar energy auditing or reporting program).

**Table 8-1:
Suggested
Improvements for
the Audited Site**

ITEM FOR IMPROVEMENT	SUGGESTED IMPROVEMENTS	ESTIMATED COSTS	ESTIMATED SAVINGS

6. Start the energy auditing program and enter the results from your audit.

7. If thermographic tests were performed (or images were documented with a digital camera), transfer all the images you captured to the computer. Consult the User's manuals of your individual camera for the proper equipment and procedures to accomplish this.

8. Import any images into the Weatherization Assistant program (or other energy auditing or reporting program). Add comments and descriptions so the subject and location of each image is clear.

9. Generate, save and print the audit report.

10. Generate, save and print any other reports associated with the audit.

11. Deliver all the reports to your instructor.

12. Save all work done on the computer, close any open programs and check with your instructor to determine whether you should shut the computer down.

13. Return all tools and materials to the appropriate places. Clean up your work area.

RESNET National Rater Test Objective Map

The RESNET national home energy rating standard spells out a listing of the knowledge base and skills set for Home Energy Ratings. Trainers and Rating Quality Assurance Designees must have a comprehensive mastery of this knowledge base and skills set and that their training curricula are sufficiently comprehensive to effectively teach these materials to prospective Home Energy Raters Prospective Home Energy Raters, to become certified, shall demonstrate through written examinations and observed exercises a practical, working knowledge of these materials sufficient to produce accurate and fair Home Energy Ratings. The RESNET Rater Trainer/Quality Assurance Designee test covers the below outline of knowledge base and skills set.

In addition to this outline a rater trainer/quality assurance designee may also want to review the RESNET Rating Standards of Practice that is posted on RESNET's web site at *www.natresnet.org/standards/practice.htm* and their rater trainer provider's rating manual.

1.0 Building Energy Performance.

- Basic energy principles

- Energy terminology, units and conversions.

- Heat transfer principles

- Conduction:

  - R-values and U-values

  - UA concepts

  - Parallel paths

- Convection

  - Film coefficients

  - Buoyancy

  - Forced air flows

- Radiation

  - Solar (absorptance + reflectance + transmittance = 1.0)

  - Far infrared (emittance = absorptance)

2.0 Moisture Principles.

- Properties
  - Dewpoint
  - Relative Humidity
  - Evaporation and condensation
- Transport Mechanisms
  - Rain and ground water
  - Capillary action
  - Air transported
  - Vapor Diffusion
  - Evaporation and condensation
- Impacts
  - Indoor Air Quality (IAQ)
  - Material and building durability
  - Human comfort
  - Energy use

3.0 Air Flow in Buildings.

- Pressure differentials and measurement techniques
- Mechanisms and drivers
- Energy and comfort implications
- Health and safety issues

4.0 Heating, Cooling, Ventilation and Hot Water Systems.

- System types
  - Direct- fired systems
  - Condensing systems
  - Heat pumps and air conditioning systems
    - Air Source
    - Ground Source

- Hydronic systems
- Combo systems
- Ductless systems
- Solar thermal systems

5.0 Efficiency.

- Measures of efficiency
- Determination of efficiency (nameplate, age-based defaults, etc.)
- Sizing and design
  - Impacts on energy use
  - Impacts on humidity control
- Controls
  - Standard thermostats
  - Programmable thermostats
  - Multi-zone
- Distribution systems
  - Duct types
  - Restricted returns
    - Closed interior doors
    - Return ducts and grills
- Leakage

6.0 Fresh Air Ventilation.

- Supply, exhaust and balanced flow systems
- Heat exchange systems
- Energy/ent halpy exchange systems
- Exchanger efficiency, fan power and duty cycle characteristics

7.0 Renewable Energy Systems.

- Active and passive space heating systems
- Solar hot water systems
- Photovoltaic systems
- Wind generation

8.0 Diagnostic Testing Procedures.

- Building airtightness
    - Multipoint pressure testing
    - C, n, $\bullet$ p and R^2

9.0 Air Distribution System Airtightness.

- Pressure pan threshold tests
- Duct air leakage measurements
    - cfm25_total
    - cfm25_out
- Pressure measurements
    - Operational (by ho me and its equipment)
    - Imposed (by blower door, etc.)
- Air heat and moisture measurements
    - Airflows
    - Temperatures
    - Relative humidity

10.0 Identifying minimum rated features as defined in the *National Home Energy Rating Technical Guideline*.

- Identify basic home construction types; ramifications of these for energy usage.
- Produce a scaled and dimensioned sketch of a home.
- Identification of insulation defects and ability to account for them in energy analysis tool inputs.
- Identify and document the features of the rated home in accordance with the requirements of Section B.5. and Appendix A of the *National Home Energy Rating Technical Guidelines*.

11.0 Identifying Potential Building Problems.

- Health and safety concerns
- Building durability issues
- Potential comfort problems
- Possible elevated energy use

12.0 Rating Procedures.

- Understanding construction documents
  - Building drawings
  - Specifications

13.0 Field Data Collection (including photo documentation).

- Physical measurements
  - Completing scaled sketches
  - Measuring building dimensions
  - Determining building orientations
  - Measuring window overhang lengths and heights
  - Determining roof slopes, gable heights, etc.
  - Calculating gross and net areas and volumes.
- Energy feature documentation
  - Energy Analysis (Software) tool data requirements
  - Developing and using field inspection forms
  - Organizing data entry procedures
- Characterizing envelope features
  - Determining wall types
  - Determining window and door types and characteristics
  - Determining envelope insulation types, thickness, thermal characteristics and weighted average thermal values
  - Determining duct system characteristics (duct types, insulation value, location with respect to the thermal and air barrier)

- Equipment efficiencies determination
  - Nameplate data
  - ARI and GAMA guides
  - Age-based defaults
  - In situ measurements
- Performance testing
  - Envelope leakage
  - Air distribution system leakage

14.0 Local Climate Impacts.

- Major US climate zones
- 97.5% and 2.5% design conditions
- Cooling and heating design trade-offs

15.0 Utility Prices.

- Revenue-based pricing
- Reliable sources

16.0 Reports.

- Minimum reporting requirements
- Improvement analysis
- Projected and confirmed ratings

17.0 Operating Procedures and Office Administration.

- National guidelines and standards
  - Accreditation Procedures
  - Technical Guidelines
  - Training & Certification Standards

18.0 Understanding the Reference Home and Rating Method.

- Reference Home as defined in B.2 of the *National Home Energy Rating Technical Guidelines* ("Twin" home concept): "The reference home is the geometric twin of the rated home, configured to a standard set of thermal performance characteristics, from which the energy budget, that is the basis for comparison, is derived."

- HERS Score computation using the Normalized Modified Loads Rating Method

19.0 Uses of a Rating.

- Builder assistance
    - Cost effective building design assistance
    - Quality assurance assistance
    - Marketing
- Program qualifications
    - EPA Energy Star
    - Utility
    - Other
- Financing advantages
    - Energy Efficient Mortgages (EEM)
    - Energy Improvement Mortgages (EIM)
- Energy Code compliance
- Added appraisal value
- Consumer education

20.0 Understanding Real Estate, Financing and Economic Terminology.

21.0 Dealing with Clients.

- Understanding the business aspects of being a energy rater
- Cultivating builder, banker and real estate partners.
- Knowing who the customer is.
- Providing excellent service.

22.0 Ethics and Disclosure.

Glossary

A

Absolute Zero The coldest temperature theoretically possible (0°K, -273.15°C, -459.67°F). At this temperature, all molecular motion stops. This temperature cannot be reached by artificial or natural means.

Absorbed The absorption of electromagnetic radiation is the way energy contained within a photon is transferred to the electrons of the atoms of a material. The electromagnetic energy is in this way transformed to other forms of energy, such as heat.

Absorbed Glass Mat (AGM) Battery A sealed battery in which the electrolyte is absorbed into a mat of fine glass fibers.

Absorption Mode The final stage in the charging cycle of a battery bank within a stand-alone alternative energy system. Power directed to the battery is slowly reduced (tapered) to avoid boiling of the electrolyte solution within the battery as it approaches full charge.

AC Disconnect A device designed to open a circuit that is designed to carry alternating current (AC).

Acid Stratification The state within a battery cell where the acid within the electrolyte "settles" to the bottom of the cell, resulting in a weak electrolyte solution at the top of the cell. This generally occurs is the battery has been kept at a high depth of discharge for too long. It is corrected by periodically equalizing the battery.

Active Closed Loop Drain-Back System Common solar thermal system that incorporates electrical pumps, a heat-exchange system and a storage tank to hold the liquid when not in use to avoid freezing.

Active Solar A solar power application involving the use of technologies to capture and convert solar energy into other energy forms (such as usable electricity (photovoltaics), light, heat, ventilation or cooling, or to store heat for future use). Active solar uses external electrical or mechanical equipment, such as pumps and fans, to increase the capacity of the system.

Adjustable System A PV mount that can be manually adjusted (usually in terms of altitude). This is usually done to increase the panel's effectiveness as the Sun's track across the sky changes throughout the year.

Albedo A measurement of how well an object reflects the light from the Sun. It is a specific form of reflectivity. It is defined as the ratio of how much radiant energy is reflected to the amount of radiant energy that strikes the object. The word is derived from Latin (*albus*) for white. The range of possible values is from 0 (dark) to 1 (bright).

Alkaline-Type Battery A class of deep cell battery where the electrolyte is an alkaline, rather than acidic mixture. They are less affected by cold temperatures than typical lead-acid batteries.

Alternating Current (AC) The type of electrical power supplied by utilities, or created by running a generator. This form of electricity reverses its direction at regular intervals. For example, 120Vac 60Hz electric power reverses its flow direction 60 times a second.

Altitude Measured in degrees, when used in PV systems, it refers to the angle of the Sun in relation to the horizon. In a wind system, the term would refer to how high up (measured in feet or meters) a reference point is when compared to the Earth's surface (or a common reference point of sea level).

American Institute of Architects (AIA) Established in 1857, the AIA is the largest US-based not-for-profit membership association for licensed architects.

Ammeter A measuring instrument used to measure the electric current present in a circuit.

Amorphous Cell A non-crystalline form of silicon deposited in thin films at low temperatures onto a variety of substrates. Often called thin film solar cells, they are generally less expensive as well as less efficient than crystalline forms of solar cells.

Amp-Hour (Ah) A battery rating that specifies the length of time a specified battery can apply its specified level of power. One amp-hour is equal to 3,600 coulombs (ampere-seconds), the electric charge transferred by a steady current of one amp for one hour.

Ampacity The current-carrying capacity (the RMS electric current) which a specified wire or device can continuously carry, while remaining within its temperature rating. The ampacity of a specified cable depends on its insulation temperature rating, its electrical properties for current flow, its ability to dissipate heat, its surroundings, and the ambient temperature.

Ampere (Amp) A measure of electric current (symbol A but also often expressed as I), specifically how many electrons are moving past a given point each second. One ampere equals 6.24×10^{18} electrons passing a single point in one second. In electronic terms, one amp is equal to the electric force of one volt acting across the resistance of one ohm.

Anglo-Persian Oil Company Founded in 1908 by William D'Arcy to exploit the discovery of a large oil field in Iran, it was later renamed the Anglo-Iranian Oil Company in 1935 and again renamed British Petroleum (BP) in 1954. In 1914 the British government bought a controlling stake in the company. In 1951 the Iranian parliament voted to nationalize the company. In an effort to regain control of the oil reserves, two years later the United States and Great Britain succeeded in overthrowing the elected government of Iran, replacing Prime Minister Mossadegh with the pro-Western Shah Mohammad Reza Pahlavi.

Angstrom An international recognized non-SI unit of measure (symbol Å) of length equal to 0.1 nanometer (there are 10 billion of these in a meter).

American National Standards Institute (ANSI) A US-based not-for-profit organization that oversees the development of voluntary consensus standards for products, services, processes, systems, and personnel in the United States. The organization also coordinates U.S. standards with international standards.

ANSI/ASHRAE/IESNA Standard 90.1 The Energy Standard for Buildings Except Low-Rise Residential Buildings. ASHRAE 90.1 is the most commonly used energy code for commercial and other non-residential buildings.

Array see *Photovoltaic (PV) Array*

Atom The basic unit of all matter, consisting of a central nucleus (typically made up of a mix of positively charged protons and neutral neutrons). Surrounding this nucleus is a cloud of negatively charged electrons.

Autumnal Equinox As the Earth revolves around the Sun, twice each year the Earth's axis is neither pointing towards or away from the Sun. The name "equinox" is derived from the Latin *aequus* (equal) and *nox* (night), because around the equinox, the night and day are approximately equally as long all over the Earth (roughly 12-hours each). The equinox occur each March (usually 20th or 21st) and each September (usually 22nd or 23rd). The equinox occurring in September has historically been referred to as the Autumnal Equinox (or Vernal Equinox). As this reflects a Northern Hemisphere bias (since September is actually in the Spring in the Southern Hemisphere), the Autumnal Equinox is increasingly referred to as the September Equinox.

Average Daily Load The amount of electricity (on average) used each day within a home, office or commercial structure.

AWG (American Wire Gauge) A system of units used to express conductor sizes in wire. AWG is a convenient system that uses whole numbers with clear relationships to each other. Wire diameters are specified in a descending relationship, whereby larger AWG gauge numbers represent smaller wire diameters.

Azimuth The angle (measured in degrees) from a reference vector (true north, for example) in a reference plane (level ground or sea, for example) to a second vector in the same plane, pointing toward something of interest (such as the location of the Sun).

B

Back Flow of Electricity A situation where electricity flows in the opposite direction than is desired. Usually prevented by blocking diodes. For example, if electricity is allowed to back-flow from a battery bank to the PV array, the array might discharge the batteries overnight.

Band Gap Energy A band gap is an energy range in a solid where no electron states exist. For insulators and semiconductors the band gap generally refers to the energy difference (in volts) between the top of the valence band and the bottom of the conduction band. The Band Gap Energy is the amount of energy required to move an electron across this gap.

Battery Bank Multiple batteries connected together. When connected in series, multiple batteries of similar characteristics behave as one battery with a larger storage capacity.

Battery Enclosure The container, box, room or other physical space within which the battery (or battery bank) resides. In alternative energy systems, enclosures protect batteries from the elements (wind, rain, hail, extreme temperatures, etc.) as well as allow for the venting of gas and heat.

Battery System All the components necessary for a battery bank to operate within an alternative energy system. This may include the batteries themselves, along with the enclosure, wires, charge controller, low-voltage discharge protection, disconnect switches, monitors, etc.)

Benzene An important industrial solvent (formula C_6H_6). It is a naturally occurring component of crude oil.

Biosphere The global zone of life on Earth. This concepts includes all plants, animals and any other living being as well as their relationship with the natural systems on land, in the oceans as well as in the atmosphere.

Bitumen A naturally occurring sticky, tar-like form of petroleum. It is so thick and heavy that it must be heated or diluted before it will flow. When mixed with stone (or aggregate) it is used to create asphalt.

Blocking Diode A diode incorporated within the wiring of a system that prevents the back-flow of electricity. This device allows the power to flow from the generating source (such as a PV panel) but does not allow it to flow back towards this source.

Bloomery An early furnace once used for smelting iron into steel. The slag from this process was called a bloom. This type of furnace has largely been replaced by blast furnaces.

Bonding see *System Bonding*

BOMA International The Building Owners and Managers Association, this US-based not-for-profit association represents commercial, corporate or government real estate owners, investors, developers, managers, and leasing/marketing representatives.

BOS (Balance of System) All the components of a photovoltaic system other than the PV panels. This includes the wiring, switches, support racks, inverter, batteries, controllers, etc. Occasionally the definition will not include the inverter, which is considered a major part (and cost) of a PV system.

British Petroleum (BP) A multi-national oil company, BP is the third largest energy company in the world, the 5th largest company of any kind worldwide and Britain's largest company. (see *Anglo-Persian Oil Company, Standard Oil of Ohio*)

Building Codes see *Code*

Bulk Charge Mode The stage of the charging cycle within a stand-alone alternative energy system where all power generated (by the PV panels, wind turbine, etc.) is directed to charging the battery bank. Any load demand is powered exclusively by the battery bank during this stage of charge.

Bulk Voltage Setting A preselected depth of discharge which, when exceeded, triggers the battery charging system to switch from floating mode to bulk charge mode.

C

C/20 Rate The symbol denoting the rate of discharge of a deep-cell battery. C/20 is used as a standard rate for comparison, indicating that the rate of discharge is such that a completely charged battery will be drained of all power within a 20-hour period of time.

Cap and Trade System A system designed to limit and/or reduce the emissions of greenhouse gases. The government determines an acceptable limit (or cap). Companies are then issued permits to emit a certain amount of pollution (within these limits). Companies that exceed their limit must purchase (or trade) carbon credits from other companies that have managed to reduce emissions to below their allocated limit.

Carbon Credit A key component of governmental attempts to mitigate the growth in concentrations of greenhouse gases. One carbon credit is equal to one ton of emitted carbon dioxide. Credits may be earned (by systems that reduce greenhouse gases already present in the atmosphere), bought, sold or traded as part of a cap and trade scheme.

Carbon Offsets see *Carbon Credit.*

Carbon Tax An environmental tax on emissions of carbon dioxide and/or other greenhouse gases.

Calories A pre-SI (International System of Units) metric unit of measurement of heat energy. In most fields, this unit of measurement has been replaced by the SI unit of energy, the joule. In many nations it still is commonly used to measure food energy. One calorie is equal to about 4.2 kJ.

Candela An SI unit of measurement (symbol cd) to indicate luminous intensity. A common candle emits light with a luminous intensity roughly equal to one candela.

Carboniferous Period The geological period of time extending from about 360 – 286 million years ago. It was a time of glaciation, low sea levels and mountain building. The name comes from Latin, meaning "coal-bearing." Many of the fossil fuel reserves (coal, oil and natural gas) currently being extracted were deposited during this period of time.

Charcoal The black residue consisting of impure carbon that is left when the water and other impurities are removed from wood. It is obtained by slowly burning the wood (in the absence of oxygen). It weighs only about 25% of the weight of the original wood fuel, and retains nearly 90% of its energy content.

Charge Controller An electrical device designed to limit the rate at which electric current is added to or drawn from electric batteries. It prevents overcharging and may prevent against over-voltage. It may also prevent complete draining of a battery, or perform controlled discharges of the battery. Also known as a charge regulator or a battery regulator.

Charge Sink A mass that can absorb an electrical charge without damage to the mass itself or the surrounding environment.

Charge Resumption Set Point (CTSP) A preset level (depth of discharge) at which a charge controller that has been preventing the charging of a battery bank resumes the charging process.

Charge Termination Set Point (CTSP) A preset level (depth of discharge) at which a charge controller shuts down and prevents further charging of the battery bank.

Charging Cycle In a battery, this indicates the complete process where a battery begins at 100% of its power storage capacity, is drained of power to some level (as indicated by its depth of discharge for that particular cycle) then is recharged to 100% capacity once again.

Chemical Energy The energy released or stored when covalent bonds within atoms are either created or separated.

Chemical Reaction The process that leads to the changing of a chemical substance from one form to another. For example, when oxygen (O_2) and hydrogen (H_2) combine to form water (H_2O), this is a chemical reaction.

Circuit Created when an acceptable external pathway is provided for the movement of the electrons from the pushing end of the voltage source to the pulling end.

Circuit Breaker A device that senses the level of current flowing through it, and is designed to interrupt the path of current flow (open circuit) if the current level gets to a certain point (the fuse rating). Circuit breakers are generally designed to allow the user to reset them (close the circuit) once the source of overcurrent has been removed.

Circulating Pump An electrical pump used to move liquid through a closed fluid transport system.

Clerestory Windows Originally used in churches or cathedrals, these vertical windows are located near the ceiling. They provide a soft light reflected from the ceiling to increase (passively) the lighting within a room. They are a form of daylighting.

Closed Loop System A solar thermal system that uses heat exchange to transfer the heat from a liquid held within a closed system to water that is heated and used within the building.

Coal A fossil fuel composed primarily of carbon along with variable quantities of other elements, including sulfur, hydrogen, oxygen and nitrogen. It is the largest source of energy for the generation of electricity worldwide, as well as one of the world's largest sources of man-made carbon dioxide emissions.

Code The codification of the general and permanent rules and regulations, often addressing safety issues. The governing code covering electrical installations within the United States is usually the National Electrical Code.

Coke A fossil fuel formed through the destructive distillation of low-ash, low sulfur bituminous coal. Cokes burn hotter and produce less smoke than coal.

Combiner A passive connection device that combines similar frequencies (voltage) originating from different equipment, to then carry the combined current in a single wire.

Combustible Capable of igniting and burning, such as wood and paper, although a combustible materials can be either a solid or a liquid.

Combustibility The measure of how easily a substance will burn.

Comfort Zone Also sometimes called thermal comfort, it is a range of temperature, air movement and humidity within which most humans "feel comfortable." It is generally recognized that this range for indoor humidity is between 30-60% with temperatures between 65-80°F (218-27°C) with an airflow velocity of less than .18 m/s.

Conduction The transfer of thermal energy between neighboring molecules. The thermal energy will always move from an area of higher temperature to an area of lower temperature. Conduction can take place in all forms of matter, including solids, liquids, gases and plasmas.

Conductivity A measurement of a material's ability to conduct thermal or electrical energy. In electrical energy, conductivity is the inverse of resistivity (how much resistance to the flow of electricity is inherent in the material). In equations it is symbolized with the Greek letter sigma (σ).

Conductor Materials composed of atoms that have three or less electrons in their valence shell, and offer very little resistance to giving up electrons. When current passes through conductors, some energy is given off as heat. Heat is often a result of too much current flowing through an undersized conducting wire, or through a bad connection.

Construction Specifications Institute (CSI) A not-for-profit organization that maintains and advances the standardization of construction language as pertains to building specifications. CSI provides structured guidelines for specification writing in their Project Resource Manual.

Continuity Test A measure of resistance across an electrical circuit. Continuity checks are always conducted with the power removed from the system being tested, in order to prevent serious damage to the testing meter.

Controllers An electric or hydraulic device that manages the flow of a liquid through a solar thermal system.

Convection The movement of molecules within fluids (liquids and gases). This transfer of heat takes place through diffusion (the random movement of molecules) and advection (the movement of heat within currents). This heat transfer will always move from areas of higher concentration (warmer) to areas of lower concentration (cooler).

Convective Cooling Passive cooling systems that take advantage of convection (hot air rises) to move warmer air away from occupants, replacing it with cooler air.

Converter see *Inverter*

Coulomb (C) An SI unit of measurement for electrical charge. A coulomb is the amount of electrical charge transported by a steady current of one ampere for one second. It can be expressed using the equation: $1C = 1A \times 1s$

Coulomb's Law A theorem describing electrical force. Developed by in the 1780s by French physicist Charles Augustin de Coulomb stating: *The magnitude of the electrostatic force between two point electric charges is directly proportional to the product of the magnitudes of each of the charges and inversely proportional to the square of the total distance between the two charges.*

Covalent Bonding A form of chemical bonding in which electrons in the outer shells of adjoining atoms are shared.

Covenants and Ordinances A legal promise or requirement to engage in or refrain from a specified action (usually associated with property use).

Current A flow of electrons, such as those moving through an electrical circuit. When a sufficient electromotive force is applied to all of the atoms between the two ends of the conductor, a flow of electrons (current) will move through the circuit. Current is measured in amperes (A).

D

Damping Ratio As it relates to thermal mass, this term reflects how well the material moderates the differences between the high and low temperature (the frequency of the wave) variations.

Day A unit of time (symbol d) equal to about 24 hours. It is not an SI unit of measurement. The term is also often used to refer to the part of the day when the Sun is shining (roughly 12 hours on average, but varies throughout the year depending on the latitude of the observer).

Daylighting The practice of placing windows or other openings (and reflective surfaces) so that natural light provides effective daytime internal lighting within a building. This is a subsystem of passive solar systems, as no external energy is required to provide the lighting.

Declination Magnetic declination (also known as grid magnetic angle in military circles, if the grid is aligned to true north) at any point on the Earth is the angle between the local magnetic field—the direction the north end of a compass points—and true north. The declination is positive when the magnetic north is east of true north. The term magnetic variation is equivalent, and is more often used in aeronautical and other forms of navigation

Deep Discharge Type Batteries A lead-acid battery designed to deliver a consistent voltage as the battery discharges.

Deforestation The clearing of naturally occurring forests through logging and/or burning of trees. Deforestation usually occurs when the wood (or charcoal derived from the wood) is sold as a commodity and/or the land is cleared for use as pasture, cropland, or development. Removal of the trees without sufficient reforestation often results in damage to the habitat, biodiversity, as well as soil and water retention. Deforested regions often degrade into wasteland (a landscape devoid of nutrients, soil and/or moisture).

Density Defined as the mass per unit of volume of a given material or substance. In mathematical equations, it is depicted by the Greek letter rho ®). Density can be described mathematically with the equation: $\rho = m$ (mass) $/ V$ (volume)

Depth of Discharge (DOD) A method of measuring a battery's state of charge. It is typically expressed as a percentage, indicating the amount of storage capacity that has been used. For example, a battery that has been drained to a point where only 20% of its total storage capacity remains, will have reached a point of 80% DOD.

Diode In photovoltaic cells, diodes are based on p-n junctions. In a p-n diode, conventional current is from the p-type side (the anode) to the n-type (the cathode), but not in the opposite direction.

Direct Compact System A solar thermal system where the water to be used is heated directly (without a heat exchanger) within the thermal collector.

Direct Current (DC) The movement of electrons whereby their movement around the circuit, from atom to atom, is always in one constant direction.

Direct Solar Gain A type of passive heating system where the heat energy contained within sunlight is used directly. The infrared radiation (heat) is emitted when the sunlight strikes the surface of an object. In a direct solar passive system, this would occur within the room which is to be heated.

Disconnect Switches A device that opens a circuit and prevents the flow of electrical current along its path. These can be manual (such as a light switch) or automatic, devices that monitor the flow of power along the circuit and automatically open the circuit when problems occur (such as a circuit breaker).

DMMs (Digital Multimeters) see *Multimeters*

Doped The process of intentionally introducing impurities into an extremely pure semiconductor to change its electrical properties. A semiconductor doped to very high levels acts more like a conductor than a semiconductor (known as a degenerate).

Drain Back A closed-loop solar thermal system that avoids freezing problems by ensuring that the liquid flows back into a storage tank that is protected from freezing temperatures.

Drain Down An open-loop solar thermal system that avoids freezing problems by ensuring that the liquid flows out of the exposed pipes when threatened with freezing temperatures.

Dry Bulb Temperature The temperature of air measured by a thermometer exposed to the air, but not exposed to moisture or sunlight.

Dual Axis Tracking System A PV mounting system designed to follow the motion of the Sun as it moves (in relation to the horizon) both in altitude and azimuth.

E

Earthing see *Grounding*

Earthship A type of passive solar home designed and marketed by Earthship Biotecture or Taos, NM. The Earthship design incorporates the concepts of thermal mass, passive solar heating and cooling, water harvesting and gray-water treatment within its design. Additionally, it is primarily constructed from salvaged "garbage"—comprised of discarded automobile tires, cans, bottles and other similar materials.

Easement A non-possessory interest to use real property in possession of another person for a stated purpose. An easement is considered as a property right in itself and is still treated as a type of property in most jurisdictions.

Edge Effect A specific form of solar radiation scattering, diverting radiant energy from the edge of clouds as photons strike water vapor within the cloud.

Elastic Potential Energy The stored energy that is in place due to the distortion of an object. When the force under which the object is placed is removed, energy is released as the object returns to its original shape or position. For example, a compressed spring contains elastic potential energy. When the spring is released, it will return to its original shape—releasing energy in the process.

Electrical Current The flow of the electrical charge of sub-atomic particles (electrons) along a circuit. The rate of this flow is measured in amperes (symbol A).

Electrical Energy see *Electrical Current*

Electrical Force A state of attraction or repulsion between two electrically charged particles defined by Coulomb's Law—which basically states that the level (magnitude) of the electrostatic force (the attraction or repulsion) depends on how strong their charge and how far apart they are. See *Coulomb's Law*.

Electrical Grid The physical components (such as transmission wires, poles, generators, transformers, etc.) connected together to generate, transmit and distribute electrical energy.

Electrical Load see *Load*

Electricity A variety of phenomena resulting from the presence and flow of electric charge. This flow serves as an energy source used to generate heat and light, as well as to produce mechanical and motive forces. The demand for electricity has produced a world full of electrical generation plants.

Electromagnetic Induction An altered AC power relationship within inductive electrical loads whereby the resulting AC current flows at some time following (lags) the application of the voltage to the circuit. The lag time is based on the amount of inductance (henries) in the load device.

Electromagnetic Radiation (EMR) Waves consisting of electric and magnetic fields that can move within a vacuum (such as space) or in matter. It is classified based on its frequency. The entire range of frequencies of EMR is referred to as the Electromagnetic Spectrum. In order of increasing frequency and decreasing wavelength, these waves include: radio waves, microwaves, terahertz radiation, infrared radiation, visible light, ultraviolet radiation, X-rays and gamma rays. EMR carries both energy and momentum, that can be transferred to any matter it may strike.

Electromagnetic Spectrum see *Electromagnetic Radiation*

Electromagnetic Waves see *Electromagnetic Radiation*

Electromotive Force (EMF) The amount of voltage existing between the different terminals of an electrical power source. It is a measurement of the potential electrical push and pull on both sides of a connected circuit or device.

Electron A sub-atomic particle that orbits around an atom's nucleus in elliptical paths called an electron shell. An electron has a negative elementary electrical charge of -1 (equal and opposite charge of a proton). The mass of an electron is believed to be so small as to be irrelevant (with no known sub-particles and essentially zero-dimensional, taking up no space).

Electron Cloud Having essentially zero mass, a wavelike orbital behavior and an unpredictable orbital pattern, the location of an electron or pair of electrons within an atom at any given point in time cannot be determined. An electron cloud is a three-dimensional representation of the probable locations within atom where the electrons may be located at any point in time.

Energy The amount (quantity) of work that can be performed by a specific force. Energy can take many forms such as kinetic, potential, or thermal.

Energy Conversion Efficiency The ratio between the useful output of an energy conversion machine (such as a automobile engine) and the energy input. It is denoted with the Greek letter "eta" (η). Energy conversion efficiency can be expressed in the equation: $\eta = P_{out} / P_{in}$

Energy Crisis Term used to describe any period of time when energy supplies are dramatically exceeded by demand, or energy prices rise sharply.

Energy Sink see *Load Dump*

Energy Star Program An international standard for energy efficient consumer products. It was first created as a U.S. government program in 1992, but has since been adopted by a number of nations around the world. Devices carrying the Energy Star logo, such as computer products and peripherals, kitchen appliances, buildings and other products, require 20%-30% less energy on average than similar non-Energy Star products.

Entropy In a closed system, the temperature within the system is always in the process of "evening out." High temperature is moving to lower temperatures, resulting in a lower, more even distribution of temperature. An example would be that a glass of ice water in a hot room will eventually warm until it reaches the same temperature as the surrounding air. As the ice melts, entropy is increasing.

Environmental Protection Agency (EPA) Established in 1970, it is the arm of the U.S. Federal government that monitors air, water, land and human health.

Ergonomics The science of designing the job, equipment, and workplace to fit the worker. Proper ergonomic design is necessary to prevent repetitive strain injuries, which can develop over time and can lead to long-term disability.

Equilibrium A condition within a system where competing influences are in balance. The system will remain unchanged until one of the influences (for example, the amount of greenhouse gas in the atmosphere) is changed.

Equalization The process of periodically "over charging" a deep cell battery. This process causes gassing which remixes the electrolyte solution, preventing or correcting sulfation and acid stratification problems within the battery cell.

Evacuated-Tube Collectors A solar thermal collector that utilizes series of modular glass tubes, mounted in parallel, each of which contains an absorber tube (in place of the absorber plate to which metal tubes are attached in a flat-plate collector).

Evaporative Cooler A device that cools the air through the evaporation of water. It is especially well suited for climates with high temperatures and low humidity (such as a desert). The process of evaporation removes heat from the surrounding air. How much heat is determined by a wet-bulb/dry-bulb temperature comparison. The greater the difference, the more cooling will take place.

Endothermic Reaction A chemical reaction that absorbs energy in the form of heat during the reaction process. It can be expressed in the equation: Reactants + Energy (heat) $\rightarrow$ Products

Exothermic Reaction A chemical reaction that releases energy in the form of heat. It can be expressed in the equation: Reactants $\rightarrow$ Products + Energy (heat)

External Costs The consequence of an economic transaction on someone that is not directly involved in the transaction. In such cases, the price of the product does not reflect the full cost in the production or consumption of a product or service.

F

Federal Energy Regulatory Commission (FERC) A U.S. federal agency with jurisdiction over all interstate electrical sales, wholesale electric rates, natural gas pricing and distribution, hydroelectric power plant licensing and oil pipeline rates.

Federal Power Act Enacted by the U.S. Congress as the Federal Water Power Act of 1920, its original purpose was to coordinate hydroelectric projects. The act created the Federal Power Commission (FPC) as the licensing authority for these power plants. In 1935 the law was renamed the Federal Power Act and the FPC's regulatory authority was expanded to include all forms of interstate electrical transmissions.

Federal Power Commission (FPC) Established by the Federal Water Power Act of 1920, the FPC is a 5-member independent commission (appointed by the U.S. President and confirmed by the Senate) tasked with regulating all interstate electrical issues as well as the natural gas industry. The FPC was replaced by the Federal Energy Regulatory Commission (FERC) in 1977.

Feedback Loops A situation where the outcome of a previous event influences (and amplifies) the current event, which in turn influences and amplifies future outcomes (a cause-and-effect chain loop). For example, warmer temperatures cause snow to melt. Melting snow exposes darker ground with a lower reflectivity than the original snow. This darker ground absorbs more heat, resulting in still warmer temperatures which in turn results in more melting snow, and so on.

Fertile Crescent An area of rich soil along the Jordan, Euphrates and Tigris Rivers roughly shaped as a crescent. This land area corresponds with portions of modern-day Iraq, Syria, Lebanon, Israel, Kuwait, Jordan, south-eastern Turkey, and south-western Iran. It is often cited as the birthplace of human civilization, including the development of agriculture, writing, the wheel, and more.

First Law of Thermodynamics see *Laws of Thermodynamics*

Fission A nuclear reaction in which the nucleus of an atom splits into smaller parts, producing free neutrons and a lighter nuclei (as well as photons in the form of gamma rays). Fission of heavy elements is an exothermic reaction that can release large amounts of energy as well as electromagnetic radiation. This is the process used to generate energy within nuclear power plants.

Fixed Mount A mounting system (in a PV system, for example) that is not designed to move or be adjusted once it has been installed.

Flat-Plate Collectors A solar thermal collector that utilizes a thin absorber sheet (of thermally stable polymers, aluminum, steel or copper, to which a black coating is applied) backed by a grid or coil of fluid tubing and placed in an insulated casing with a glass or polycarbonate cover.

Floating Mode The state of charge of a deep-cell battery within an alternative energy system where the battery bank is alternately charged and drained of power (floats) within a range of 80-100% of capacity (0-20% depth of discharge).

Fluid Transport System System of pipes to transport a liquid, such as water or in a solar thermal system, glycol.

Flush Mounting see *Stand Off Mounting*

Foot-Candle The amount of luminous flux that would strike the inside surface of a one-foot sphere if a light source of one candela was located in the exact center of the sphere. It can also be defined as being equal to one lumen equally distributed within one square foot. It is not an SI unit of measurement, but is commonly used in the lighting industry.

Force An external agent that changes the motion of a free body (something unattached to anything else) or causes stress upon a fixed body (a substance that cannot be moved). It is often described as the push or pull that may cause an object with mass to changes its velocity. Force (symbol F) is measured in newtons (N) and can be expressed in the equation: F (force) = m (mass) x a (acceleration)

Fossil Fuels Fuels such as oil, natural gas, or coal that are the product of decomposed organisms buried many millions of years ago. These fuels contain a high percentage of carbons and hydrocarbons that produce carbon dioxide (CO_2) as a byproduct of their use.

Free Electron A valence electron from an atom's outer shell that has been physically separated from the atom. In this condition, the electron is referred to as a free electron and represents a negative electrical charge.

Fuse A safety device that is placed in the line of an electrical source to sense the level of current flowing through the line. It is designed to interrupt the path of current flow (open circuit) when the current level surpasses the fuse rating.

Fusion The process by which multiple like-charged atomic nuclei join together to form a heavier nucleus. It is accompanied by the release or absorption of energy. Nuclear fusion occurs naturally within stars (such as the Sun).

G

Gasoline A petroleum-derived liquid fuel, primarily used within internal combustion engines. It is the primary fuel used worldwide within the transportation sector.

Gassing Within a battery, this refers to the process by which a portion of the electrolyte within the cell converts to gas (boils) releasing hydrogen, oxygen and various corrosive gases.

Gel Cell Battery A VRLA battery with a gelled electrolyte (the sulfuric acid is mixed with a silica fume, which makes the resulting mass gel-like and immobile).

Gravitational Potential Energy The potential energy stored in an object or system that is the result of gravitational force. For example, if a book is placed on a high shelf, it gains gravitational potential energy. If the book falls to the floor, this potential energy is converted to kinetic energy as it falls. Hydropower takes advantage of gravitational energy as water flows from a higher elevation to a lower elevation.

Greenhouse Effect The heating of the surface of a planet due to atmospheric gases that absorb and trap infrared radiation (heat energy). Many scientists believe that greenhouse gases (such as methane and carbon dioxide) emitted by human activities have in recent decades resulted in a significant increase in global surface temperatures due to this effect.

Greenhouse Gases Gases in the atmosphere that absorb and emit radiation within the thermal infrared range of the electromagnetic spectrum. Higher concentrations of these gases result in more thermal energy concentrated at the surface of a planet, resulting in higher surface temperatures. Common greenhouse gases in the Earth's atmosphere include water vapor, carbon dioxide, methane, nitrous oxide, ozone, in addition to chlorofluorocarbons.

Grid see *Electrical Grid*

Grid-Tied System An alternative energy system (such as wind and/or solar) that is connected to the utility's electrical grid. Excess power that is generated can then be "sold back" to the utility company, and power can be drawn from the grid when needed.

Ground (GND) The reference point in an electrical circuit from which all other voltages are measured. It also can be defined as the common return path for an electrical current, a direct physical connection to the Earth.

Ground Fault A situation that occurs on an electrical circuit wen an unintended pathway opens between the current source and a grounded surface. If this pathway is a person, the result may be a lethal shock.

Ground Fault Protection A system or device that protects an electric circuit (and those who may come in contact with the circuit) from the consequences of unintended ground faults. An example of such a device is a ground fault interrupter (GFI), also called a residual current device (RCD) or a residual current circuit breaker (RCCB).

Ground Reflection A form of solar radiation scattering, where the albedo properties of the Earth's surface reflect a portion of the light to nearby surfaces (such as a PV module).

H

Heat Exchanger A device built for efficient heat transfer from one medium (usually a liquid) to another, whether the media are separated by a solid wall so that they never mix, or the media are in direct contact.

Heliostats A device that tracks the movement of the Sun (usually a mirror) and directs it towards a stationary target or receiver. From the Greek word *helios* (Sun) and *stat* (stationary).

Hertz A measure of frequency (symbol Hz). It is defined as the number of complete cycles per second. It is named after the German physicist Heinrich Hertz, who made important scientific contributions to electromagnetism.

Horse Power A non-SI unit of measurement for power. It is often used in consumer products to denote the power capacity of the engine or turbine or electric motor. One mechanical horsepower equals 550 foot-pounds per second or 745.7 watts. A metric horsepower equals 75 kgf-meter per second or 735.499 watts. One horsepower rating on an electric motor equals 746 watts.

Hot Testing Testing an electrical circuit to determine if current is present.

Hubbert's Peak Oil The moment in time when the world reaches its maximum level of oil extraction. From that moment on, the amount of oil produced worldwide will decline. In 1956 M. King Hubbert accurately predicted that the United State's oil production would peak between 1965-1970. He later predicted worldwide oil production would peak in 1995. It is now generally accepted that world oil production did peak in 2006.

Hybrid System Indicates a system that incorporates two distinctly different sub-systems, each of which could operate independently if required to do so. In an electrical system, this term is used to refer to a system that incorporates several methods of producing power. For example, if a stand-alone PV system is combined with a stand-alone wind power system, the result will be referred to as a hybrid. Additionally, grid-tied PV systems typically do not incorporate battery banks (the utility serves that function). A grid-tied system that also incorporates a battery-bank (and all the components necessary for a stand-alone system) may also be referred to as a hybrid.

Hydrometer An instrument used to measure the specific gravity of a liquid (the relative density ratio of that liquid to the density of water). It is used in testing the charge level of lead-acid batteries.

I

Illuminance The total light power (luminous flux) striking a specified surface area. Illuminance was often called brightness (although this concept is more a descriptive term rather than a quantitative term). Illuminance is measured in lux (lx).

Indirect Solar Gain A type of passive heating system where the heat energy contained within sunlight is used indirectly. The infrared radiation (heat) absorbed into a material is then radiated through its mass and into the interior of a room to be heated. Sunlight does not enter the room directly as part of this system.

Indoor Air Quality (IAQ) A term referring to the air quality within and around buildings and structures, especially as it relates to the health and comfort of building occupants.

Inductance The property in an electrical circuit where a change in the current flowing through that circuit induces an electromotive force (EMF) that opposes the change in current. The amount of difference between the application of the voltage (the push/pull on the circuit) and the actual flow of current is based on this.

Inductive Load A load created by an induction motor, a type of asynchronous AC motor where power is supplied to the rotating device by means of electromagnetic induction. A characteristic of this type of load is a large energy spike required at startup.

Induction Motor An alternating current (AC) motor where power is supplied to the rotating device by means of electromagnetic induction.

Industrial Age The time period in the late 1700's- early 1800's, where older work methods began to be replaced by, and enhanced through the use of machines. Largely agricultural societies in Europe and North America became machine-based manufacturing communities. Sources of power shifted from animal and human – to fossil fuel.

Infrared Radiation (IR) A portion of the electromagnetic spectrum, typically felt as heat. IR is energy with a wavelength longer than visible light (400-700 nm), but shorter than terahertz radiation (100μm - 1 mm). About 47% of the electromagnetic spectrum is infrared radiation.

Insolation The measurement of radiation energy received on a given surface (such as the photovoltaic cell), and specified in terms of average irradiance in watts per square meter. Term derived from the words *incident solar radiation*.

Institute of Electrical and Electronics Engineers (IEEE) An international not-for-profit professional association focused on the advancement of technology related to electricity. It has the most members of any technical professional organization in the world, with more than 365,000 members in around 150 countries.

Inter-Row Shading In large PV installations, the situation that may occur when shadows cast by one row of PV panels falls upon panels aligned in a row behind.

Insulator Material that resists the flow of electricity. Also called a dielectric, the electrons in the outer shell of these materials are tightly bonded and not easily shared with neighboring atoms. Common electrical insulators include rubber, plastics, paper, and glass.

Integrated Collector Storage (ICS) A solar thermal system where the water storage tank is part of the solar collector system. Also called a solar batch heater.

Internal Combustion Engine An engine where the combustion of a fuel (usually a fossil fuel such as gasoline) mixed with an oxidizer (usually air) takes place internally within the engine, within a combustion chamber. This explosion results in an expansion of combusted gases, applying force to a movable component of the engine (such as a piston or turbine). This movement results in useful mechanical energy.

Internal Resistance A concept that models the electrical consequences of the complex chemical reactions inside a battery. It indicates or measures the loss of current delivered by a battery cell as current flows through it. Internal resistance generally increases over time as a battery ages, but is usually in the range of 1 ohm for most commercial batteries.

International Building Code (IBC) A model building code first published in 2000 developed by the International Code Council (ICC). It has been adopted throughout most of the United States.

International Code Council (ICC) A not-for-profit association responsible for the development of codes addressing building safety and fire prevention during the construction of residential, commercial and institutional (schools, churches, etc.) buildings.

International Energy Conservation Code (IECC) A building code created by the International Code Council in 2006. It is a model code adopted by many state and municipal governments in the United States for the establishment of minimum design and construction requirements for energy efficiency.

International Organization for Standardization (ISO) An international standard-setting body composed of representatives from various national standards organizations (such as ANSI and SCC). Founded in 1947, the organization promulgates worldwide proprietary industrial and commercial standards.

International Residential Code (IRC) A building code created by the International Code Council. This comprehensive, stand-alone residential code establishes minimum regulations one- and two-family dwellings of three stories or less.

Inverter An electrical device that converts direct current (DC) to alternating current (AC). The resulting AC can be created in such a way as to meet the required voltage and frequency for use in appropriate transformers, switches and control circuits.

Ion An atom that has given up an electron and is now out of balance, exhibiting a positive electrical charge.

Islanding The condition in which power is generated from a distributed electrical system (such as a small wind or solar power system connected to the electrical grid) onto the electrical grid even though power from the electric utility is no longer present. This may occur (for example) when the grid goes down due to storm damage. A wind system connected to the grid may continue to push power onto the power lines. This can create an extremely dangerous situation for people working on the lines who believe they are "dead."

Isolated Solar Gain A type of passive heating system where the heat energy contained within sunlight is used indirectly. The infrared radiation (heat) absorbed into a material is radiated through its mass and into the interior of a room to be heated. Additionally, heat from sunlight is collected directly in an adjacent space (such as a Trombe Wall or sun room), then moved (either actively or through passive convection) into the space that is to be heated. Sunlight does not enter the room that benefits from isolated solar gain directly as part of this system.

I-V Curve A graphic representation of the relationship between the output of amps and volts for a given PV module under a given set of operating conditions.

J

Joule A metric unit of measurement use (symbol J) to measure energy. It was named for James Prescott Joule (19th century British physicist who studied the nature of heat). It is equal to the amount of force of one newton acting to move an object a distance of one meter. It can be defined by the equation: $1 J = 1 kg \times m^2 / s^2$

Junction Box A metal or plastic container used for electrical junctions, usually intended to conceal them from sight and to protect them from the elements and tampering.

K

Kelvin An SI unit (symbol K) used to measure temperature. In the Kelvin scale, absolute zero is referenced as zero kelvin (0 K). Temperature intervals (the difference between 3 K and 4 K, for example) are: $1 K = 1°C = 1.8 °F$.

Kerosene A combustible hydrocarbon liquid derived distilling coal. Also known as paraffin or paraffin oil (the name kerosene was trademarked by Abraham Gesner in 1854) in many parts of the world.

Kilowatt-Hour (kWh) A measurement of energy consumed or generated at a steady rate equal to one thousand watts of power flowing for a period of time equal to one hour. Utility companies measure energy in terms of the kilowatt-hours (kWh). It can be expressed in the equation $1 kWh = 1 kW \times 1 h$ (hour). This term does not express how fast the energy is generated or consumed (which would be kW/h, kilowatts *per* hour). For example, during periods of low energy use, it might take 6 hours to consume one kWh. During periods of high energy use, one kWh might be consumed in 30 minutes.

Kinetic Energy It is the energy an object possesses due to its motion. It can also be defined as the work that must be done to accelerate a given mass from a state of rest to its current velocity. KE is defined by the equation: $KE = 1/2 m$ (mass) $\times v^2$ (velocity squared)

L

Lanyard A rope or cord often worn around the neck or wrist to carry something. Usually it is used where there is a risk of losing the object or to ensure it is visible at all times.

Latitude Refers to the location of a place on Earth (or other planetary body) north or south of the equator. Usually denoted by the Greek letter phi (φ).

Law of Conservation of Energy A basic principle in physics that states that the energy within an isolated system (such as the universe) cannot be created or destroyed—there is a fixed amount of energy in the system that will never increase or decrease. The energy within the system can only change forms, from potential energy to kinetic energy, for example, or from electrical energy to light and heat (as in a light bulb).

Laws of Thermodynamics A group of four laws (or fundamental principles) describing how heat and work are transported within thermodynamic processes (activities that convert energy to heat and work. The Zeroth Law states that if two objects have exactly the same temperature, no heat will flow between them. The First Law states that heat is a form of energy, and as a form of energy it can neither be created or destroyed (Law of Conservation of Energy). The Second Law states that as work is done, heat energy is always moving from where it is warm to where it is cooler. This is known as entropy. The Third Law states that no transfer of energy to work is perfect, so as a result, the temperature of a system can never get to absolute zero.

Light Diffuser A device attached to a light fixture that spreads out or scatters the light, reducing the harshness or glare created by the light source (soft light).

Light Irradiance (E) A term for the power of electromagnetic radiation at a surface, per unit area, when the electromagnetic radiation strikes the surface. The SI unit of measurement is W/m^2 (watts per square meter). This is often referred to as the light's intensity.

Light Shelf A horizontal light-reflecting overhang that is placed above eye-level and has a high-reflectance upper surface. This surface is then used to reflect sunlight through a window and onto the interior ceiling and/or deeper into a room within a building. It is a form of daylighting.

Light Tube A device placed into a roof (also called solar tubes) to admit light to a focused area of the interior or the building. These often resemble recessed light fixtures in the ceiling, but are completely passive in nature. They do not allow as much heat transfer as skylights because they have a less exposed surface area.

Line Side A directional indication (such as left and right) indicating the side of a component within an alternative energy system that is closest to the utility interface.

Liquid Vented Battery Lead-acid batteries that allow gases produced within them to vent into the surrounding atmosphere.

Load The output terminal on a circuit. The term may also apply to the electricity that is used by devices connected to that output terminal.

Load Dump Within a stand-alone alternative energy system, it is a storage device (such as a water tank) that is capable of accepting and storing excess energy the system may produce from time-to-time so that the extra power is not simply wasted.

Load Resistance Electrical resistance as defined by Ohm's Law is a measure of the "friction" against the current flow at a given level of power (measured in watts). As power levels vary (based on load demands), resistance levels within the circuit will also vary.

Location The physical space where a system (such as PV panels or a wind turbine tower) will be placed.

Low Voltage Discharge Protection A device that protects against the deep discharge of a battery. Batteries may be damaged if allowed to discharge too much of their energy. May be a stand-alone device or incorporated into the battery charge controller.

Lumens The SI measurement unit (symbol lm) used to indicate the perceived power of light (luminous flux).

Luminous Flux The measure of the perceived power of light (adjusted to reflect the human eye's sensitivity to the various wavelengths of visible light). Also sometimes called luminous power, it is measured in lumens. Essentially, the higher the luminous flux (the more lumens) the greater the amount of light emitted.

Luminous Intensity The measure of the power of light emitted by a light source in a particular direction. The SI unit for luminous intensity is a candela. Where luminous flux measures the total amount of light emitted from a source, the luminous intensity measures only the amount emitted in a specific direction (a steradian – the unit of measure of a solid angle). For example, a light source emitting in all directions will have a certain luminous flux. If half of the light's sphere is covered, the luminous flux will be cut in half. But the light emitted from the uncovered portion will have exactly the same luminous intensity as it did before (of course the portion covered will now have a luminous intensity of zero).

Lux An SI unit (symbol lx) measuring illuminance. One lux is equal to one lumen per square meter.

M

Master Format A standard for organizing specifications and other written information for commercial and institutional building projects in the U.S. And Canada.

Maximum Power Point A specific point on an I-V curve (a plot of amperes and volts) of a PV panel where total power (I x V) is at its highest level.

Maximum Power Point Tracking Device An electrical device that tracks and adjusts the power output from an alternative energy system to best match that point on the I-V curve where the amount of watts produced is at its highest level. Such a device improves the efficiency of a system under changing environmental conditions.

Maximum Power Current (Imp) Operating under ideal conditions, the maximum current (amps) a PV panel will produce.

Maximum Power Voltage (Vmp) Operating under ideal conditions, the maximum voltage a PV panel will produce.

Mechanical Energy The energy required to move a physical object (solid, liquid or gas) from one place to another. This energy can be kinetic (in motion) or potential. It typically refers to movement on the observable level, rather than on the molecular level.

Megawatt (MW) Equal to one-million watts of electrical power.

Modified Square Wave Inverter An inverter that produces a wave form of output somewhere between a sine wave and a square wave. The output from this type of inverter avoids some of the problems associated with square wave inverters, but cannot be used in grid-tied electrical systems.

Molecule A stable, electrically neutral group of at least two atoms, held together by strong covalent chemical bonds. A molecule may be made of a single element (such as oxygen – O_2) or a combination of elements (such as water – H_2O).

Monocrystalline Cell A photovoltaic cell made from a single crystal of silicon.

Multi-Junction Cell A sub-class of photovoltaic cell developed for higher efficiency. They consist of multiple thin films, each with a different band gap that causes it to absorb light most efficiently at a certain portion of the electromagnetic spectrum. As a result, the many layers allow the cell to capture more of the solar spectrum and convert it into electricity.

Multimeters A multitester, also known as a volt/ohm meter or VOM, is an electronic measuring instrument that combines several measurement functions in one unit. A typical multimeters may include features such as the ability to measure voltage, current (amps) and resistance (ohms). There are two categories of multimeters, analog multimeters (VOMs) and digital multimeters (DMM or DVOM.)

Multi-Stage Controller More flexible than a single-stage controller, these charge controllers are designed to accommodate the various charging stages of a battery bank (float mode, bulk charge mode and absorption mode).

N

National Electrical Code (NEC) A document that describes recommended safe practice for the installation of all types of electrical equipment. Its stated purpose is for the "practical safeguarding of persons and property from hazards arising from the use of electricity." Written and published by the NFPA, it is also referred to as NFPA 70.

National Electrical Grid see *Electrical Grid*

National Fire Protection Association (NFPA) A not-for-profit US-based association charged with creating and maintaining minimum standards and requirements for fire prevention and suppression activities, training, and equipment, as well as other life-safety codes and standards. Specifically, NFPA writes and publishes the National Electrical Code (NEC, also referred to as NFPA 70).

National Association of Home Builders (NAHB) A US-based trade association that seeks to promote the policies that make housing a national priority. It was established in 1942 and currently has more than 200,000 members.

NFPA 5000: Building Construction and Safety Code A code written and published by the NFPA that addresses those construction, protection, and occupancy features necessary to minimize danger to life and property. Competes directly with the International Building Code.

Natural Cooling see *Passive Cooling*

Natural Gas Consisting primarily of methane and associated with fossil fuels, it is found primarily in coal beds, as methane clathrates, and is created by methanogenic organisms in marshes, bogs, and landfills. It is an important fuel source, a major feedstock for fertilizers, and a potent greenhouse gas.

Negative Charge The charge state of an electron particle. Electrical charges are measured in coulombs, which is equivalent to about 6.25×10^{18} e (e is the charge on a single electron or proton).

Negative Electrical Charge see *Negative Charge*

Net Metering An electricity billing policy for consumers who own (generally small) alternative energy systems (such as wind or solar) that are connected to the utility's electrical grid. Excess power generated by the PV system (for example) is sold to the utility company. Under net metering, a homeowner receives retail credit (paid for power at the same rate they are paying the utility company for power) for at least a portion of the electricity they generate. Special electricity meters are required that accurately record power flow in both directions, allowing a no-cost method of effectively banking excess electricity production for future credit. However, the rules vary significantly by country and by state/province.

Neutron A sub-atomic particle exhibiting no electrical charge whatsoever and a mass slightly larger than a proton. It is part of the nucleus of an atom.

Newton It is the metric unit of measurement of force (symbol N). Named after Sir Isaac Newton, it is equal to the amount of force needed to accelerate one kilogram of mass at a rate of one meter per second per second. It can be defined by the equation: $1 \text{ N} = 1 \text{ (kg} \times \text{m)} / \text{s}^2$

Nickel-Cadmium Battery An alkaline-type battery that utilizes nickel-cadmium rather than lead plates.

Night It is not an SI unit of measurement. The term is also often used to refer to the part of the day when the Sun is below the horizon (roughly 12 hours on average, but varies throughout the year depending on the latitude of the observer).

Nominal Voltage In a PV system, this term refers to the voltage of the battery the system a PV module is best suited to charge. It does not refer to the maximum or minimum voltage produced by the module.

North American Electric Reliability Council (NERC) A non-profit corporation formed in 1968 (funded by the electric utility industry), mandated by Congress in response to the 1965 electrical blackout that affected much of the northeastern U.S. The NERC's mission is to ensure the reliability of electrical power systems operating within the U.S., Canada and a portion of Baja California, Mexico. In 2006 the NERC changed its name (but not the acronym) to the North American Electric Reliability Corporation.

Northern Hemisphere The half of the Earth's surface located north of the equator.

N-Type Semiconductor A material obtained by carrying out a process of doping, by adding some amount of an element with more electrons (N for *Negative*) to a semiconductor element with fewer electrons in order to increase the number of free charge carriers. In this case the charge carriers are negatively charged.

Nucleus The cluster of protons and neutrons located in the center of an atom's structure.

O

Occupational Safety and Health Administration (OSHA) An agency of the United States Department of Labor, and created by Congress under the Occupational Safety and Health Act, on December 29, 1970. Its mission is to prevent work-related injuries, illnesses, and deaths by issuing and enforcing standards for workplace safety and health.

Ohm's Law A mathematical formula expressing the relationship between voltage, resistance and current flow in an electrical circuit. Expressed by the equation: I (current in Amperes) = V (volts) / R (resistance). Resistance is measured in ohms (symbol Ω, the Greek letter Omega). Named for German physicist Georg Ohm who published his treatise in 1827.

Ohms Ohms (Ω) are the unit of electrical impedance according to the International System of Units (SI). In the direct current case, they symbolize the unit of electrical resistance, named after Georg Simon Ohm.

Oil Cartel A formal agreement between oil-producing companies or countries to increase profits by controlling such factors as price, output amounts, sales territories, market share, distribution and other key factors.

OPEC – Organization of Petroleum Exporting Countries An oil cartel comprised of 12 nations, including: Algeria, Angola, Ecuador, Iran, Iraq, Kuwait, Libya, Nigeria, Qatar, Saudi Arabia and the United Arab Emirates. The organization has maintained its headquarters in Vienna, Austria since 1965.

Open Circuit An open-circuit condition exists when there is a break in the path of a circuit, preventing current from flowing along the circuit. A light switch in the "off" position creates such a situation, interrupting the flow of electrons along the circuit by creating a gap or an open circuit.

Open Circuit Voltage (Voc) The difference of electrical potential between two terminals of a device when there is no external load connected (the circuit is broken or open. Under these conditions there is no external electric current between the terminals. Theoretically this is the maximum voltage a PV module is capable of generating.

Open Loop System A type of solar thermal system where the water to be used is heated directly by the solar thermal collector. It is open in the sense that usable hot water flows into the system (from a water utility or well), and flows out (as usable hot water).

Ottoman Empire Also known as the Turkish Empire or simply Turkey, the empire lasted from 1302 to 1922. At its height (16th -17th Centuries), the empire controlled much of southeastern Europe, western Asia and north Africa.

Overcharge When power is continually applied to charged storage batteries, they can be overcharged. This creates a potentially dangerous situation because overcharged batteries can overheat and possibly explode.

Overcurrent A situation where a larger than intended electric current exists through a conductor, leading to excessive generation of heat and the risk of damaging infrastructure and equipment and causing fires.

P

Parallel Circuit A method of connecting identical voltage sources together (positive terminals are connected to positive terminals) such that the total voltage level is identical to that of an individual voltage source. However the current delivery capability is equal to the sum of the currents produced by each individual source. For example, three 6-volt, 15 amp batteries connected in parallel will create a 6-volt, 45 amp circuit.

Passive Cooling A passive system (uses no outside mechanical or electrical energy source) designed to assist in cooling a structure. Systems often incorporate components that block sunlight during warm weather, facilitate the movement of air within the structure or remove warm air while allowing cooler air to enter the structure.

Passive Solar Solar energy applications that include designing homes and buildings to use the heat and light received directly from the sun for space heating, water heating, ventilation, distillation, and solar lighting. They do not incorporate any outside mechanical or electrical energy source within the system (as contrasted with active solar).

Peak oil see *Hubbert's Peak Oil*

Peak Sunlight Intensity see *Light Irradiance*

Phantom Load The electricity consumed by electronic devices while they are switched off or in a standby mode.

Photochromic A material that changes color when exposed to changes in the intensity of light. Light-sensitive sunglasses are an example of a product made with a photochromically-sensitive material.

Photon An elementary particle within an electromagnetic field, the basic unit of light and all other forms of electromagnetic radiation. They exhibit properties of both waves and particles, and have zero mass.

Photosynthesis A process by which trees and plants convert energy from the Sun, along with water (H_2O) and carbon dioxide (CO_2) to produce glucose (food for the plant) and oxygen (O_2).

Photovoltaics (PV) Green technology and research related to the application of solar cells for energy, which convert sunlight directly into electricity. The manufacture of solar cells and photovoltaic arrays has greatly expanded in recent years.

Photovoltaic (PV) Array A grouping of multiple PV panels connected together. Individual panels may be wired together in a series circuit to provide additional voltage capabilities, in parallel to provide greater current flow capabilities, or in a series-parallel combination to match the voltage and current requirements of a given load device.

Photovoltaic (PV) Cells A device that converts light directly into electricity by the photovoltaic effect. Sometimes the term *solar cell* is reserved for devices intended specifically to capture energy from sunlight, while the term *photovoltaic cell* is used when the light source is unspecified.

Photovoltaic (PV) Module A packaged interconnected assembly of photovoltaic cells. Known commonly as a solar panel, it is a component of a larger PV system and is the portion of the system that directly converts sunlight to an electrical current.

Polarity The determination as to which side of a voltage cell exhibits a positive charge, while the other side exhibits a negative charge.

Pollution Prevention (P2) Programs Established by the U.S. EPA, the term refers to a number of initiatives designed to reduce the amount of pollution generated by a process, whether it is consumer consumption, or industrial in nature.

Polycrystalline Cell A photovoltaic cell made from many crystallites of silicon of varying size and orientation.

Positive Charge The charge state of a proton sub-atomic particle. Electrical charges are measured in coulombs. which is equivalent to about 6.25×10^{18} e (e is the charge on a single electron or proton).

Positive Electrical Charge see *Positive Charge*

Potential Energy Energy that is stored in a system. This stored energy can be converted into other forms of energy such as kinetic energy or work. The SI (standard unit or measurement) unit potential energy is measured in is a joule.

Power The amount of work that can be done in a given unit of time, or the amount of energy that can be transferred in a given unit of time. It is measured in watts. It can be expressed in the equation: P (power) = w (work) / t (time)

Pressure The amount of force for a given area (symbol P or p) applied in a direction perpendicular to the surface of the object in question. Atmospheric pressure, for example is the amount of force (gravitational weight) of a column of air from the surface of the Earth (the surface of the object being measured) to the edge of space.

Price shock An unexpected and unpredictable dramatic change in the price of a product or commodity (either positive or negative, but usually used in terms of dramatically rising prices) caused by some external event.

Proton A sub-atomic particle with an elementary electrical charge of +1. It is part of the nucleus of an atom, typically paired with neutrally charged neutrons. In most atoms the positive electrical charge of the proton is balanced by a similar number of negatively charged electrons.

Proterozoic Era A geological period of time extending from 2,500 – 542 million years ago. The name comes from Greek meaning "earlier life"—and it represents the period of time prior to the first abundant complex life appearing on Earth.

P-Type Semiconductor A material obtained by carrying out a process of doping. When the doping material is added, it takes away (accepts) weakly-bound outer electrons from the semiconductor atoms (creating a positive charge). This type of doping agent is also known as an acceptor material and the vacancy left behind by the electron is known as a hole. Thus the dopant atom can accept an electron from a neighboring atom's covalent bond.

Public Utility Commissions (PUCs) Independent committees (usually with a state-wide jurisdiction and appointed by the Governor) assigned the responsibility of regulating privately owned electric, natural gas, telecommunications, water, railroad, rail transit, and passenger transportation companies.

Pulse Width Modulated Controller A form of multi-stage controller that better accommodates the absorption stage of charging by rapidly pulsing (turning on and off) the charge as the battery reaches a state of full charge.

Q

Quantum Physics The set of principles that describe the physical reality at the atomic level of existence. In other words, the study of the very very small.

R

Radiant Energy Visible or invisible energy that is in the form of electromagnetic waves.

Rate of Discharge As it relates to batteries, this indicates how quickly stored power is drained from the battery. Typically the faster a battery is drained, the less power available within the battery cells. Usually indicated with a designation such as C/20—where the number (in this case 20) indicates the number of hours in which a battery is drained from full capacity to completely discharged.

Reactance An AC circuit parameter in which the load poses an opposition to the changing current push being applied. This is opposition to AC current flow from inductance or capacitance, instead of resistance.

Reflected In electromagnetic radiation, it refers to the change of direction of a wavefront when it strikes the interface of another media (this could be a material, or the edge of an atmosphere, or a surface of a liquid, etc.). The wavefront then returns to th medium from which it originated. For example, sunlight entering the atmosphere from space might strike a cloud surface and the wavefront be turned (or reflected) back into space. If it doesn't return to its original source, it is not reflected but is scattered or transmitted.

Reflectivity A ratio measuring the reflective nature of a material. It is a fraction representing the amount of radiation reflected by an objects surface divided by the amount of radiation striking that surface. A reflectivity of zero would indicate that all radiant energy was absorbed by the object.

Reflector A surface (such as a mirror) that contain properties highly suitable to reflecting or scattering electromagnetic waves (such as light).

Regulation An administrative code or ruling by a branch of government that usually has the force of law.

Respiration Commonly known as breathing, the process that enables animals to expel carbon dioxide (the primary product of cellular respiration) and replace it with oxygen from fresh air.

Resistance The opposition to the flow of a steady electrical current by a circuit or component. It can be expressed in a mathematical equation (Ohm's Law): I (current in Amperes) = V (volts) / R (resistance). Resistance is measured in ohms (symbol Ω, the Greek letter Omega).

Resource Neutral A system that consumes no more of any resource than can be replaced within the life of that unit. In other words, the product or service could continue to be produced in any quantity for an unlimited period of time without risk of depleting any of the resources used in creating that product or service.

RMS Refers to the measurement of AC voltage with a standard multi meter, with the result being expressed as volt-amperes (VA), rather than watts.

Roof Pond A passive heating and cooling system that incorporates a swimming pool like structure on the roof of a building. During cool periods, heat from the Sun is absorbed into the water (the pool is uncovered during the day). The pool is then covered at night and the heat contained within it radiated through the bottom into the building. During warm periods of time, the pool remains covered during the day. It is then uncovered at night, drawing radiant heat from within the building and releasing it into the cool night air.

Root Mean Square (RMS) Also known as the quadratic mean, it is a statistical measurement of the magnitude of a quantity that varies from positive to negative (such as a sine wave).

Rural Electrification Administration One of the New Deal agencies created under U.S. President Franklin Delano Roosevelt. The REA was created in 1935 with the primary goal of promoting rural electrification. In the 1930s, the U.S. lagged significantly behind Europe in providing electricity to rural areas due to the unwillingness of power companies to serve farmsteads.

S

Scattered In physics, this describes the event when radiation (such as light or sound) are forced to deviate from a straight path (its trajectory). This may occur when it strikes an object or through no-uniformities within the medium through which it is traveling. Radiation that does not return to the original source when it strikes a surface is may be scattered, often called diffuse reflection.

Schematic Diagram A symbolic wiring diagram depicted the technical details of an electric or electronic circuit.

Sealed Battery Lead acid batteries marketed as no-maintenance (as the liquid contained within cannot be monitored or adjusted). Despite the name, these batteries still allow gases produced within to escape when overcharged.

Second Law of Thermodynamics see *Laws of Thermodynamics*

Semiconductor A material having a resistivity value between that of a conductor and an insulator. The conductivity of a semiconductor material can be varied using an external electrical field.

Series Circuit The connection of batteries, solar panels, or other DC power sources in such a way as to attach positive terminals to negative terminals in a daisy-chain configuration. In a series circuit, the voltage of the circuit equals the sum of all the individual component voltages. The current (amps) remains at the level of the individual components. For example, three 6-volt, 15 amp batteries connected in series will create a 18-volt, 15 amp circuit.

Short Circuit A condition whereby a wire or conductor is placed across the power terminals in the absence of a suitable load. Current flow through the circuit and inside the power source (battery) moves as quickly as the internal process can generate more free electrons. The acceleration of current causes he power source to heat up, which in turn can cause it to overheat. If the power source is a battery, it may explode.

Short Circuit Current (Isc) The current flowing between two terminals of a PV module (through a tester, which creates a short circuit). Theoretically this is the maximum current a PV module is capable of generating.

Shunt Controller An electronic device that prevents damage to components (such as batteries) within a system by diverting excess power (or excess voltage) away from the system to a ground or storage device that can safely dissipate the excess power.

SI The International System of Units (abbreviated SI from the French *le Système international d'unités*) is the modern form of the metric system. It is the world's most widely-used system of measurement.

Silicon The second most abundant element (after oxygen), making up 25.7% of the Earth's crust by mass. The most common metalloid, it is less reactive than its chemical analog carbon. It has the chemical symbol of Si and an atomic number of 14. A semiconductor used in the construction of photovoltaic cells.

Sine Wave A wave pattern found often in nature (such as ocean waves, sound waves, etc.) characterized by smooth curved (rounded) wave patterns. The sine wave is important in physics because it retains its wave shape when added to another sine wave of the same frequency and arbitrary phase.

Sine Wave Inverter An inverter that produces a sine wave form of output rather than a square wave form. The output from this type of inverter matches the form of electricity provided by electrical utilities. It is the only choice of inverter that can be used with grid-tied energy systems.

Single Axis Tracking System A PV mounting system designed to follow the motion of the Sun as it moves (in relation to the horizon) only in relation to its azimuth.

Single-Wall Heat Exchanger A heat exchange system that transfers heat from a liquid held within a closed loop directly through the wall of the pipe to water stored within a tank.

Sinusoidal Wave see *Sine Wave*

Site Assessment The process of walking around and looking directly at local conditions under which a system will be installed.

Skylight Windows or domes placed on the roof of buildings, allowing sunlight to enter into the interior of the structure. They are a form of daylighting.

Solar Array see *Photovoltaic (PV) Array*

Solar Energy Radiated energy received from the Sun in the form of light and heat.

Solar Insolation Map A graphic depiction of the amount of solar radiation (sunlight) that strikes a given location over a period of time.

Solar Noon The time during a day with the highest sun elevation, which will depend on longitude, latitude and date.

Solar Oven A device or container (also called a solar cooker) that uses sunlight as its energy source. Thermal energy from sunlight is trapped within a container, increasing the temperature within a box that allows for the cooking of food. Because they use no fuel and they cost nothing to run, humanitarian organizations are promoting their use worldwide to help slow deforestation and desertification caused by collecting wood as fuel for cooking.

Solar Panel see *Photovoltaic (PV) Module*

Solar Power Towers A type of utility-scale solar thermal system that concentrates solar radiation by reflecting it from a number of movable mirrors onto a central tower.

Solar South As opposed to magnetic south, solar south would be in the direction of the southern most point on the Earth (as determined by its relationship with the Sun).

Solar Thermal see *Thermal Solar*

Solar Thermal Collector A device (or module) within a thermal solar system that collects the heat from solar radiation and transfers it to a liquid flowing through it. It is comparable to a PV module within a PV system, as the portion of the system that converts the energy from the Sun into usable power (in this case in the form of heat rather than in the form of electricity).

Solar Window The period of time each day considered optimal for collecting solar radiation (usually determined to be between 9 am and 3 pm).

Southern Hemisphere The half of the Earth's surface that is located south of the equator.

Specific Heat Capacity The measure of heat energy required to increase the temperature of a unit of mass by a certain temperature interval. For example, the amount of energy required to raise the temperature of a liter of water from 10°C to 11°C would be the water's specific heat capacity.

Spectrum A condition that is not limited to a specific set of values but can vary infinitely within a continuum. A rainbow is an example of a spectrum, where an infinite continuum of colors are contained within its boundaries.

Spring Equinox As the Earth revolves around the Sun, twice each year the Earth's axis is neither pointing towards or away from the Sun. The name "equinox" is derived from the Latin *aequus* (equal) and *nox* (night), because around the equinox, the night and day are approximately equally as long all over the Earth (roughly 12-hours each). The equinox occur each March (usually 20th or 21st) and each September (usually 22nd or 23rd). The equinox occurring in March has historically been referred to as the Spring Equinox (or Vernal Equinox). As this reflects a Northern Hemisphere bias (since March is actually in the Autumn in the Southern Hemisphere), the Spring Equinox is increasingly referred to as the March Equinox.

Square Wave Inverter An inverter that produces a square wave form of output rather than a sinusoidal form. Considered an old technology, these inverters produce a form of power that is not compatible with sensitive electrical devices.

SRCC Certification Program A performance rating system for solar thermal collectors established by the Solar Rating and Certification Corporation (SRCC). In order for a collector model to be certified and rated by SRCC, the collector must first pass a series of tests performed on a sample unit which has been randomly selected by SRCC from the manufacturer's production. The series of tests are conducted according to the methods specified in SRCC Standard 100 by an independent laboratory accredited by SRCC.

Stand-Alone System An electrical system (wind, solar, fuel cell, etc.) that is not connected to the electrical grid. Stand-Alone Systems provide all the energy used by the home or business. They are often used in remote areas where no utility-provided electricity is available.

Stand Off Mounting A rooftop mounting system for PV arrays, where panels are mounted on brackets or rails which are then directly attached to the roof structure.

Standard Oil of Ohio Formed by John D. Rockefeller and Henry Flagler in the late 1800's, this petroleum refining and distribution company (also known as Sohio) was part of the anti-trust breakup of Standard Oil in 1911. British Petroleum (BP) merged with Sohio (called Boron in states other than Ohio) in 1968. By 1991 all Sohio (as well as Boron) gasoline stations were re-branded as BP within the United States.

Standard An established norm or requirement for an industry segment or product. It is usually a formal document that establishes uniform engineering or technical criteria, methods, processes and practices.

Standard Test Conditions (STC) A common set of environmental conditions under which the performance characteristics of PV cells are measured. These standard conditions have been set at a level of irradiance of 1000 W/m^2 at an atmospheric pressure found at sea level (AM 1.5) at 25°C (77°F).

Standards Council of Canada (SCC) A federal Crown corporation with the mandate to promote efficient and effective voluntary standardization within Canada.

Statute A formal written enactment of a legislative authority that commands or prohibits something, or declares policy. Similar in nature to a law, but distinct from a regulation as it is a legislative, rather than administrative instrument.

Storage Tank A container in which liquid is held.

Subsidies A form of financial assistance usually paid by a government to a business.

Sulfation The process whereby a lead-acid battery loses its ability to hold a charge after it is kept in a discharged state too long. This allows the crystallization of lead sulfate within the battery cell.

Summer Solstice A solstice is an astronomical event that happens twice each year, when the tilt of the Earth's axis is most inclined toward (Summer Solstice) or away (Winter Solstice) from the Sun.

Sun Chart A graph of the azimuth and altitude of the Sun for a particular location. It is a graphic representation of the track the sun will follow referenced by time of day as well as time of year. A sky view of obstructions (trees, buildings, etc.) for a specific location can be superimposed on the sun chart to indicate if that location will have suitable sunlight available to make a photovoltaic system practical.

Sun Room A room constructed on the side of a home (usually in the direction of predominant sunlight) with many windows that allow direct solar gain during winter months.

Sunlight The total spectrum of electromagnetic radiation given off by the Sun. When it strikes the Earth, direct sunlight includes infrared, visible and ultraviolet light. It is also sometimes defined as direct irradiance from the Sun (insolation) measured on the ground of at least 120 watts per square meter. Sunlight striking the outer edge of the Earth's atmosphere has a insolation of 1,366 watts per square meter. As it filters through the atmosphere, the average insolation of sunlight striking the Earth's surface is 1,000 watts per square meter.

Swamp Cooler see *Evaporative Cooler*

System Bonding The process of intentionally connecting all metallic non-current carrying components of a system together so that every component within the system will have the same electrical potential. This is a safety measure to reduce the risk of electrical shocks.

T

Tapering Mode see *Absorption Mode*

Temperature The physical properties of a material or system that corresponds with the common notions of hot and cold. For a solid, the sense that it is increasing in temperature (getting hotter) corresponds with increased molecular motion or vibration within the material. In most of the world (except Belize, Liberia, Myanmar and the United States—which use the Fahrenheit scale) temperature is measured using the Celsius scale. The Celsius scale was based on the freezing and boiling point of water (0°C and 100°C respectively at one atmosphere pressure). The Fahrenheit scale is thought to be referenced by the freezing point of salt water (or brine) at about 0°F and the temperature of the human body (at the time measured to be about 100°F – actually on average closer to 98.6°F).

Temperature Coefficient The relative change of a physical property when the temperature is changed by one degree Kelvin.

Temperature Compensation A feature sometimes incorporated within a charge controller that compensates the charge level based on the temperature of the battery.

Tennessee Valley Authority (TVA) A federally owned corporation created by the U.S. Congress in 1933 to provide electrical generation, flood and navigation control, and economic development within the Tennessee River valley. The TVA was designed not only as an electricity provider, but also as a regional economic development agency that would use federal experts and electricity to rapidly modernize the region's economy and society (a region particularly hard hit by the Great Depression).

Thermal Chimney A passive convective cooling system that can be incorporated into a structure, designed to draw warm air out of a living space and vent it to the atmosphere through a chimney.

Thermal Cycle In passive solar systems, a thermal cycle refers to the period of time that starts at one set of conditions (such as a fixed ambient temperature and humidity) and continues until it returns to that same set of conditions. For example, a thermal cycle might refer to a 24-hour period, when environmental conditions are observed at dawn. When conditions return to a similar state (at dawn the next day), one thermal cycle has taken place. But an annual thermal cycle might also be observed for the same location during which time, 365 daily thermal cycles have occurred. So the length of time is not a factor in determining what constitutes a thermal cycle.

Thermal Diode A device that allows heat to flow in only one direction.

Thermal Energy A form of energy that can be felt as an increase in temperature (heat).

Thermal Efficiency The measurement of a device that compares the work produced with the heat energy of the fuel input. The less work produced for a given level of fuel, the lower the thermal efficiency of that device. As stated in the First Law of Thermodynamics, the thermal efficiency must always be less than 100%, since the amount of work produced can never exceed the energy contained in the fuel used to produce the work (energy cannot be created).

Thermal Lag The amount of time it takes heat energy absorbed into a mass to radiate out of that mass. This property is used as a comparative measurement, so the amount of energy released is not fixed, nor are the conditions under which the measurement is taken. For example, the comparison could be to determine the comparative thermal lag between two materials as they release 5°F of heat as ambient temperatures decline 20°F. Or it could compare how quickly two materials release 1°C as ambient temperatures decline 15°C.

Thermal Mass The capacity of a body to store heat. In the field of building design, thermal mass provides "inertia" against temperature fluctuations. It can be calculated by multiplying the thermal heat capacity of a substance by the mass of that substance that is present.

Thermal Solar An active or passive system that utilizes solar radiant energy to heat a liquid, then uses this stored heat energy directly (in the form of heat or hot water) or indirectly, using the heat energy to drive electric-generating turbines.

Thermal Storage Capacity The amount of heat that can be retained (stored) within a given mass.

Thermochromic A material that changes color when exposed to changes in temperature. A "mood ring" is an example of a product made with a thermochromically-sensitive material.

Thermosiphon A method of passive heat exchange based on natural convection that circulates liquid without the necessity of a mechanical pump.

Third Law of Thermodynamics see *Laws of Thermodynamics*

Tracking Mount A mounting system that allows a PV panel to move in relation to the Sun, maximizing the panel's exposure to solar radiation.

Tracking System see *Tracking Mount*

Transmitted In physics, this describes the event when radiation (such as light or sound) travels through a substance and is neither absorbed or deflected.

Trombe Wall A Sun-facing wall developed by French engineer Félix Trombe in 1956. It incorporates a thermal mass combined with an air space and vents to serve as a passive isolated solar gain system.

U

Underwriters Laboratories (UL) An independent product safety certification organization that has been testing products and writing standards for safety for more than a century.

UL Mark One of a number of labels that indicate a product has been tested and found to meet Underwriters Laboratories' safety criteria for that specific product to the level indicated by that specific mark.

UL Classified Mark Indicates that a product has been tested by Underwriters Laboratories for only certain (but not all) safety hazards.

Utility Grid Interconnection Agreement A required legal contract between a utility company and the owner/operator of a small electrical generating system that is connected to the utility's power lines. Sample agreements are available from the U.S. Federal Energy Regulatory Commission (FERC).

Utility Interface A device (usually determined by the utility company) that connects an alternative energy system (such as wind or solar) to the utility's electrical grid. The device's primary function is to ensure that no electricity flows to the grid when the grid is "down." It also will modify the power quality to match the characteristics of the electricity provided by the utility. If a net-metering agreement is in effect, the utility interface may also monitor current flow (both from the utility and from the homeowner).

Utility-Scale PV Systems Large photovoltaic or solar thermal systems incorporated within a utility's electrical generating system.

UV Radiation The electromagnetic radiation within sunlight with a wavelength shorter than that of visible light but longer than x-rays, in the range 10 nm to 400 nm, and energies from 3 eV to 124 eV. Most people are aware of the effects of UV through the painful condition of sunburn, but the UV spectrum has many other effects, both beneficial and damaging, on human health.

V

Valence Electrons Residing in the outer atomic shell, these are the only electrons capable of being separated from an atom to become free electrons.

Visible Radiation The portion of the electromagnetic spectrum that is visible to the human eye. Wavelengths within in this range (about 380 to 750 nanometers) is called visible light or simply light.

Voltage (V) The electromotive force (EMF) that places the electrical push and pull on the different terminals of a power source.

Voltage Drop The reduction in voltage in an electrical circuit between the source (such as a PV panel) and load.

Volt It is a unit of measurement (symbol V) to denote electromotive force. The value of potential difference across a conductor when a current of one ampere dissipates one watt of power in the conductor. It is also equal to one joule of energy per coulomb of charge. It can be expressed with the equation: $1 V = 1 W (watt) / 1 A (ampere)$

Volume The three-dimensional space any solid, liquid, plasma, vacuum or theoretical object occupies. It is often presented in units such as cubic inches, cubic centimeters, liters, etc. One-dimensional figures (such as lines) and two-dimensional shapes (such as squares or circles) are assigned a zero volume in three-dimensional space.

W

Water Wall A wall constructed in such a way as to incorporate water as a major portion of its mass. This system takes advantage of the relatively good thermal storage capacity and thermal lag of water when compared with other possible building materials.

Watts A unit of measurement (symbol W) used to describe power. It measures the rate of energy conversion. One Watt is equal to one joule (J) of energy per second. A watt can be used to measure mechanical energy as well as electrical energy. In mechanical energy it can be expressed with the equation: $1 W = 1 kg (kilogram) \times m^2 (meter squared)/s^3 (seconds cubed)$. In electrical energy it can be expressed with the equation: $1 W = 1 V (volt) \times 1 A (ampere)$.

Wavelength In a sine wave, it can be defined as the distance from the crest of one wave to the crest of the next or adjacent wave pattern. Wavelength is commonly designated by the Greek letter lambda (γ).

Wet Bulb Temperature The minimum temperature that can be achieved by evaporative cooling of a damp surface (exposed to moving air).

Whale Oil A clear liquid was obtained from the blubber of whales, primarily from three breeds: the Right, Bowhead and Sperm Whale. First used in lamps and to create candles, whale oil was largely replaced by petroleum products during the late 1800's.

Wind Loading A form of structural dynamics, where the force placed on a structure will vary during changing wind speeds. In PV installations, for example, the force of the wind moving over solar panels can produce a great deal of pressure (either pushing or pulling) on the building.

Wire A single, usually cylindrical string of metal. In electricity, this metal serves as a conductor to carry an electrical current along a circuit. The metal is often sheathed in an insulating material (a plastic coating). A bundle of wires within an outer sheathing is referred to as a cable.

Work In physics, it is defined as the amount of energy transferred by a force across a distance (pushing a rock up a hill would be defined as work). It is defined by the equation w (work) = F (force) $\times$ d (distance).

Wrought Iron No longer commercially produced in any large scale, it is a pure iron with a very low carbon content. It has largely been replaced with steel. The word "wrought" is an old version of the past tense form of the verb *to work*. Literally the term means *worked iron*.

Z

Zenith The direction pointing directly above a specific location.

Zeroth Law of Thermodynamics see *Laws of Thermodynamics*

Acronyms

A	Amperes	O_2	Oxygen molecule
AC	Alternating Current	OSHA	Occupational Safety and Health Administration
AFC	Alkaline Fuel Cells		
AH	Amp/Hour	PAFC	Phosphoric Acid Fuel Cell
AWG	American Wire Gauge	PEM	Proton Exchange Membrane
BTL	Biomass To Liquid	PPM	Parts Per Million
BTUs	British Thermal Units	PSI	Pounds per Square Inch
C	Carbon	PV	Photovoltaic
CH_3OH	Methanol	PWM	Pulse Width Modulation
CH_4	Methane	rms	Root mean square
CO	Carbon Monoxide	SI	International System of Units
Co_2	Carbon Dioxide	SOFC	Solid Oxygen Fuel Cells
CompTIA	Computing Technology Industry Association	SPDT	Single Pole, Double Throw
DC	Direct Current	SPST	Single Pole, Single Throw
DMFC	Direct Methanol Fuel Cells	TIA	Telecommunications Industry Association
DMM	Digital MultiMeters	UND	University of North Dakota
DOE	Department of Energy	ULSD	Ultra-Low Sulfur Diesel
DOT	Department of Transportation	V	Voltage
EERC	Energy and Environmental Research Center	VA	Volt-Amperes
EMF	Electromotive force	VAWT	Vertical Axis Wind Turbine
ETA-I	Electronics Technicians Association – International	Vmp	Rated Voltage
		Voc	Open Circuit Voltage
GND	Ground	VOM	Volt-Ohm-Milliammeter
GTL	Gas To Liquid		
H	Hydrogen		
H_2O	Water molecule		
HAWT	Horizontal Axis Wind Turbine		
Hz	Hertz or cycles per second		
Imp	Rated Current		
ISA	International Society for Automation		
Isc	Short Circuit Current		
K	Potassium		
K_2CO_3	Potassium Carbonate		
kWh	Kilowatt-hour		
mA	Milliamperes		
MCFC	Molten Carbonate Fuel Cell		
MW	Megawatts or Million Watts		
Na	Sodium		
NaCL	Sodium Chloride		
NaOH	Sodium Hydroxide		
NEC	National Electrical Code		
NFPA	National Fire Protection Association		
NREL	National Renewable Energy Laboratory		
O	Oxygen		

Index

CPSIA information can be obtained at www.ICGtesting.com
Printed in the USA
BVOW041658121011

273391BV00003B/8/P